French
Paintings

A CATALOGUE OF THE COLLECTION OF THE METROPOLITAN MUSEUM OF ART

VOLUME

III

French Paintings

A CATALOGUE OF THE COLLECTION OF
THE METROPOLITAN MUSEUM OF ART

III
XIX-XX Centuries

Charles Sterling
Curator of Paintings, The Louvre

Margaretta M. Salinger
Associate Research Curator of European Paintings,
The Metropolitan Museum of Art

The Metropolitan Museum of Art

Distributed by New York Graphic Society, Greenwich, Connecticut

Designed by Peter Oldenburg. Printed by Plantin Press in Monotype Granjon on Warren Lustrogloss paper. Bound by J. F. Tapley Co. Covers and jackets printed by Clarke & Way.

First printing, March 1967, 10,000 copies.

Contents

Introduction

THIS THIRD volume brings the catalogues of the Museum's French paintings up to date. It contains the works of French artists made during the last quarter of the nineteenth century and the first half of the twentieth, from Gustave Moreau to Soutine.

In their own time the Impressionists were a small group of scarcely known painters working independently of the academic art then fashionable and in revolt against the Salon. Today they are almost the only French artists of the last one hundred years to be popularly recognized and esteemed. Indeed during the last thirty years, and especially since the second World War, their works have been the ones most sought after by collectors and museums. Accordingly, as these pictures have become rare, they have brought enormous prices hitherto unheard of on the international art market.

In America French Impressionist pictures were sought after early by certain discriminating collectors with prophetic taste, even before they found a market in France. Extraordinary among these were Mr. and Mrs. H. O. Havemeyer, who, aided by their friend the artist Mary Cassatt, brought together one of the most distinguished collections of Impressionist paintings in the world. The pictures bequeathed to the Metropolitan by the Havemeyers, a group unsurpassed in this country, form one of the principal glories of the Museum.

The paintings of the Post-Impressionist and subsequent schools have been gradually added and include many generous gifts from contemporary collectors. The policy in acquiring them has been to select works that seem to have enduring quality rather than those made well known through momentary fashion.

The biographies and individual entries here have been treated as in the other volumes of the Museum's catalogues. The painters have been arranged in approximately chronological order, giving emphasis, however, to the chief movements and their influence rather than to the date of birth. In this way artists working in related styles are grouped together, and the artificial juxtapositions of a strictly chronological list are avoided.

For each painter there is first a brief biography intended only to provide the salient facts in his career and to clarify his relationship to other artists. Following this his works owned by the Museum are listed in the order of their production, according to factual or stylistic evidence.

Every picture is illustrated in half-tone. The material on which it is painted, the medium used, and the dimensions are given. Detailed descriptions, color notes, and references to condition are provided only where they are particularly significant.

Publications about French painting have been so numerous in recent years that the listing of references in these catalogues must necessarily be selective. Sources contemporary with the painters and subsequent writing that makes a serious contribution to our knowledge have been emphasized, and an attempt has been made to give at least one reference that includes a good reproduction in color.

The history of each picture has been traced as far back as possible, often to the studio of its artist. Square brackets enclose the names of dealers who have held the picture. The last line of each entry gives the name of the donor or of the fund that made the acquisition possible.

Volume III, like Volume II, was begun by Charles Sterling, Curator of Paintings of the Louvre, who carried out the work with his characteristically thorough and scholarly method until 1956. Most of the pictures acquired since that year are by Impressionist or Post-Impressionist artists. The original and sensitive entries for these are the work of Margaretta Salinger of the Museum's Department of European Paintings, who enjoyed the indispensable assistance of Mary Ann Wurth Harris and Claire Wever. The Editorial Department of the Museum, especially Jean Leonard, have patiently attended to the form of these catalogues and to the details of publication. The Museum is grateful for the help generously given by the directors and staff of the many institutions that have opened their archives and made all their resources available to the authors and for the friendly advice and information supplied by numerous private individuals.

THEODORE ROUSSEAU, *Curator of European Paintings*

French
Paintings

III

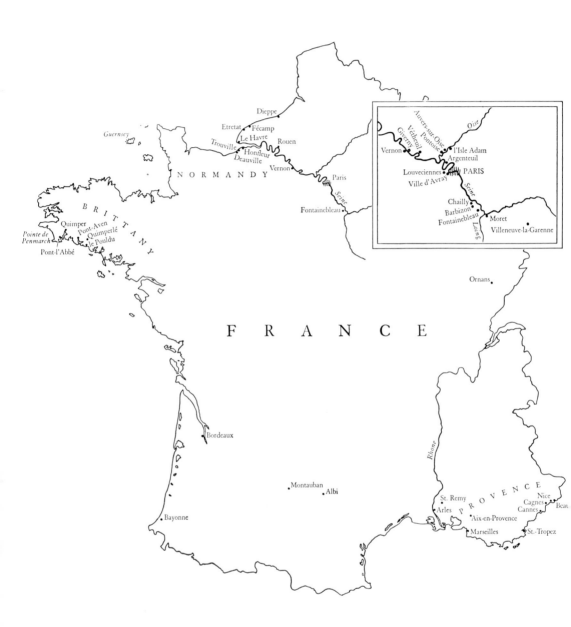

Guernsey

Dieppe

Etretat · Fécamp

Le Havre

Trouville · Rouen

Honfleur

Deauville

Vernon

N O R M A N D Y

B R I T T A N Y

Quimper · Pont-Aven

Quimperlé

le Pouldu

Pointe de
Penmarch

Pont-l'Abbé

Paris

Seine

Fontainebleau

Auvers-sur-Oise

Oise

Pontoise

Vétheuil

Giverny

Vernon · l'Isle Adam

Argenteuil

Louveciennes · PARIS

Ville d'Avray

Seine

Chailly

Barbizon

Fontainebleau · Moret

Loing

Villeneuve-la-Garenne

Ornans

F R A N C E

Bordeaux

Rhône

Montauban

Albi

P R O V E N C E

St. Remy · Nice

Cagnes · Beau.

Arles · Cannes

Aix-en-Provence

Bayonne

Marseilles · St.-Tropez

Moreau

Gustave Moreau. Born in Paris in 1826; died there in 1898. Moreau, the child of an architect, was born into a well-to-do family and received a careful education. He studied in the atelier of François Édouard Picot at the École des Beaux-Arts, where Cabanel and Bouguereau were his fellow students. He subsequently became the pupil of Théodore Chassériau. During the late fifties he spent considerable time in Italy. At intervals between 1852 and 1880 he exhibited at the Salon, achieving recognition at the Salon of 1864 with the Museum's painting of Oedipus and the Sphinx (see below). Although he was adversely criticized for the bizarre quality of his imagination, he gradually made an impression on official circles, where he was regarded as an artist who was both traditional and original. In 1881 he received a commission to illustrate the *Fables* of La Fontaine and worked for nearly five years to produce the sixty-five water colors that compose the series. At the end of his life Moreau was made a professor at the École des Beaux-Arts. He had always enjoyed complete freedom from financial care and only rarely sold his pictures. At his death he left to France a very large portion of his output, which today forms the Musée Gustave Moreau in Paris.

From Chassériau Moreau took an inclination toward literary content and the exotically picturesque, but aside from a certain influence on his color and his drawing, Moreau's style shows little dependence upon his master. He was deeply impressed by the paintings that he saw in Italy, but his experience of Italian art was absorbed completely in his personal style. He shared this interest in Italian art with Burne-Jones and the other English Pre-Raphaelites, and indeed, with his visionary spirit and his painstaking technique, he is the only French artist who can be likened to the Pre-Raphaelite painters.

Moreau's originality lies in the aura of mysticism with which he enveloped biblical and mythological subjects, in the desire for richness that led him to pile up in his pictures exotic stuffs and antique or oriental jewels, and in his glowing colors and complex textures. The most ambitious of his creations are so replete with detail that they produce the effect of enlarged miniatures, a characteristic summarized with biting irony by Degas, who said that Moreau put "the gods on leashes made of watch chains." The charge frequently made that Moreau's painting was too literary is refuted by a group of some two hundred small oils and water colors done late in his life, when his works were becoming increasingly abstract. These small pictures have little or no identifiable subject matter and affirm his expressed prophetic belief that a new form of painting was beginning.

Moreau played an extraordinary role as a teacher. Highly intelligent and tolerant of the independence of others, he guided several of the most original twentieth-century painters, especially Rouault and Matisse. His intellectual and fantastic art also made a deep impression on Odilon Redon.

Oedipus and the Sphinx   21.134.1

The sphinx was a fabulous winged monster of classical mythology, with the head and breasts of a woman, who besieged the city of Thebes, devouring everyone who could not solve her riddles. Oedipus sought out the sphinx at Thebes and by solving her riddle caused her death. The grateful Thebans made him king.

Moreau sent this large painting, which he had just completed, to the Salon of 1864, after an interval of nine years in which he had not exhibited. It has the same subject as and bears a general resemblance in composition to a famous picture by Ingres,[1] painted in 1808, that Moreau could have seen when it was exhibited in Paris in 1846 and 1855. Certain details, like the idea of showing the foot of the corpse in the foreground, Moreau borrowed directly from Ingres. For the posture of the sphinx, who claws the chest of Oedipus, he seems to have been indebted to a poem by Heinrich Heine in the *Buch der Lieder*, of which he owned a copy.[2] In style Moreau's Oedipus and the Sphinx shows clearly the influence of the painting of the Italian fifteenth century. Mantegna especially inspired him and he used Mantegna's favorite medium of *grisaille* for one of his repetitions of the Oedipus (formerly in the Duruflé collection).

The ornate antique setting that Moreau conceived abounds with details, some of which have been interpreted symbolically, as for instance, the butterfly and the snake twined around the pedestal, which have been said to represent good and evil.[3] Édouard Schuré (Ref., 1900) saw in the sphinx the symbol of nature ultimately vanquished by man.

Although the painting, when it appeared at the Salon, inspired some sarcastic criticism and was made the butt of one of Daumier's cartoons,[4] it met on the whole with great success. Degas, usually so caustic, is said to have defended it as a work of art.[5]

Moreau made very careful preparations for painting this picture, including more than thirty sketches, some ten of which are studies of a large bird's wing, which served as model for the wing of the sphinx.[6] There are also two large cartoons. After its favorable reception at the Salon Moreau repeated the composition in a number of water colors and in two paintings that have the appearance of sketches, but bear the date May 1864, which proves that they were made after the picture had been put on exhibition in the Salon. One of the water colors, in the Luxembourg, is more broadly treated than the oil, shows much chiaroscuro, and has a landscape recalling those of Leonardo da Vinci.

Oil on canvas. H. 81¼, w. 41¼ in. (206.4 x 104.7 cm.).

Signed and dated (at lower left): *Gustave Moreau 64.*

Notes: 1. Louvre, no. 421; ill. in H. Lapauze, *Ingres* (1911), opp. p. 88. 2. Ref., von Holten, 1957, p. 44. 3. Ref., von Holten, 1960. 4. Ref., von Holten, 1957, ill. p. 36. 5. Ref., Loisel, 1912, p. 15. 6. For studies and preparatory drawings see especially *Catalogue sommaire . . . Musée Gustave Moreau* (1904).

REFERENCES: E. About, *Salon de 1864* (1864), pp. 137ff., complains of a certain servility in the execution of this painting and of the wooden quality of the figure of Oedipus but appreciates Moreau's departure from tradition in unseating the sphinx from her accustomed plinth // F. Aubert, *Le Pays* (1864), likens it to the paintings of the fifteenth century // L. Auvray, *Salon de 1864* (1864), pp. 54–57, considers the picture disagreeable, scorns the ambivalent, contradictory criticism it received // H. de Callias, *L'Artiste*, series 8, v (1864), p. 219, admires the picture, calling it a study rather than a painting and relating it to the work of the Pre-Raphaelites and the early Italians // *L'Artiste*, series 8, v (1864), publishes an album of sketches by the artists of the Salon, including in the second section, dated June 10, 1864, p. 24, a drawing by Moreau of this picture, which it describes as the "*tableau-lion du salon*," and critical quotations about it by P. de Saint-Victor and J. Rousseau // M. du Camp, *Les Beaux-Arts* (1867), pp. 109–117, praises both the content and the execution, finds Moreau's interpretation more spiritual than that of Ingres // [J.] Castagnary, *Salon de 1864*, reprinted in *Salons (1857–1870)* (1892), I, pp. 198–202, condemns its literary quality and derides the details, calling the picture a pastiche of the Italian Renaissance // J. Clarétie, *L'Artiste*, series 8, VI (1864), p. 4, discusses the reaction

of the public and artists to the painting at the Salon // C. Clément, *Journal des débats* (May 12, 1864) // T. Gautier, *Le Moniteur universel* (May 27, 1864), p. 766, defends it, finds in it the influence of Mantegna and notes a touch of Hamlet in the Oedipus // L. Lagrange, *Gaz. des B.-A.*, XVI (1864), pp. 506–508, ill. opp. p. 506 (engraving), praises it with reservations // P. de Saint-Victor, *La Presse* (May 7, 1864), calls it a pastiche // T. Thoré [W. Bürger], *Salon de 1864*, reprinted in *Salons de W. Bürger, 1861 à 1868* (1870), II, pp. 14–19, 22, admits the originality of the interpretation but condemns the literary quality, the technique, and the style // P. Mantz, *Gaz. des B.-A.*, XXIII (1867), p. 330, finds Moreau's "archaic and unhealthy" manner best exemplified in this painting; acknowledges certain qualities of tone and touch in it but complains of its lack of unity // T. Gautier, *L'Illustration*, LIII (May–June 1869), reprinted in *Tableau à la plume*, n.d., pp. 279f., attempts to explain the success of this picture in an analysis of its effectively novel combination of unlikely artistic elements // C. Phillips, *Mag. of Art*, VIII (1885), p. 230, observes that this was the first picture establishing Moreau's personality // P. Leprieur, *L'Artiste* (1889), I, pp. 169–171, 348, 354, 357, 444, 449f., studies this painting in relation to other works by Moreau, minimizes its eclecticism // L. Thévenin, *L'Esthétique de Gustave Moreau* (1897), p. 14 // J. Breton, *Nos Peintres du siècle*, n.d., pp. 178f., complains of its labored execution and its eclecticism // G. Geffroy, *L'Oeuvre de Gustave Moreau (L'Oeuvre d'art: Revue mensuelle illustrée)*, n.d., pp. 3–6 // A. Renan, *Gustave Moreau* (1900), pp. 27, 45, 50–52, 131, ill. opp. p. 40 (engraving) // O. Redon, in a letter (Jan. 29, 1900), published in *Lettres d'Odilon Redon* (1923), p. 38, and quoted in R. Bacou, *Odilon Redon* (1956), I, p. 254, recalls the deep impression this painting had made on him at the Salon of 1864 // E. Schuré, *Revue de Paris* (Dec. 1, 1900), pp. 617f.; reprinted in *Précurseurs et revoltés* (1904) // P. Flat, *Musée Gustave Moreau* [1903?], p. 17 // Abbé Loisel, *L'Inspiration chrétienne du peintre Gustave Moreau* (1912), pp. 15, 28, interprets the theme as man opposed to nature // L. Deshairs and J. Laran, *Gustave Moreau* [1913], pp. 25–28, pls. v, vi (cartoons and water color), quotes contemporary critics // *Gustave Moreau (Les Peintres illustrés)* (1914), pp. 36f. // C. Léger, *Courbet selon les caricatures et les images* (1920), p. 54, publishes a cartoon showing Moreau's sphinx disturbing Courbet's sleep // G. Coquiot, *Des Gloires déboulonnées* (1924), p. 107, quotes critics // M. Praz, *The Romantic Agony* (1933), pp. 295f., discusses it in a consideration of Moreau's treatment of the sphinx theme // A. Tabarant, *La Vie artistique au temps de Baudelaire* (1942), p. 391, calls Gustave Moreau the hero of the Salon of 1864, quoting the praise of numerous critics in the press of the period // C. Chassé, *Le Mouvement symboliste dans l'art du XIXe siècle* (1947), p. 34 // J. C. Sloane, *French Painting between the Past and the Present* (1951), pp. 171f., 174 (note 46), 175, fig. 68 // B. Polak, *Het Fin-de-siècle in de Nederlandse Schilderkunst* (1955), pp. 38f., discusses it in a study of the sphinx in the art and literature of the nineteenth century // R. von Holten, *Symbolister: Tidskrift för Konstvetenskap*, xxxii (1957), pp. 36–46, 50 (notes), ill.; and *L'Art fantastique de Gustave Moreau* (1960), pp. 2–9, fig. 6, analyzes it in detail, discusses other treatments of the theme, especially that of Ingres and the critical reception of the picture; and *Gustave Moreau* (exhib. cat.), Musée du Louvre, Paris (1961), pp. 27f., no. 10, pl. 6 // D. Ashton, *Odilon Redon, Gustave Moreau, Rodolphe Bresdin* (exhib. cat.), Museum of Modern Art, New York, and Art Institute of Chicago (1961–1962), pp. 115, 179, no. 175, ill. p. 113, gives a careful analysis and interpretation.

EXHIBITED: Paris, Salon de 1864, no. 1388; Musée du Louvre, Paris, 1961, *Gustave Moreau*, no. 10; Museum of Modern Art, New York, and Art Institute of Chicago, 1961–1962, *Odilon Redon, Gustave Moreau, Rodolphe Bresdin*, no. 175.

EX COLL.: Prince Jérôme Bonaparte (from 1864); William H. Herriman, Rome.

BEQUEST OF WILLIAM H. HERRIMAN, 1921.

Redon

Bertrand Jean (called Odilon) Redon. Born at Bordeaux in 1840; died in Paris in 1916. Redon, who had a French father and a Creole mother, spent his youth at Peyrelabade (Gironde), where his family had an estate to which he always remained deeply attached and to which he frequently returned, attracted by the melancholy landscape of that region. He was also impressed by the country of the Pyrenees, which he visited briefly in 1861. Having decided very young that he wanted to become an artist, he took lessons in Bordeaux with a local painter, Stanislas Gorin, but at his father's wish he also studied under a number of architects in Bordeaux. He failed, however, in the examinations for architecture at the École des Beaux-Arts in Paris. Some time after 1863 he presented himself there again as a painter and was permitted to enroll in the studio of Gérôme, with whom he studied for a short time only, finding himself in little sympathy with the teaching offered there. He spent a great deal of time in the Louvre and developed an enormous interest in Rembrandt, later fortified by travel in the Low Countries, and also in Goya, to whom he dedicated in 1885 a set of lithographs. During his student years he met the painter-engraver Rodolphe Bresdin, who not only became an influential friend but instructed him in the elementary graphic techniques. He subsequently learned more about lithography from Fantin-Latour. Another friend was the botanist Armand Clavaud, who introduced him to the writings of Flaubert, Baudelaire, and Poe, and to Hindu literature. In later life he also enjoyed the friendship of the writer Huysmans and the poet Mallarmé. Redon himself had a gift for expressive and critical writing, as shown in his autobiographical study *À Soi-même*, and in the series of articles that he published in *La Gironde* in 1868, analyzing the works displayed in the Salon of that year.

Although Redon was a visionary and in his early years devoted more time to solitary contemplation than to productive activity, he was very much aware of the work of his contemporaries and was by no means isolated from them. At Bordeaux he had seen paintings by Millet and Corot, early pictures by Moreau, and works by Delacroix, for whom he felt great enthusiasm, copying his paintings both in Bordeaux and in Paris at the Louvre. He met Courbet and Corot, who became his friend and adviser, and later on knew the symbolists Maurice Denis and Paul Sérusier and also Bonnard and Vuillard. In 1884 he helped to organize the Salon des Indépendants and became its president. He also sent fifteen entries to the eighth and last Impressionist exhibition, which took place in 1886.

It was as a maker of prints that Redon had first appeared, in 1867, at the Salon, and indeed up to about 1900 his work in this field was at least as important as his painting. All through his life, however, he also painted pictures. During the seventies he worked at Barbizon and in Brittany, creating landscapes very much in the style of Barbizon but based, like his charcoal studies, on a minute and exact scrutiny of nature, from which his more fanciful compositions later took flight. His first still lifes, dating from the beginning of the eighties, betray the influence of Fantin-Latour. In the decade between 1880 and 1890 he also produced several series of lithographs. The Apocalypse of Saint John, his last set of lithographs, came out in 1899, and the rest of his life was devoted almost exclusively to paintings, drawings, and pastels. At the Salon of 1904 an entire gallery was given over to the works of Redon, revealing the great variety of his production and the many changes it had undergone.

The art of Redon, independent of both academic and impressionistic aesthetics, demonstrates his own expressed intention "to place the logic of the visible at the service of the invisible." It is this deliberate reliance on all that he gleaned from a close study of natural forms that gives to his most imaginative productions an eerie and compelling reality. In upholding the validity of the artist's imagination Redon laid the foundations for symbolism and was a forerunner of surrealism and expressionism. Also of importance and value to other artists were his technical innovations, like the use of charcoal in finished compositions to establish a mysterious atmosphere. His originality combined with his wide literary and musical culture to make Redon one of the most considerable figures in the artistic life of France around the turn of the century.

Madame Arthur Fontaine 60.54

Redon's good friends the industrialist Arthur Fontaine and his wife held somewhat the same position in Paris that had been occupied a quarter of a century before by the Georges Charpentiers (see Renoir, p. 149). They gathered at their apartment in Paris writers and musicians, including Claude Debussy, and they enjoyed the friendship of Paul Claudel, André Gide, and Francis Jammes. They also collected the works of Redon. In September 1901 they visited the artist at the small seaside resort of St.-Georges-de-Didonne, near Royan, where the Redons had been spending the summer, and it was here that Redon did this portrait of Madame Fontaine in pastel, as well as one in sanguine of her husband. She was also painted twice by Vuillard,[1] and she appears with Degas and Paul Poujaud in one of Degas's famous intimate photographs.[2] Madame Fontaine, born Marie Escudier, obtained a divorce from Arthur Fontaine in 1909 and later married Dr. Abel Desjardins.

Signed, dated, and inscribed (at upper left): fait à St-Georges-de-Didonne/ Septembre-1901-/ODILON REDON.

Pastel on paper. H. 28½, w. 22½ in. (72.4 x 57.2 cm.).

Notes: 1. C. Roger-Marx, *Vuillard* (1945), ill. opp. p. 105, and after p. 108. 2. P. A. Lemoisne, *Degas* (1946), 1, ill. opp. p. 218, fig. a.

REFERENCES: E. Bernard, *L'Occident* (April 1903), reprinted in *Théories* (1920), p. 137, mentions this portrait of "Mme A. F..." in a discussion of Redon's use of decoration to enhance a portrait // F. Daulte, *Le Dessin français de Manet à Cézanne* (1954), pp. xx, 58, no. 28, ill. in color pl. 28, considers it one of Redon's most finished portraits, observing that it, like the other pastels of this time, is distinguished by its rich color // R. Bacou, *Odilon Redon* (1956), 1, p. 153, II, p. 54, no. 76, pl. 76, calls this picture the masterpiece of this kind of portrait (with a frame of flowers), catalogues it; and *Odilon Redon* (exhib. cat.), Musée de l'Orangerie, Paris (1956–1957), pp. 49f., no. 89, pl. XLI // K. Berger, *College Art Journal*, XVI (1956–1957), p. 29, ill. // K. Berger, *Odilon Redon* (1965), p. 211, no. 393, pl. 22.

EXHIBITED: Durand-Ruel, Paris, 1903, *Odilon Redon*, no. 17 (as Portrait de Mme A. F.); Paris, 1904, Salon d'Automne, Salle Odilon Redon, no. 26 (as a *dessin*, Portrait de Mme A. F.); Galerie Druet, Paris, 1908, *Odilon*

60.54

Redon, no. 23 (pastel, Portrait de Mme F.; possibly this picture); Galerie Barbazanges, Paris, 1920, *Odilon Redon*, no. 98 (as La Brodeuse, lent by M. Desjardins); Musée des Arts Décoratifs, Paris, 1926, *Odilon Redon*, no. 104 (lent by Mme Desjardins); Gazette des Beaux-Arts, Paris, 1934, *Les Étapes de l'art contemporain, II: Gauguin et ses amis*, no. 84 (as Portrait de Marie Desjardins, lent by Dr. Abel Desjardins); Bernheim-Jeune, Paris, 1934, *Cent Ans de portraits français*, no. 61; Galerie Charpentier, Paris, 1944, *La Vie familiale*, no. 112 (as Mme Desjardins brodant); and 1945, *Portraits français*, no. 84 (as Portrait de Mme D.); Bernheim-Jeune, Paris, 1948, *Exposition de la Femme*, no. 70 (as La Brodeuse, lent by M. Desjardins); Musée de l'Orangerie, Paris, 1949–1950, *Eugène Carrière et le symbolisme*, no. 147 (as Portrait de Mme Arthur Fontaine, lent by a private collector); Musée des Arts Décoratifs, Paris, 1952, *Cin-*

quante Ans de peinture française dans les collections particulières, no. 133 (as Portrait de Mme Arthur Fontaine, lent anonymously); Musée de l'Orangerie, Paris, 1956–1957, *Odilon Redon*, no. 89 (as Portrait de Madame Arthur Fontaine, lent by Jean Arthur Fontaine); Musée National d'Art Moderne, Paris, 1958, *De l'Impressionnisme à nos jours*, no. 170 (as La Brodeuse, 1901; lent by a private collector).

EX COLL.: Mme Arthur Fontaine (after c. 1912 Mme Abel Desjardins), Paris; Jean Arthur Fontaine, Paris (from 1946).

PURCHASE, MR. AND MRS. HENRY ITTLESON JR. FUND, 1960.

Flowers in a Chinese Vase   59.16.3

Redon apparently owned a variety of vases, in which Madame Redon arranged bouquets that formed the subject of his numerous still lifes of flowers. This one, of delicately patterned porcelain, reappears in a painting signed and dated 1916, from a private collection, that was exhibited at the World's Fair of 1940 (*Masterpieces of Art*, no. 353, ill. p. 237).

The Museum's picture, looser in style, was surely painted at least a decade earlier, for a label on the back of the canvas indicates that it was lent to an exhibition in New York City in 1906 by Pottier, a Parisian dealer and framemaker. This was seven years before Redon's works became known in America at the Armory Show. See also Bouquet in a Chinese Vase below.

Signed (at lower left and on bottom of vase): ODILON REDON.

Oil on canvas. H. 28⅝, w. 21¼ in. (72.7 x 54 cm.).

REFERENCES: F. Watson, *The Arts*, IX (1926),

59.16.3

ill. p. 13 // K. Berger, *Odilon Redon* (1965), p. 204, no. 308.

EXHIBITED: New York, 1906, *Redon*, no. 11 (lent by Pottier); Carroll Galleries, New York, 1915, *Second Exhibition of Contemporary French Art*, no. 16 (Vase of Flowers—pink background; owned by the gallery); John Herron Art Institute, Indianapolis, 1915, *Paintings by Odilon Redon*, no. 8 (Vase of Flowers: pink background, oil, lent by the Carroll Galleries); Metropolitan Museum, 1920, *Fiftieth Anniversary Exhibition*, cat. p. 10 (lent by John Quinn); and 1921, *Impressionist and Post-Impressionist Paintings*, no. 94 (lent by John Quinn); Museum of French Art, New York, 1922, *Odilon Redon*, no. 4 (lent by John Quinn); Art Center, New York, 1926, *Memorial Exhibition of . . . the John Quinn Collection*, no. 31 (Vase of Flowers, possibly this picture).

EX COLL.: [Pottier, Paris, in 1906]; [Carroll Galleries, New York, in 1915]; John Quinn, New York (by 1920, until 1925; Cat., 1926, p. 14; Vase of Flowers on pink background, 21 x 28½ in.); Mrs. J. Montgomery Sears, Boston; Mabel Choate, New York.

BEQUEST OF MABEL CHOATE IN MEMORY OF HER FATHER, JOSEPH HODGES CHOATE, 1958.

Bouquet of Flowers 56.50

This still life, showing lilacs, anemones, and other flowers, dates, according to Klaus Berger, about 1905. The vase in which the bouquet is arranged has been preserved and belongs to Redon's son Arï.

Signed (at lower center): ODILON REDON.

Pastel on paper. H. 31⅝, w. 25¼ in. (80.4 x 64.2 cm.).

REFERENCES: K. Berger (verbally, 1961), dates this picture about 1910 or 1911; *Odilon Redon* (1965), p. 215, no. 454, dates it about 1905.

EX COLL.: [Jacques Seligmann, Paris and New York, until 1932]; Mr. and Mrs. George B. Post, New York (from 1932).

GIFT OF MRS. GEORGE B. POST, 1956.

56.50

Pandora   60.19.1

Pandora was reputed to be the most beautiful woman ever created but idle and silly. Overcome by curiosity, she disobediently opened a box, in which were imprisoned all the evils that plague mankind. Redon has represented her delicately delineated form in the midst of flowers and trees, with no suggestion of the afflictions that proceeded from her box. This picture was probably painted about 1910, a period when he did a number of female nudes in the guise of mythological heroines.

Signed (at lower right): ODILON REDON.

Oil on canvas. H. 56½, w. 24½ in. (143.5 x 62.2 cm.).

REFERENCES: L. G. Cann, *International Studio*, LXXVIII (1923), ill. p. 103 // *Paintings and Pastels by Odilon Redon* (exhib. cat.), Paul Rosenberg, New York (1959), no. 18, places it in the years 1908–1909 // J. Rewald, *Odilon Redon, Gustave Moreau, Rodolphe Bresdin* (exhib. cat.), Museum of Modern Art, New York, and Art Institute of Chicago (1961–1962), pp. 44, 174, no. 45, ill. p. 88, dates it about 1910 // K. Berger, *Odilon Redon* (1965), p. 194, no. 172.

EXHIBITED: Carroll Galleries, New York, 1915, *Second Exhibition of Contemporary French Art*, no. 23 (owned by the gallery); John Herron Art Institute, Indianapolis, 1915, *Paintings by Odilon Redon*, no. 7 (lent by the Carroll Galleries); Museum of French Art, New York, 1922, *Odilon Redon*, no. 1 (lent by John Quinn); Art Center, New York, 1926, *Memorial Exhibition of . . . the John Quinn Collection*, no. 28; De Hauke & Co., New York, 1928, *Odilon Redon*, no. 9 (lent by Alexander Bing); World's Fair, New York, 1940, *Masterpieces of Art*, no. 350; Paul Rosenberg, New York, 1959, *Paintings and Pastels by Odilon Redon*, no. 18 (lent by Alexander M. Bing); Museum of Modern Art, New York, and Art Institute of Chicago, 1961–1962, *Odilon Redon, Gustave Moreau, Rodolphe Bresdin*, no. 45.

Ex coll.: [Carroll Galleries, New York, in
1915]; John Quinn, New York (by 1922, until
1925; Cat., 1926, p. 14, ill. p. 106); Alexander
M. Bing, New York (by 1928, until 1959).

Bequest of Alexander M. Bing, 1959.

The Chariot of Apollo   27.29

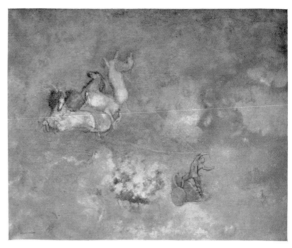

27.29

In 1878 Redon, in a study of Delacroix, praised
that artist's ceiling in the Louvre showing the
Chariot of Apollo, and in the same year he
noted in his journal his admiration for a painting of Phaëthon by Gustave Moreau. His own
treatments of the theme dealing with the
horses of the sun, driven by Apollo or by
Phaëthon, seem, however, to have come mostly later, between 1905 and 1916. During these
years he made oils, pastels, and water colors
with this subject. Our picture seems to represent Apollo or the sun god Helios rather than
the presumptuous Phaëthon, son of Helios,
who could not control the fiery horses and
was destroyed by Jove.

Formerly called Apollo.

Signed (at lower left): ODILON REDON.

Oil on canvas. H. 26, w. 32 in. (66 x 81.3 cm.).

References: B. B[urroughs], *Met. Mus. Bull.*,
xxii (1927), p. 90, ill. // S. Sandström, *Le
Monde imaginaire d'Odilon Redon* (1955), pp.
30f., fig. 26, dates this picture about 1900 //
R. Bacou, *Odilon Redon* (exhib. cat.), Musée
de l'Orangerie, Paris (1956–1957), p. 79, under no. 156 (another version) mentions our
picture, discusses Redon's treatment of the
theme // R. von Holten, *L'Art fantastique de
Gustave Moreau* (1960), p. 55 (note 6), cites
this painting as an example of a work by
Redon related to that of Gustave Moreau
(in a letter quoted in R. Bacou, *Odilon Redon*, 1956, I, p. 257) // J. Rewald, *Odilon
Redon, Gustave Moreau, Rodolphe Bresdin* (exhib. cat.), Museum of Modern Art, New
York, and Art Institute of Chicago (1961–
1962), p. 174, no. 46, dates it about 1910 //

K. Berger, *Odilon Redon* (1965), p. 192, no.
153, calls it a sketch for a painting in the
Petit Palais.

Exhibited: Virginia Museum of Fine Arts,
Richmond, 1950; Society of the Four Arts,
Palm Beach, 1951, *Portraits, Figures, and Land-
scapes*, no. 32; Phoenix Fine Arts Association,
Phoenix (Arizona), 1955, an exhibition to co-
incide with the World Symposium on Applied
Solar Energy; Corcoran Gallery of Art, Wash-
ington (D. C.), 1956, *Visionaries and Dreamers*,
no. 25; Milwaukee Art Center, 1958–1959,
Man's Concept of Outer Space; Museum of
Modern Art, New York, 1961–1962, and Art
Institute of Chicago, 1962, *Odilon Redon,
Gustave Moreau, Rodolphe Bresdin*, no. 46;
Arkansas Arts Center, Little Rock, 1963, *Five
Centuries of European Painting*, cat. pp. 40f.

Anonymous Gift, 1927.

Etruscan Vase with Flowers   53.140.5

This bouquet illustrates Redon's method of
basing his work on both direct representation
and memory. He has mingled real flowers with
imaginary ones that recall the fantastic flowers
invented by the eighteenth-century artist
Jean Baptiste Pillement. The composition,
free but consciously decorative, and the very

delicate technique led Mademoiselle Roseline Bacou of the Louvre, a specialist in Redon's work, to conclude that it was painted about 1910.

Tempera on canvas. H. 32, w. 23¼ in. (81.3 x 59.1 cm.).

REFERENCES: L. G. Cann, *International Studio*, LXXVIII (1923), ill. p. 104 // K. G. Sterne, *Parnassus*, III (1931), p. 9, lists this picture // S. Sandström, *Le Monde imaginaire d'Odilon Redon* (1955), p. 168, fig. 132, dates it 1900–1905 // J. Rewald, *Odilon Redon, Gustave Moreau, Rodolphe Bresdin* (exhib. cat.), Museum of Modern Art, New York, and Art Institute of Chicago (1961–1962), p. 173, no. 26, ill. p. 70, dates it 1900–1905 // K. Berger, *Odilon Redon* (1965), p. 204, no. 311, dates it c. 1912.

EXHIBITED: Carroll Galleries, New York, 1915, *Second Exhibition of Contemporary French Art*, no. 17; John Herron Art Institute, Indianapolis, 1915, *Paintings by Odilon Redon*, no. 11 (lent by the Carroll Galleries); Metro-

politan Museum, 1921, *Impressionist and Post-Impressionist Paintings*, no. 92 (lent by John Quinn); Museum of French Art, New York, 1922, *Odilon Redon*, no. 2 (lent by John Quinn); Brooklyn Museum, New York, 1926, *Special Loan Exhibition of Paintings by Modern French and American Artists* (no cat. published; lent anonymously, according to the museum's records); De Hauke & Co., New York, 1928, *Odilon Redon*, no. 16 (lent anonymously); Museum of Modern Art, New York, 1931, *Lautrec and Redon*, no. 84 (lent by a private collector, New York); and 1931, *The Collection of Miss Lizzie P. Bliss*, no. 117; Addison Gallery, Andover (Mass.), 1931, *The Collection of Miss Lizzie P. Bliss*; John Herron Art Institute, Indianapolis, 1932, *Modern Masters from the Collection of Miss Lizzie P. Bliss*, no. 87; Museum of Modern Art, New York, 1934, *The Lillie P. Bliss Collection*, no. 50; and 1934, *Fifth Anniversary Exhibition*, no. 21; Phillips Memorial Gallery, Washington (D. C.), 1941, *Function of Color in Painting*, no. 143 (lent by the Museum of Modern Art); Cincinnati Art Museum, 1944, *Pictures for Peace*, no. 28 (lent by the Museum of Modern Art); Museum of Modern Art, New York, 1952, *Les Fauves*, no. 7; Musée de l'Orangerie, Paris, 1956–1957, *Odilon Redon*, no. 184; Museum of Modern Art, New York, 1961–1962, and Art Institute of Chicago, 1962, *Odilon Redon, Gustave Moreau, Rodolphe Bresdin*, no. 26; Munson-Williams-Proctor Institute, Utica (New York), and in the Armory of the Sixty-ninth Regiment, New York, 1963, *Armory Show, 50th Anniversary Exhibition*, cat. p. 202, ill. p. 65 (an asterisk indicates that it is "believed to have been included in the 1913 exhibition, but . . . not listed in the original catalogue").

EX COLL.: [Carroll Galleries, New York, 1915?]; John Quinn, New York (by 1921, until 1925; Cat., 1926, p. 14); Lizzie P. Bliss, New York (until 1931); Museum of Modern Art, New York (1931–1951; Cat., 1942, no. 511, and 1948, no. 634).

MARIA DeWITT JESUP FUND, 1951; ACQUIRED FROM THE MUSEUM OF MODERN ART, LIZZIE P. BLISS COLLECTION.

53.140.5

Bouquet in a Chinese Vase 64.266

The vase in this painting seems to be the same one as in the Flowers in a Chinese Vase (above), but seen from another side. Here there are poppies, marigolds, and other flowers mostly in shades of red and orange, set against a copper-colored background. This bouquet, treated with greater definition than the other, is probably a little later in date, perhaps about 1912–1914.

Signed (at lower left): ODILON REDON.

Oil on canvas. H. 25½, w. 19½ in. (64.9 x 49.7 cm.).

REFERENCES: Francesco Sapori, *La Dodicesima Esposizione d'Arte a Venezia* (1920), p. 51 // A. Brookner, *Burl. Mag.*, CIV (1962), p. 130, fig. 35, comments on its effect of sparseness and intensity, likening it to music.

EXHIBITED: Venice, 1920, *XII Esposizione Internazionale d'Arte della Città di Venezia*, no. 51; Matthiesen Gallery, London, 1959, *Odilon Redon*, no. 75 (lent from a private collection, England); Roland, Browse and Delbanco, London, 1961, *Flowers*, no. 1; Alex Reid and Lefevre, London, 1962, *XIX and XX Century French Paintings*, no. 13.

64.266

EX COLL.: [Gallery Tanner, Zurich]; Mrs. E. Reichenbach, London (by 1959, in 1961); [Alex Reid and Lefevre, London, in 1962]; [Sam Salz, New York, until 1964].

PURCHASE, MR. AND MRS. HENRY ITTLESON JR. FUND, 1964.

Pissarro

Camille Jacob Pissarro. Born in 1830 at Saint Thomas, in the Virgin Islands, then a Danish possession; died in Paris in 1903. Pissarro's father was a Frenchman of Portuguese descent, and his mother was Creole. Pissarro was sent to school in Paris and there learned to draw. Back in Saint Thomas he worked for five years at his father's business but eventually got permission to study painting, and in 1855 he returned to Paris, where he worked at the École des Beaux-Arts and the informal Académie Suisse. He began by painting landscapes of the Antilles from memory but soon turned to scenes of Paris. These early paintings were sometimes done in the silvery gray tones used by Corot, who had encouraged him and given him advice, and occasionally showed the strong contrasts and heavy impasto of Courbet. Pissarro was admitted to the Salon in 1859 and contributed to its exhibitions at intervals throughout the sixties. In 1863 he exhibited three pictures at the famous Salon des Refusés, which attracted the attention of the critic Castagnary. During the sixties he began to lighten his color and by 1865, when he allied himself with the Impressionists, especially Monet, whom he had met at the Académie Suisse, and Renoir, he had achieved their kind of chromatic enrichment in the lights and shadows.

Pissarro was developing toward an impressionistic style when the Franco-Prussian War and the invasion of Paris drove him to London, where he was further stimulated in this direction by his study of the works of Turner and Constable. He saw much of Monet, who was also in London, and it was at this time that he met Durand-Ruel, who became his chief patron and his dealer. During the war about a thousand of Pissarro's pictures, left in his studio in Paris, were destroyed by the Prussians.

After the war Pissarro's style definitely crystallized into Impressionism, and until about 1882 he produced purely impressionistic works. Abandoning the official Salon, he contributed steadily, from the first showing in 1874, to the exhibitions of the Impressionist group and became its most enthusiastic and faithful member. His way of seeing was basically very like that of Monet, who exerted a decided influence on him. Established at Pontoise, however, Pissarro also spent much time with Cézanne and was briefly attracted to his solid forms and definite rhythms. It was Pissarro who directed Cézanne toward Impressionism; it was also he who converted Gauguin to painting outdoors and introduced him to the members of the group.

In 1884, after exhibiting at the Salon des Indépendants, Pissarro came in contact with Seurat and Signac and was influenced by Neo-Impressionism. He experimented with the pointillist, or divisionist, technique, but he was well aware that his impulsive temperament was cramped by such a rigid system, and his divisionist period was limited to the years between 1886 and 1890.

When Pissarro enthusiastically returned to impressionist freedom he entered a new period of growth. A retrospective exhibition of his works organized by Durand-Ruel in 1892 brought him success after three decades of bitter poverty and struggle. He settled at Eragny (Eure) but made many trips in search of new subject matter; he painted at Moret, Le Havre, and Dieppe and went more than once to London. In 1893 he began his first series of views of Paris streets glimpsed from the windows of various buildings. Later, following Monet's precedent, he undertook several series of pictures with the same motif: bridges, the cathedral of Rouen, the boulevards of Paris, the square of the Comédie Française, the Garden of the Tuileries, the Place du Carrousel, the Pont Neuf, and the Quai Malaquais.

Pissarro played a dual role in the French Impressionist movement. He was primarily an original artist, alert and curious, and though he submitted to various influences he never lost his own tender and poetic personal tone. He understood, perhaps even more intimately and directly than Monet, the spirit of the countryside and the life of growing things. Although he specialized in landscape, his interests were wide and he painted genre scenes, portraits, and still lifes and also mastered various engraving techniques. Beyond his contribution as a painter Pissarro was at the same time a great propagandist for Impressionism and brought several young artists into the ranks. He had a gift for teaching which he exercised generously, his spirit was incorruptible, and in the face of physical hardship and need he showed a serene courage that won the high regard of the foremost artists of his time. Although his vast output was unequal, his importance among the Impressionists will never be questioned.

Jallais Hill, Pontoise (La Côte du Jallais, Pontoise) 51.30.2

When shown at the Salon of 1868 this wide landscape, though hung too high, attracted the attention of Zola and Castagnary. It is the chief work of Pissarro's earliest, pre-Impressionist style and shows traces of Corot and also of Courbet, whose influence is especially evident in the use of deep greens against the vivid blue of the sky. It is Manet's inspiration, however, that accounts for the dramatic contrasts of light and dark and the broad, free brush stroke, which imbue this vision of nature with a completely new quality of freshness. Cézanne painted the same scene, very probably when he was visiting Pissarro in 1881 (Tyson coll., Philadelphia; L. Venturi, *Cézanne*, 1936, I, p. 314, no. 319, II, pl. 86).

Formerly called Hillside at Jallais, Pontoise.

Signed and dated (at lower right): *C. Pissarro / 1867.*

Oil on canvas. H. 34¼, w. 45¼ in. (87 x 114.9 cm.).

51.30.2

REFERENCES: J. Castagnary, *Salon de 1868*, reprinted in *Salons (1857–1870)* (1892), I, p. 278, praises this picture // E. Zola, *L'Événement illustré* (May 19, 1868), reprinted in *Salons* (1959), pp. 128f., expresses admiration for it, prefers it to Pissarro's other entry, L'Hermitage, at this Salon // C. Pissarro, in a letter to Durand-Ruel (Mar. 4, 1881), published in L. Venturi, *Les Archives de l'impressionnisme* (1939), II, p. 9, lists among the pictures he plans to show at the Impressionist exhibition of 1881 a painting, possibly this one, called La Côte du Jalais *(sic)*, pris sur le vieux chemin d'Ennery // M. Hamel, *Les Arts*, XIII (1914), no. 147, p. 26 // A. Tabarant, *Pissarro* (1925), p. 19 // *Art News*, XXVII (Mar. 9, 1929), p. 26 // L. R. Pissarro and L. Venturi, *Camille Pissarro* (1939), I, pp. 20, 85, cat. no. 55, II, pl. 10, no. 55, consider it the masterpiece of Pissarro's new manner in 1867 // J. Rewald, *The History of Impressionism* (1946), p. 162, ill.; (revised and enlarged edition, 1961), ill. p. 186 // J. Leymarie, *Impressionism* (1955), I, pp. 68, 71–73, ill., analyzes it, compares it to Corot's St.-André-du-Morvan of 1842 // J. Rewald, *Camille Pissarro* (1963), pp. 70f., ill. in color, comments on the robust approach and the solidity, stating that Daubigny intervened to have it accepted for the 1868 Salon.

EXHIBITED: Paris, Salon of 1868, no. 2015; 35 Boulevard des Capucines, Paris, 1881, *6e Exposition de peinture* ("Impressionist exhibition"), no. 72 (possibly ours, Paysage pris sur le vieux chemin d'Ennery, près Pontoise, see Venturi, *Les Archives . . .*, 1939, II, p. 9); Galerie Manzi et Joyant, Paris, 1914, *Rétrospective Camille Pissarro*, no. 5; Art Institute of Chicago, 1934, *A Century of Progress*, no. 260 (lent by William Church Osborn); Toledo Museum of Art, 1946, and Art Gallery of Toronto, 1947, *The Spirit of Modern France*, no. 46 (lent by W. C. Osborn); Metropolitan Museum, 1941, *French Painting from David to Toulouse-Lautrec*, no. 96 (lent by W. C. Osborn); Wildenstein, New York, 1945, *Camille Pissarro*, no. 2 (lent by W. C. Osborn).

EX COLL.: [Durand-Ruel, Paris]; [William H. Holston, New York, in 1929]; William Church Osborn, New York (from 1929).

BEQUEST OF WILLIAM CHURCH OSBORN, 1951.

A Cowherd on the Route du Chou, Pontoise   56.182

This picture presents a lively contrast to the earlier Jallais Hill, Pontoise (see above), which is a view of the same countryside. Painted seven years later, in the year of the first Impressionist exhibition, it is lighter in tone, showing the fleeting brush stroke and the shimmering surface of the Impressionist style. The major difference, however, lies in its greater unity of mood, atmosphere, and composition.

Formerly called Landscape near Pontoise.

Signed and dated (at lower left): *C. Pissarro. 1874.*

Oil on canvas. H. 21⅝, w. 36¼ in. (54.9 x 92.1 cm.).

REFERENCE: L. R. Pissarro and L. Venturi, *Camille Pissarro* (1939), I, pp. 40, 116, cat. no. 260, II, pl. 52, no. 260.

EXHIBITED: Musée des Arts Décoratifs, Paris, 1925, *Cinquante Ans de peinture française*, no. 57 (lent by Paul Rosenberg); Metropolitan Museum, 1956, *Summer Loan Exhibition* (lent by Mrs. Walter Sachs); Wildenstein, New York, 1965, *C. Pissarro*, no. 27.

EX COLL.: [Paul Rosenberg, Paris, in 1925]; Mrs. Arthur K. Salomon, New York (in 1939); Mrs. Walter Sachs (Edna H.), New York.

GIFT OF EDNA H. SACHS, 1956.

The Public Garden at Pontoise   64.156

Pontoise is a very old town about twenty miles outside of Paris, with historic connections that go back to Louis XIV, St. Louis, and the Gauls. A feature of its public gardens, which are pictured here, is the maze or labyrinth, from which there is a view of the valley of the Oise. Pissarro, who lived and worked

56.182

64.156

in Pontoise for a decade from 1872 to 1882, included another view of the park, painted the year before ours, among his five contributions to the first Impressionist exhibition. The loose and free brush strokes that he uses in the Museum's painting to suggest the foliage and the strolling figures are completely in the style of the early Impressionists, and related especially to that of Monet.

Signed and dated (at lower left): *c. pissarro 1874.*

Oil on canvas. H. 23⅝, w. 28¾ in. (60 x 73 cm.).

REFERENCES: A. Tabarant, *Pissarro* (1925), pl. 16 // T. Duret, *Histoire des peintres impressionnistes* (1939), p. 37, ill. // L. R. Pissarro and L. Venturi, *Camille Pissarro* (1939), I, p. 116, no. 257, II, pl. 51, no. 257.

EXHIBITED: Paul Rosenberg, New York, 1957, *Masterpieces Recalled*, no. 8 (lent by Mr. and Mrs. Arthur Murray); Metropolitan Museum, *Paintings from Private Collections*, 1961, no. 66 (lent by Mr. and Mrs. Arthur Murray); Wildenstein, New York, 1965, *Camille Pissarro*, no. 26.

EX COLL.: [Durand-Ruel, Paris, by 1925, in 1939]; [Paul Rosenberg, New York, until 1944]; Mr. and Mrs. Arthur Murray, New York (1944–1964).

GIFT OF MR. AND MRS. ARTHUR MURRAY, SUBJECT TO A LIFE ESTATE IN THE DONORS, 1964.

La Mère Larchevêque   56.184.1

This excellent characterization of a middle-aged countrywoman demonstrates Pissarro's insight and comprehension in his paintings of peasants. It is more than a portrait; for beyond the individualized likeness there is also, as often in Rembrandt's work, a picture of a social level and a way of life.

Signed and dated (at upper left): *C. Pissarro 80.*

Oil on canvas. H. 28¾, w. 23¼ in. (73 x 59 cm.).

56.184.1

REFERENCES: M. Hamel, *Les Arts*, XIII (1914), no. 147, p. 32 // L. R. Pissarro and L. Venturi, *Camille Pissarro* (1939), I, pp. 45, 153, cat. no. 513, II, pl. 105, no. 513 // L. Venturi, *Impressionists and Symbolists* (1950), p. 77, fig. 74 // J. Rewald, *Camille Pissarro* (1963), pp. 118f., ill. in color, praises this picture for its simplicity and depth.

EXHIBITED: Galerie Manzi et Joyant, Paris, 1914, *Rétrospective Camille Pissarro*, no. 40; Leicester Gallery, London, 1920, *C. Pissarro*, no. 67; Galerie Nunès et Fiquet, Paris, 1921, *Collection de Madame Veuve C. Pissarro*, no. 38; Durand-Ruel, Paris, 1928, *C. Pissarro*, no. 34; Musée de l'Orangerie, Paris, 1930, *Centenaire de la naissance de Camille Pissarro*, no. 122; Galerie Marcel Bernheim, Paris, 1934, *Pissarro et ses fils*; Leicester Gallery, London, 1935, *Fifty Years of Portraits*, no. 101 (lent by Mme Rodo Pissarro); Galerie de l'Élysée, Paris, 1936, *C. Pissarro*, no. 10; Metropolitan Museum, 1960, *The Nate and Frances Spingold Collection*.

EX COLL.: Mme Camille Pissarro, Paris (1903–1928); Ludovic Rodo Pissarro, Paris (1928–1947); [Sam Salz, New York, 1947–1948/49];

Mr. and Mrs. Nate B. Spingold, New York (from 1948/49).

A Washerwoman at Eragny 64.154.1

Pissarro spent a good part of the late summer and autumn months of 1893 at Eragny. This picture, like many done in the nineties, shows the lasting effect on Pissarro's style of the pointillism that he had abandoned several years before.

Signed and dated (lower left): *C. Pissarro. 93.*

Oil on canvas. H. 18, w. 15 in. (45.7 x 38.1 cm.).

REFERENCE: L. R. Pissarro and L. Venturi, *Camille Pissarro* (1939), I, p. 201, no. 861, II, pl. 176, no. 861.

EXHIBITED: Durand-Ruel, Paris, 1894, *C. Pissarro*, no. 29; Wadsworth Atheneum, Hartford (Conn.), 1959, *The Music Makers*, no. 12 (lent by Mr. and Mrs. Richard Rodgers).

EX COLL.: [Durand-Ruel, Paris, 1894]; Richard Rodgers, New York (in 1959–1964).

64.154.

A Bather in the Woods 29.100.126

Pissarro, who seldom painted the nude, wrote to his son Lucien, in the summer of 1893, that he had prepared several compositions of peasant girls bathing (C. Pissarro, *Lettres à son fils Lucien*, John Rewald, ed., 1950, p. 302, letter headed Paris, July 3, 1893). This painting of a young woman sitting on the bank of a stream is one of a group of nude studies made between 1893 and 1896. It is dated 1895 and seems to follow a painting done the year before of a young woman in the same posture and with the same setting but clothed (Pissarro and

29.100.126

Venturi, no. 901). A third very similar painting, also of a clothed model, is dated 1895 like our picture (*ibid.*, no. 903). Although Pissarro had consciously abandoned the divisionist technique in 1890, our painting shows traces of it, apparently retained in his effort to create a more intense luminosity.

Signed and dated (at lower left): *C. Pissarro. 1895.*

Oil on canvas. H. 23¾, w. 28¾ in. (60.3 x 73 cm.).

REFERENCES: L. R. Pissarro and L. Venturi, *Camille Pissarro* (1939), I, p. 206, cat. no. 904, II, pl. 183, no. 904 // C. Pissarro, *Letters to his Son Lucien* (edited by J. Rewald, 1943), p. 273, in a letter of Oct. 20, 1895, comments on Portier's sale of the picture to Hayashi

// J. Rewald, *C. Pissarro* (1954), pls. 28, 29 (detail); *Camille Pissarro* (1963), pp. 140f., ill. in color, suggests that it shows the artist's difficulty in overcoming divisionism and in working from imagination // F. Seiberling, *Impressionism and Its Roots* (exhib. cat.), The University of Iowa (1964), pp. 8, 48, no. 40, ill. p. 45, finds Pissarro adhering in it to the earlier, "classical" phase of Impressionism.

EXHIBITED: Wildenstein, New York, 1956, *Nude in Painting*, no. 28; Arkansas Arts Center, Little Rock, 1963, *Five Centuries of European Painting*, cat. p. 47; The University of Iowa, Iowa City, 1964, *Impressionism and Its Roots*, no. 40; Wildenstein, New York, 1965, *C. Pissarro*, no. 59.

EX COLL.: [Portier, Paris, 1895]; private collection of Tadamasa Hayashi, Tokyo, Paris, and New York (1895–1913; sale, American Art Association, New York, Jan. 8–9, 1913, no. 146); [Durand-Ruel, New York, in 1913]; H. O. Havemeyer, New York.

THE H. O. HAVEMEYER COLLECTION. BEQUEST OF MRS. H. O. HAVEMEYER, 1929.

Steamboats in the Port of Rouen
58.133

In the spring of 1896, and again in the fall, Pissarro painted in Rouen, a city of which he was especially fond, trying to capture "effects of fog and mist, of rain, of the setting sun, and of gray weather, motifs of bridges seen from every angle, quays with boats . . ." (C. Pissarro, *Lettres à son fils Lucien*, John Rewald, ed., 1950, p. 400, letter dated Feb. 26, 1896). This picture belongs to a large series made that fall in Rouen, many of them painted apparently from his room at the Hôtel d'Angleterre on the Cours Boïeldieu. At least seven of these show the same diagonal view of the quay and its boats in the foreground and across the water the buildings of Saint-Sever, a suburb of Rouen (Pissarro and Venturi, nos. 957–960, 965, 967, 969). In 1898 Pissarro returned to the same site and made further paintings of the harbor (*ibid.*, nos. 1039–1043, 1047–1054). This idea of studying one subject under changing conditions of weather and light had been enthusiastically developed by Monet.

Signed and dated (at lower right): *C. Pissarro. 96.*

Oil on canvas. H. 18, w. 21½ in. (45.7 x 54.6 cm.).

REFERENCE: L. R. Pissarro and L. Venturi, *Camille Pissarro* (1939), I, p. 214, cat. no. 958, II, pl. 194, no. 958.

EXHIBITED: Galerie de l'Élysée, Paris, 1936, *C. Pissarro*, no. 14.

EX COLL.: [Georges Petit, Paris; sale, *Quatrième Vente de la dissolution de la Société Anonyme des Galeries Georges Petit*, Hôtel Drouot, Paris, Dec. 15, 1933, no. 103]; Alphonse Bellier, Paris; Arthur J. Neumark, New York.

GIFT OF ARTHUR J. NEUMARK, 1958.

The Boulevard Montmartre on a Winter Morning
60.174

On the eighth of February, 1897, Pissarro wrote from Eragny to his son Lucien in London that he was going on the tenth to Paris, where he had engaged a room at the Grand Hôtel de Russie. This hotel was situated on the corner of the Rue Drouot, where the Boulevard des Italiens joins the Boulevard

58.133

Montmartre. From his room he intended to paint a series of boulevard scenes at different seasons and in varying kinds of weather, which he thought might be attractive to his dealer Durand-Ruel. Pissarro mentioned these paintings again in March, and on April 29 he said that he had almost finished the series and hoped that his son could see it at Durand-Ruel's. The next year, in 1898, Pissarro wrote that he had been given a large exhibition room all to himself at Durand-Ruel's, where he showed "twelve Avenues, seven to eight Avenues and Boulevards," and some other studies (C. Pissarro, *Lettres à son fils Lucien*, John Rewald, ed., 1950, pp. 431, 433, 438, 454). The Museum's painting is one of twelve scenes of the Boulevard Montmartre surely painted from Pissarro's hotel room (Ref., Pissarro and Venturi, 1939, I, II, nos. 986–995, 997, 998).

Signed and dated (at lower left): *C. Pissarro.* '97.

Oil on canvas. H. 25½, w. 32 in. (64.9 x 81.3 cm.).

REFERENCES: W. Dewhurst, *The Studio*, XX (1903), p. 96, ill.; and *Impressionist Painting* (1904), ill. between pp. 50 and 51 // *Brush and Pencil*, XIII (1904), ill. p. 432 // L. R. Pissarro and L. Venturi, *Camille Pissarro* (1939), I, p. 216, no. 987, II, pl. 199, no. 987.

EXHIBITED: Durand-Ruel, Paris, 1898, *C. Pissarro*, no. 14; Institute of Modern Art, Boston (Mass.), 1939, *The Sources of Modern Painting*, no. 69 (lent by Durand-Ruel); Knoedler and Durand-Ruel, New York, 1940, *Paintings of London-Paris*, no. 4; Durand-Ruel, New York, 1941, *The Art of Camille Pissarro in Retrospect*, no. 23 (lent anonymously).

EX COLL.: Durand-Ruel, Paris (private collection); Stanley Newbold Barbee, Beverly Hills (California); [Knoedler, New York, 1951–1952]; Mr. and Mrs. Ernest G. Vietor, New York and Greenwich (Connecticut) (1952–1959); Mrs. Ernest G. Vietor, New York and Greenwich (1959–1960).

GIFT OF KATRIN S. VIETOR (MRS. E. G.), IN LOVING MEMORY OF ERNEST G. VIETOR, 1960.

60.174

The Old Market at Rouen and the Rue de l'Épicerie 60.5

When Pissarro visited Rouen in 1898 he made three oil paintings of the point where the old market place (Anciennes Halles) joins the Rue de l'Épicerie, which leads to the south transept of the cathedral. This picture apparently records the activity there on Fridays, when the market was held; the other two show the marketplace without its stalls and with only a few figures in the street (Pissarro and Venturi, nos. 1037, 1038). Fifteen years before, in 1883, Pissarro had made a water color of the same subject, and he also did an etching with the same composition as the water color (*Masters of Modern Art*, exhib. cat., Marlborough Fine Art Limited, London, 1960, no. 24, ill., the water color; *Brush and Pencil*, XIII, 1903–1904, ill. p. 414, the etching). Claude Monet too recorded this site, viewed from the market square, in a picture in the collection of André Maus in Geneva, which Douglas Cooper dates tentatively about 1894 (ill. in *Claude Monet*, exhib. cat., Royal Scottish Academy, and Tate Gallery, 1957, no. 97, pl. 241).

In our painting the buildings in the foreground are treated with many broad, simple areas of color, in contrast to the background, where the richly varied architecture of the cathedral towers is handled with a rough and

60.5

scintillant impressionistic technique. In 1924 at the Leclanché sale this picture brought a sum that exceeded any previously paid for a work by Pissarro.

Formerly called La Rue de l'Épicerie à Rouen.

Signed and dated (at lower left): *C. Pissarro / 1898.*

Oil on canvas. H. 32, w. 25⅝ in. (81.3 x 65.1 cm.).

REFERENCES: C. Mauclair, *The French Impressionists* [1903], ill. p. 135 // *Le Figaro artistique* (Nov. 20, 1924), ill. // *Le Bulletin de l'art ancien et moderne* (Dec. 1924), p. 290, comments on the record sum of 83,000 francs brought by this picture at the Leclanché sale; (Jan. 1925), ill. p. 27 // S. de Ricci, *Beaux-Arts*, II (1924), p. 320, ill., comments on the significance of the auction price // L. R. Pissarro and L. Venturi, *Camille Pissarro, son art et son oeuvre* (1939), I, p. 225, no. 1036, II, pl. 208, catalogue it // C. Pissarro, *Letters to his Son Lucien* (edited by J. Rewald, 1943), p. 329, fig. 66 (photograph of the site), in a letter from Rouen, Aug. 19, 1898, writes of choosing this scene as a subject // A. Chamson and F. Daulte, *Chefs-d'oeuvres français des collections suisses*, in *Art et Style* (1959), no. 50 (unnumbered plate), in color // J. Rewald, *The History of Impressionism* (revised and enlarged edition, 1961), ill. p. 570 (with a photograph of the site, which he states was destroyed during the second World War).

EXHIBITED: Kunstmuseum, Bern, 1957, *Camille Pissarro*, no. 98 (lent by a private collector, Geneva); Petit-Palais, Paris, 1959, *De Géricault à Matisse, Chefs-d'oeuvre français des collections suisses*, no. 110 (lent by a private collector, Geneva); Wildenstein, New York, 1965, *C. Pissarro*, no. 68; Knoedler, New York, 1966, *Impressionist Treasures*, no. 24.

EX COLL.: Louis Bernard, Paris (until 1901; sale of Monsieur L. B., Hôtel Drouot, Paris, May 11, 1901, no. 47); Maurice Leclanché, Paris (1901–1924; sale, Hôtel Drouot, Nov. 6, 1924, no. 62); Auguste Savard, Paris (1924–1939/40); Roger Varenne, Geneva (1939/40–1960).

PURCHASE, MR. AND MRS. RICHARD J. BERNHARD FUND, 1960.

Manet

Édouard Manet. Born in Paris in 1832; died there in 1883. Manet belonged to an affluent bourgeois family. When his father, an important member of the Ministry of Justice, opposed his wish to become a painter he considered a career with the navy and made a crossing as apprentice pilot, sailing to Rio de Janeiro. On his return he entered the studio of the successful painter Thomas Couture. Although Manet rejected the academic standards of his master, he stayed with Couture for seven years, learning from him to model his style on the great colorists of the past and to emphasize textures and contrasts of light and dark. He also set himself to learn from nature, studying live models at the Académie Suisse and landscape at Fontainebleau. Between 1853 and 1856 he made trips to the Low Countries and also to Italy, Germany, and Austria.

During his early years Manet made many copies in the Louvre, especially of the paintings of Velazquez, Titian, Rubens, and Delacroix. In most of his works painted before 1870 he based his compositions on pictures by Chardin, Murillo, Goya, Rubens, and Raphael, disguising his borrowings with modern settings. In this way he hoped to demonstrate that he could give new life to the painting of his own time without breaking with tradition. Like Courbet he chose subjects from contemporary life such as The Absinthe Drinker and The Concert in the Tuileries. The Louvre's Déjeuner sur l'Herbe (Picnic), which shows two nude women in a landscape in the company of two men in contemporary dress, created a scandal at the Salon des Refusés in 1863, in spite of the fact that it actually was based on two Renaissance works, Giorgione's famous Concert Champêtre and an engraving after Raphael. A work filled with pictorial imagination, the painting Olympia, which was accepted for the Salon of 1865, provoked diatribes of harsh moral disapproval because of the individualized and realistic nude. In both these pictures, as in his less sensational paintings of contemporary events and in his marines and still lifes, much of the shock was due to Manet's highly original manner of painting. As his way of seeing became more personal and more consistent he simplified his drawing, color, and chiaroscuro to strengthen his forms, which accordingly became flatter and less representational.

The Spanish Singer, in the Salon of 1861, was the first of a series of paintings with realistic Spanish subjects, and is one of a number of these pictures owned by this museum, including A Boy with a Sword, Mademoiselle Victorine as an Espada, A Young Man in the Costume of a Majo, and A Torero Saluting. Manet's travels in the fifties had given him the opportunity to see, especially in Vienna, a number of paintings by Spanish artists that impressed him profoundly. Also, as a young man in Paris he could have known the gallery of four hundred Spanish paintings belonging to Louis Philippe, as well as the collection of nearly two hundred belonging to Marshall Soult, which was sold in 1852 and was especially rich in works by Murillo and Velazquez. In 1865 a short trip to Spain gave him a chance to study at first hand the works of Velazquez and those of Goya, whose technique he later imitated and whose compositions he borrowed. It is a paradoxical fact, however, that Manet's visit to Spain diminished his interest in Spanish subject matter. From this time on he celebrated French, especially Parisian, life.

In 1867 at the Paris World's Fair Manet held a private exhibition of his works in a building erected at his own expense near the one that Courbet had put up. This showing assured for him a position of widespread influence as the master of the avant-garde movement. Claude Monet, Pissarro, and Cézanne drew inspiration from his work. Théodore Duret and Émile Zola supported him, but many critics continued their hostile attacks.

After the Franco-Prussian War, from about 1872 on, Manet fared better. He sold a number of pictures to Durand-Ruel and to the singer Faure. Following Monet's example, he began to work outdoors as the Impressionists did, and his paintings became much lighter in color. Like Degas he developed such themes as the racetrack. But even these Impressionist influences and the enthusiastic support given the new cause by his pupil Berthe Morisot, who became his sister-in-law, did not weaken his wish for acceptance by the official Salon. Because of this ambition he never contributed to the Impressionist exhibitions. But in spite of this caution many of his works were rejected by the jury of the Salon, especially those, like Nana, that were treated in the spirit of naturalistic literature. His impressionist style became increasingly broad, giving even his finished pictures the immediate and unstudied effect of large sketches. Works of this sort, like Boating, which was accepted by the Salon, had an imposing appearance that attracted attention. His masterpiece in this manner, painted in 1881, is The Bar at the Folies Bergères (Courtauld Collection, London).

During the last eight years of his life Manet's success was assured. He received many commissions and made a great number of portraits of young women in Parisian society. About 1879, feeling the early symptoms of a serious illness, he sometimes worked in colored crayon and pastel, which tired him less than painting in oil. Shortly before his death he was obliged to stop painting out of doors, and he worked in his room on still life, especially flower pieces, and on some portraits, including the Museum's sketches of Faure.

In the history of modern painting Manet is of prime importance. It was he who began the simplification of the artist's vision and the resultant flattening of form, thus foreshadowing Gauguin and Matisse. He was the first to break away from the attachment to content, banishing all formulas and anecdotes in order to concentrate fully on plastic problems and true pictorial values. He was at the same time the first progressive painter of his generation to take inspiration from the old masters. Museums were developing rapidly during the nineteenth century, and Manet, much more than his academic contemporaries, reflects their influence. Like Picasso in our own time, he deliberately and methodically studied the art of the past.

The Bark of Dante   29.100.114

When Manet was young, one of the most celebrated "modern" pictures was Dante and Virgil in Hell, generally known as the Bark of Dante, painted in 1822 by Delacroix and exhibited in the Luxembourg Museum.[1] Manet paid a visit to Delacroix to get his permission to copy it, probably in 1854. According to Antonin Proust, who accompanied him, Delacroix was extremely gracious but surprised the young painter by advising him, with dogmatic seriousness, to follow in the footsteps of Rubens. Manet made two copies of the Bark of

Dante, one precise and literal (Ref., Jamot and Wildenstein, 1932, I, p. 114, no. 2; II, pl. 4, fig. 15), which went from the Chéramy collection to the Museum at Lyons, and ours, slightly smaller and much more summary. These two paintings, so different from each other, must have been done about the same time, at the end of 1854 or the beginning of 1855. Probably Manet began by making the faithful copy and then went on to do the freer and more personal interpretation. There are preliminary drawings for the Lyons version. In our painting Manet concentrated on re-creating Delacroix's composition in terms of colored masses. The lumpy patches of white paint reveal the influence of Couture, in whose studio Manet continued to work until the beginning of 1856. Somewhat over a decade later Delacroix's Bark of Dante was copied by Cézanne.[2]

Oil on canvas. H. 13, w. 16⅛ in. (33 x 41 cm.).

Notes: 1. Louvre, no. 207; U. Christoffel, *Eugène Delacroix* (1951), pl. 3. 2. L. Venturi, *Cézanne* (1936), I, p. 94, no. 125, II, pl. 31, no. 125.

References: T. Duret, *Histoire d'Édouard Manet et de son oeuvre* (1902), p. 192, no. 5, lists this painting // C. de Sainte-Croix, *Édouard Manet* (*Portraits d'hier*, no. 19, Dec. 15, 1909), p. 20, mentions it among copies made at the Louvre (1856–1858) // T. Duret, *Manet and the French Impressionists* (1910), p. 210, no. 5 // J. Meier-Graefe, *Édouard Manet* (1912), pp. 18f., note 1, alludes to it as a work of 1859 // A. Proust, *Édouard Manet, Souvenirs* (1913), pp. 23f., gives an account of Manet's visit to Delacroix for permission to copy The Bark of Dante // E. Moreau-Nélaton, *Manet* (1926), I, p. 24, fig. 9 // A. Tabarant, *La Renaissance*, XIII (1930), pp. 58f., dates our copy at the end of 1854 or the beginning of 1855, regards it as earlier than the copy in Lyons, notes that Mme Manet's account book records the sale of the painting to Vollard on October 30, 1894; *Manet, Histoire catalographique* (1931), p. 31, cat. no. 8, decides that the Lyons copy was painted before ours // P. Colin, *Édouard*

29.100.114

Manet (1932), pp. 16f., 73, lists ours as the second copy, dating it about 1855 // P. Jamot and G. Wildenstein, *Manet* (1932), I, pp. 20, 74, 114, cat. no. 1, date it 1854; II, pl. 220, fig. 485 // W. Uhde, *The Impressionists* (1937), p. 11, discusses the qualities in Delacroix's picture that may have attracted Manet // G. Jedlicka, *Édouard Manet* (1941), pp. 133f. // J. Rewald, *The History of Impressionism* (1946), pp. 23f., ill., dates it 1854; (revised and enlarged edition, 1961), p. 25, ill. // M. Florisoone, *Manet* (1947), p. xvii // A. Tabarant, *Manet et ses oeuvres* (1947), pp. 19, 533, no. 7, and *passim*.

Exhibited: Galerie Vollard, Paris, 1895; Metropolitan Museum, 1930, *The H. O. Havemeyer Collection*, no. 80; Wildenstein, New York, 1948, *Loan Exhibition of Manet*, no. 1; Bordeaux, 1963, *Delacroix, ses maîtres, ses amis, ses élèves*, no. 363.

Ex coll.: Mme Manet, Paris (until 1894); [Ambroise Vollard, Paris, from 1894]; Mrs. H. O. Havemeyer, New York (before 1902, until 1929; Cat., 1931, p. 150).

The H. O. Havemeyer Collection. Bequest of Mrs. H. O. Havemeyer, 1929.

Fishing in Saint-Ouen, near Paris (La Pêche)   57.10

This may be Manet's earliest landscape, painted at the beginning of the sixties or

57.10

and the same spire in the background.[1] The other is a small oil sketch in the collection of Baron von der Heydt at Zandvoort, which has been thought of as a study for our painting and is indeed often entitled La Pêche.[2] This little sketch is really a study that Manet made in 1863 when first preparing to paint the Louvre's Déjeuner sur l'Herbe; it was not used in the final version.

Early in this century a copy of our painting that had belonged to the painter's widow came on the market as a work by Manet himself and caused considerable disagreement until it was finally pronounced to be certainly not by him (Ref., Tabarant, 1947).

even before. Its setting, according to Madame Manet's notebook, is a real one, the banks of the river Seine at Île Saint-Ouen, in the region of Gennevilliers, where the Manet family owned property. As in most of his early works Manet has adapted motifs from pictures by the old masters. Two works by Annibale Carracci, Hunting and Fishing, in the Louvre (no. 1233, La Chasse; no. 1232, La Pêche), provided the chief elements. There are also direct borrowings from Rubens, whose Landscape with a Rainbow in the Louvre (no. 2118) supplied the rainbow, the dog, and the crossed saplings. Since these motifs appear in reverse in our picture Manet may have known Bolswert's engraving of the Rubens rather than the painting itself. The pair of figures at the lower right are related in costume and pose to Rubens's portraits of himself and his second wife, Hélène Fourment, in his painting of the Park of the Château of Steen in the Kunsthistorisches Museum in Vienna (no. 326). Manet, in adapting this couple, gave them the features of himself and his fiancée, Suzanne Leenhoff, whom he was to marry in 1863. It has been suggested that the child fishing on the opposite bank is Suzanne's son, Léon Koëlla-Leenhoff, who was about nine years old at the time the picture was painted and who also posed for Manet's Boy with a Sword (see below).

Two other works by Manet have similar compositions. One is the very early etching called Les Voyageurs (The Travelers), which shows the same river landscape, the same trees

Signed (at lower left): éd. Manet.

Oil on canvas. H. 30¼, w. 48½ in. (76.8 x 123.2 cm.).

Notes: 1. M. Guérin, L'Oeuvre gravé de Manet (1944), no. 1. 2. Ref. Jamot and Wildenstein, 1932, I, p. 124, no. 74, II, pl. 182, fig. 366.

REFERENCES: T. Duret, Histoire d'Édouard Manet (1902), pp. 100, 201, no. 33, lists this picture among paintings done in 1861-1862, but in text dates it 1859, identifies the couple at lower right as Manet and his wife, recognizes the landscape as the Seine at Saint-Ouen // C. de Sainte-Croix, Édouard Manet (Portraits d'hier, no. 19, Dec. 15, 1909), p. 21, lists this among the works of 1859–1860 // T. Duret, Manet and the French Impressionists (1910), pp. 75, 215, no. 33 // J. Meier-Graefe, Édouard Manet (1912), p. 124, pl. 59, dates it 1862, observes a connection between the handling of trees in this painting and in Déjeuner sur l'Herbe // E. Moreau-Nélaton, Manet (1926), I, pp. 29f., fig. 16, dates it about 1860, says Manet entitled it Paysage // P. Jamot, Gaz. des B.-A., xv (1927), pp. 37–42, ill., dates it before 1860, comments on the costumes, considers two paintings by Annibale Carracci in the Louvre as Manet's inspiration for this composition; p. 43, illustrates La Pêche by Carracci // A. Tabarant, Manet, Histoire catalographique (1931), p. 60, cat. no. 35, dates the painting 1861, relates it to Manet's etching called Les Voyageurs, identifies the child on the river bank as Léon

Koëlla-Leenhoff, wrongly giving his age as twelve years; p. 576, no. 35 // G. Bazin, *L'Amour de l'art*, XIII (1932), pp. 153–155, credits Charles Sterling with the discovery of Manet's borrowing from two Rubens paintings, Parc du Château de Steen in Vienna and the landscape with a rainbow in the Louvre; figs. 17–22 (details of ours and the related pictures) // P. Jamot and G. Wildenstein, *Manet* (1932), I, pp. 57, 117, cat. no. 30, say the picture was signed by Mme Manet, painted in Manet's Rue Guyot studio after his sketches of Île Saint-Ouen, and inspired by Carracci's La Pêche; II, pl. 4, fig. 13 // M. Florisoone, *Manet* (1947), p. xvii, pl. 11 // A. Tabarant, *Manet et ses oeuvres* (1947), pp. 34–36, 61f., 534, no. 29, and *passim*, discusses fully our picture and the copy ascribed to Mme Manet's nephew Édouard Vibert // N. G. Sandblad, *Manet* (1954), pp. 42–45, 89f., 170f., notes 46f., fig. 3 (confuses this painting with La Pêche in Baron von der Heydt's collection), relates elements in our painting to engravings by Schelte à Bolswert after the two Rubens paintings (figs. 2, 4) // J. Rewald, *The History of Impressionism* (revised and enlarged edition, 1961), p. 128.

EXHIBITED: Avenue de l'Alma, Paris, 1867, *Exposition particulière de Manet*, no. 50 (called Paysage); Galerie Matthiesen, Berlin, 1928, *Ausstellung Manet*, no. 5 (lent from a private collection, Paris); Bernheim-Jeune, Paris, 1928, *Manet*, no. 15 (possibly this painting); Musée de l'Orangerie, Paris, 1932, *Manet*, no. 14 (lent by Durand-Ruel, Paris); Venice, 1934, *Esposizione Biennale Internazionale d'Arte*, XIX, French Pavilion, cat. p. 282, no. 1 (lent by Durand-Ruel); San Francisco (California), 1940, *Golden Gate International Exhibition*, no. 274 (lent by Durand-Ruel, New York).

EX COLL.: Eugène Manet, Paris (until 1885); Mme Édouard Manet, Paris (1885–1897); private collection of Durand-Ruel, Paris (1897–1950); Jean d'Alayer d'Arc, Société Artistique Georges V, Paris (1950–c. 1956); [Sam Salz, New York].

PURCHASE, MR. AND MRS. RICHARD BERNHARD FUND, 1957.

The Spanish Singer 49.58.2

Manet himself regarded this picture as one of his most successful and important, and it was he who entitled it Le Chanteur Espagnol (The Spanish Singer). Soon after the picture was finished in 1860, Théophile Gautier called it a Guitarrero (Guitarist), and this title has been used by many other writers. The model has been said to be a musician named Jeronimo Bosch, who belonged to the Spanish troupe playing at the Hippodrome in Paris and who even performed for the Manet family and their guests at home. This identification, however, is disproved by two portraits of Bosch, a lithograph by Manet (Ref., Guérin, 1944, no. 70) and a print by Bracquemond (H. Beraldi, *Les Graveurs du XIXe siècle; III: Bracquemond*, 1885, p. 21, no. 18). Tabarant suggests that the idea of doing such a picture came to Manet because of the great popularity in Paris of the Andalusian guitarist Huerta, but that it was an unknown Sevillian model rather than Huerta who posed for the picture (Ref., 1947). Manet boasted that he had painted the head in two hours and that he had never added a brush stroke to it afterward. After the picture was finished a visitor asserted that he had made the performer play with his left hand an instrument strung for the right (Ref., 1913), but left-handed players do perform on instruments strung in this way.

Spanish subject matter, which had been used a long time before by the romanticists, was familiar to the French public, and both the subject and style of this picture, which follow Spanish seventeenth-century painting, were readily understandable. It did not, therefore, appear revolutionary to the public or the critics. When it was exhibited at the Salon of 1861, though hung in a bad position, it created a genuine sensation and attracted the attention of painters of the older generation like Delacroix and Ingres and advanced critics like Gautier and Baudelaire. It was awarded an honorable mention, possibly through Delacroix's intervention.

Actually this painting was a manifesto of a new art, chiefly because of the freshness of its color and the bold contrasts of light and dark, which differed greatly from the academic way of handling shadow and at the same time from Courbet's treatment of darks. Its vivid and deliberate realism had a decisive effect on Manet's young contemporaries.

In 1861 Manet made an etching after The Spanish Singer (Ref., Guérin, 1944, no. 16), of which the Museum owns two states. He also made a repetition of the picture in water color for his friend Antonin Proust (Ref., Richardson, 1958, pl. 4). The singer Jean Baptiste Faure, who had already acquired the oil painting, later bought this water color, which is today in the collection of Emery Reves at Roquebrune, France. (See Manet's portraits of Faure below.)

Formerly called The Guitarist.

Signed and dated (at right): *ed. Manet 1860*.

Oil on canvas. H. 58, w. 45 in. (147.3 x 114.3 cm.).

Note 1. *Arts: lettres, spectacles, musique* (Mar. 29–Apr. 4, 1961), no. 815, p. 9.

REFERENCES: T. Gautier, *Abécédaire du Salon de 1861* (1861), pp. 264f., draws attention to this painting when it was in the Salon of 1861, observes in it the influence of Velazquez and Goya // *Le Courrier artistique* (Oct. 15, 1861), p. 34, lists it among pictures exhibited at 26 Boulevard des Italiens // H. Callias, *L'Artiste*, series 7, XII (1861), p. 7 // L. Lagrange, *Gaz. des B.-A.*, XI (1861), p. 52 // C. Baudelaire, *Le Boulevard* (Sept. 14, 1862), reprinted in *Oeuvres complètes de Charles Baudelaire* (1925), v, p. 416, notes that it made a great impression at the Salon of 1861, comments on Manet's realism and grasp of the Spanish spirit // P. Mantz, *Gaz. des B.-A.*, XIV (1863), p. 383, predicts for Manet a powerful development // E. Zola, *L'Artiste (Revue du XIXe siècle)*, series 8, XIV (1867), p. 55, reprinted in *Salons* (1959), p. 94, comments on the ease with which the public accepted this picture // E. Bazire, *Manet* (1884), pp. 20, 22, ill. p. 11 (sketch for the etching), quotes Gautier's praise of it but observes that it was not universally acclaimed // L. Gonse, *Gaz. des B.-A.*, XXIX (1884), pp. 137–139, ill. // J. Péladan,

L'Artiste, I (1884), pp. 106f. // T. Duret, *Histoire d'Édouard Manet et de son oeuvre* (1902), pp. 17f., 196, no. 23, observes that Manet used a Spanish model; *Manet and the French Impressionists* (1910), pp. 14, 212, no. 23, ill. p. 15 // J. Laran and G. Le Bas, *Manet* [c. 1912], pp. 21f., pl. III, illustrates the etching, quotes contemporary critics // J. Meier-Graefe, *Édouard Manet* (1912), pp. 55, 310, pl. 29, asserts that the Spanish singer, I. Bosch, was Manet's model for this and also for a lithograph made by Manet's friend Bracquemond // A. Proust, *Édouard Manet, Souvenirs* (1913), pp. 40–42, 144, gives Manet's account of the rapid painting of this picture and how it was pointed out to him that he had made the guitarist finger the instrument with the wrong hand; mentions the water color of this subject // W. H. Wright, *Modern Painting* (1915), p. 67, sees in this picture traces of Goya, Murillo, Velazquez, and Courbet // T. Klingsor, *L'Amour de l'art*, III (1922), p. 258, ill. p. 266, stresses Manet's advanced technique in handling light and dark // E. Waldmann, *Édouard Manet* (1923), pp. 32, 109, ill. p. 24, mentions the permanent impression the picture made on Manet's public // L. Rosenthal, *Gaz. des B.-A.*, XII (1925), pp. 208–211, ill. p. 205 // E. Moreau-Nélaton, *Manet* (1926), I, pp. 31f., 133, fig. 21; II, fig. 342, illustrates it hanging in the posthumous exhibition of 1884, publishes it in Manet's list of the pictures he was to sell Durand-Ruel, with his asking price // A. Tabarant, *Manet, Histoire catalographique* (1931), pp. 57–59, cat. no. 34; p. 524, no. 30, catalogues the water color made after this painting // P. Jamot and G. Wildenstein, *Manet* (1932), I, pp. 21f., 75, 119, cat. no. 40; II, pl. 13, fig. 36 // D. C. Rich, *Parnassus*, IV (Feb. 1932), pp. 1–4, ill. // P. Durand-Ruel, *Mémoires*, published in L. Venturi, *Les Archives de l'impressionnisme* (1939), II, p. 190, gives his record of the picture // M. Guérin, *L'Oeuvre gravé de Manet* (1944), no. 16, publishes five states of the etching made after this painting // *Manet raconté par lui-même et par ses amis* (1945), pp. 89, 119–121, 188, 235, quotes contemporary criticism // J. Rewald, *The History of*

Impressionism (1946), pp. 44f., 225, ill. p. 45, gives an account of the favorable reception by the critics; comments on a contemporary liking for Spanish old masters, citing an article by Champfleury on Courbet; records Desnoyer's account of the strong impression the painting made on young contemporary artists; (revised and enlarged edition, 1961), pp. 50–52, 187, 272, ill. in color p. 53 // A. Tabarant, *Manet et ses oeuvres* (1947), pp. 41f., 102, 534, no. 38, and *passim*, suggests that the popularity of the guitarist Huerta inspired this picture, for which Manet used a Sevillian as model // J. C. Sloane, *French Painting between the Past and the Present* (1951), pp. 185, 192, fig. 55 // D. Cooper, introduction to *The Courtauld Collection* (1954), p. 22, note 1, identifies The Guitar Player exhibited by Durand-Ruel in London in 1872 as this picture // G. H. Hamilton, *Manet and His Critics* (1954), pp. 24–28, 40, 111, 120, pl. 3, reports on the picture's reception in the Paris press // N. G. Sandblad, *Manet* (1954), pp. 17, 46f., identifies the model as Huerta // J. L. Vaudoyer, *E. Manet* [c. 1955], no. 8, ill. (the painting and a large detail of the head) // J. Richardson, *Édouard Manet* (1958), p. 118, no. 4, pl. 4 (the water color), discusses the model, suggests that the composition was derived from a print by Goya (presumably L. Delteil, *Francisco Goya*, 1922, no. 30) and a painting by Greuze which Manet probably knew from the engraving (presumably the Oiseleur guitariste, see Ref., Vallery-Radot, 1959); and in a letter (1960), discusses the model // J. Lethève, *Impressionnistes et Symbolistes devant la presse* (1959), pp. 19, 22, 279, note 3 // H. Perruchot, *La Vie de Manet* (1959), pp. 98, 100, 102f., 104, 108, 122, 136, 187, 230 // J. Vallery-Radot, *Gaz. des B.-A.*, LIV (1959), p. 215, finds the pose similar to that of Greuze's Oiseleur guitariste, which exists in three versions in oil as well as in a drawing and an engraving (figs. 1, 2) // P. Courthion, *Manet* (1961), p. 64, ill. p. 65 in color, calls it a polished work, reminiscent of Courbet in the way the paint is applied.

EXHIBITED: Paris, Salon of 1861, no. 2098; 26 Boulevard des Italiens, Paris, 1861, *Exposition de peinture;* Avenue de l'Alma, Paris, 1867, *Exposition particulière de Manet*, no. 3; Glaspalast, Munich, 1869, *Internationale Kunst-Ausstellung*; Durand-Ruel, London, 1872, *Fourth Exhibition of the Society of French Artists*, no. 38 (as The Guitar Player); École des Beaux-Arts, Paris, 1884, *Exposition des oeuvres d'Édouard Manet*, no. 8 (lent by Faure); Paris, 1889, *Exposition centennale de l'art français*, no. 486; Durand-Ruel, Paris, 1906, *Exposition de 24 tableaux et aquarelles par Manet formant la collection Faure*, no. 7; Durand-Ruel, New York, 1913, *Loan Exhibition of Paintings by Édouard Manet*, no. 3; and 1928, *French Masterpieces of the Late XIX Century*, no. 10 (lent anonymously); and 1934, *Great French Masters*, no. 30 (lent anonymously); The Century Association, New York, 1936, *Exhibition of French Masterpieces of the Nineteenth Century*, no. 10 (lent by William Church Osborn); Wildenstein, New York, 1937, *Édouard Manet . . .*, no. 3 (lent by Mr. and Mrs. William Church Osborn); World's Fair, New York, 1940, *Masterpieces of Art*, no. 283 (lent by William Church Osborn); Knoedler, New York, 1941, *Loan Exhibition in Honor of Royal Cortissoz*, no. 22 (lent anonymously); Wildenstein, New York, 1948, *Loan Exhibition of Manet*, no. 5 (lent by William Church Osborn).

EX COLL.: [Durand-Ruel, Paris, from 1871/72–before 1884]; Jean Baptiste Faure, Paris (by 1884–1906); [Durand-Ruel, Paris, 1906]; William Church Osborn, New York (1906–1949).

GIFT OF WILLIAM CHURCH OSBORN, 1949.

A Boy with a Sword   89.21.2

The model for this painting was Léon Koëlla-Leenhoff, who himself asserted that he had posed for it in Manet's studio on the Rue Guyot toward the end of 1861, when he was not quite ten years old. The date 1861 and a second signature, which had both been added around the beginning of this century, were removed in a recent cleaning. The long heavy sword is a seventeenth-century weapon that Manet borrowed for the picture from his friend the painter Monginot, and the costume is of the same period. Léon, or Léon Édouard as he is named in the record of his birth, was born in 1852, the son of Suzanne Leenhoff, a Dutch pianist who eleven years later became Manet's wife. He was usually known as her youngest brother, but it has frequently been hinted that he was the natural child of Manet. As a young man he worked for a time as bank clerk under Auguste De Gas, the father of Edgar Degas the painter. He later became the proprietor of a successful firm that sold agricultural products.

In its decided contrasts of light and shadow the Boy with a Sword clearly shows the Spanish influence that is so marked in much of Manet's work during the first half of the sixties. Indeed the silhouette against the low horizon, the stance of the boy, and the diagonal of the sword vividly recall Ribera's painting of a club-footed boy that was in Paris in Manet's time and was given to the Louvre in 1869. Since Manet's painting had a fairly smooth surface and an agreeable and traditional subject not unusual during the first Empire, the public received it with less hostility than other works by Manet. Catalogues of Manet's work mention a small repetition of this picture (now in the collection of Mrs. Mellon Bruce, New York), but it seems to be a reduced copy, bearing an apocryphal signature.

This picture and The Woman with a Parrot, both presented to the Museum by Erwin Davis in 1889, were the first of Manet's works to enter public collections in this country. An undated letter from Manet preserved in the Metropolitan Museum's library refers to the sale of this picture by Durand-Ruel to Alden Weir, who bought it for Davis.

Signed (at lower left): *Manet.*

Oil on canvas. H. 51⅝, w. 36¾ in. (131.1 x 93.4 cm.).

REFERENCES: E. Zola, *L'Artiste*, series 8, XIV (1867), p. 55, reprinted in *Salons* (1959), p. 94, praises this picture, commenting on Manet's relation to Spanish painters, but observes that he himself prefers other works by Manet // A. Wolff, *Le Figaro* (May 1, 1883), predicts that this painting will be hung in the Louvre // E. Bazire, *Manet* (1884), pp. 54–56, 139, publishes Manet's sketch for his etchings of this picture, quotes Zola, identifies the boy as Léon Leenhoff // J. Péladan, *L'Artiste* (1884), I, p. 106 // A. Wolff, *La Capitale de l'art* (1886), pp. 220, 227, notes the influence of Velazquez in this picture // E. Durand-Gréville, *Gaz. des B.-A.*, XXXVI (1887), p. 74 // A. J. Eddy, *Brush and Pencil*, I (1897–1898), pp. 137f., 140 // T. Duret, *Histoire d'Édouard Manet et son oeuvre* (1902), pp. 19, 203, no. 41 (no. 42 refers to a small replica by Manet in the possession of M. Gérard in Paris); *Manet and the French Impressionists* (1910), pp. 16, 201f., 216, no. 41 // E. Waldmann, *Kunst und Künstler*, IX (1910), pp. 91, 96f., ill., observes that in this picture Manet worked for the first time with complete independence // J. Laran and G. Le Bas, *Manet* [c. 1912], pp. 23f., pl. IV, observes that it was exhibited in 1861 // J. Meier-Graefe, *Édouard Manet* (1912),

pp. 64 (note 1), 130 (note 4), 202 (note 1), 313, pl. 194 (etching), states that Manet borrowed the sword from Monginot, who had studied with him in Couture's studio, and gave him in return a sketch of the picture; gives an account, apparently erroneous, of Durand-Ruel's purchase of the painting from Manet in 1872 // A. Proust, *Édouard Manet, Souvenirs* (1913), pp. 120, 136, 152, 154 // W. H. Wright, *Modern Painting* (1915), p. 67, mentions this with the pictures of Manet's immaturity that were inspired by the "one-figure arrangements of Velazquez, Mazo and Carreño" // K. M. Roof, *Life and Art of Chase* (1917), p. 94, supposes that William Merritt Chase advised J. Alden Weir to buy this painting from Durand-Ruel for Erwin Davis in 1881 // D. Phillips, in *Julian Alden Weir, an Appreciation* (1921), pp. 20f., gives 1883 as the date of Weir's purchase of this picture for Davis // J. E. Blanche, *Manet* (1925), pp. 31, 42, pl. 4 // L. Rosenthal, *Gaz. des B.-A.*, XII (1925), p. 212, ill., in a study of the Spanish influences on Manet, observes that this painting recalls Velazquez rather than Goya // E. Moreau-Nélaton, *Manet* (1926), I, pp. 44f., 51, 133, fig. 48; II, p. 90, gives an account of Manet's dealings with Martinet, quotes an entry in Manet's notebook recording the sale to the dealer Fèvre (*sic*, for Febvre) // P. Jamot, *Revue de l'art*, LI (1927), pp. 33f., asserts that Victorine Meurend rather than Léon Leenhoff posed for this painting // A. Tabarant, *Manet, Histoire catalographique* (1931), pp. 68f., cat. no. 42, quotes Léon Koëlla-Leenhoff's statement that he posed for this picture when not quite ten years old in Manet's studio on the Rue Guyot, regards the small painting of the same subject cited by Duret (see above) as not by Manet but a copy // P. Jamot and G. Wildenstein, *Manet* (1932), I, pp. 35f., 119, cat. nos. 42, 43, II, pl. 12, fig. 35, give a complete history of the picture, say wrongly that Erwin Davis acquired it in 1880, reject the small copy // *French Art, 1200–1900* (commemorative cat. of exhib.), London (1933), pp. 99, no. 422, pl. 117 // P. Durand-Ruel, *Mémoires*, published in L. Venturi, *Les Archives de l'impressionnisme* (1939),

II, pp. 192, 210f., note 1, gives an account of his ownership of the picture, with the erroneous implication that he bought it directly from the artist, and his account of the 1881 sale of a group of pictures, including this one, which had been made over to Edwards as collateral for a loan // M. Guérin, *L'Oeuvre gravé de Manet* (1944), nos. 11–14, illustrates many versions and states of Manet's etching after this picture // H. Huth, *Gaz. des B.-A.*, XXIX (1946), pp. 232f., note 10, fig. 6 // A. Tabarant, *Manet et ses oeuvres* (1947), pp. 45, 183, 534, no. 44 // G. H. Hamilton, *Manet and his Critics* (1954), pp. 38f., 96, 98, 111, 120, 260, 265f., quotes early criticism of this picture // J. L. Vaudoyer, *E. Manet* [c. 1955], no. 9, illustrates the painting and a large detail // H. Perruchot, *La Vie de Manet* (1959), pp. 109f., ill. in color between pp. 96 and 97 // D. W. Young, *The Life and Letters of J. Alden Weir* (1960), pp. 145f., relates that Weir bought this picture in Paris in 1881 for Davis // P. Courthion, *Manet* (1961), p. 28, refers to it as one of Manet's too carefully painted pictures // T. Reff, *Burl. Mag.*, CIV (1962), pp. 183–185, fig. 2, discusses the sword carried by the boy and compares it with another representation of the same sword in Manet's etching that formed the second frontispiece of a collection of eight etchings (fig. 1; Ref. Guérin, 1944, no. 29).

EXHIBITED: A gallery in the Rue de Choiseul, Paris, 1861/62 (see Ref., Wolff, 1886); Bordeaux, 1862; 26 Boulevard des Italiens, Paris, 1863; Brussels, 1863, *Exposition générale des beaux-arts*, no. 755; Avenue de l'Alma, Paris, 1867, *Exposition particulière de Manet*, no. 4; National Academy of Design, New York, 1883, *Pedestal Fund Art Loan Exhibition*, no. 153 (lent by Erwin Davis); and 1886, *Works in Oil and Pastel by the Impressionists of Paris*, no. 303 (lent by Erwin Davis); Royal Academy, London, 1932, *French Art, 1200–1900*, no. 423; Pennsylvania Museum of Art, Philadelphia, 1933, *Manet and Renoir* (see *Pennsylvania Mus. Bull.*, XXIX, 1933, p. 17); Honolulu Academy of Arts, 1949–1950, *Four Centuries of European Painting*, no. 23; Art

Gallery of Toronto, 1950, *Fifty Paintings by Old Masters*, no. 23; Des Moines Art Center, 1953; Parrish Art Museum, Southampton (New York), 1957, *William Merritt Chase, a Retrospective Exhibition*, p. 14; Haus der Kunst, Munich, 1958, *Aufbruch zur Modernen Kunst*, no. 79.

EX COLL.: [Febvre, Paris, 1872]; [Durand-Ruel, Paris, from 1872]; Edwards, Paris (sale, Collection d'un amateur, Hôtel Drouot, Paris, Feb. 24, 1881, no. 39; see Ref., Durand-Ruel, 1939); Feder, Paris, 1881; [Durand-Ruel, Paris, 1881]; Erwin Davis, New York (from 1881; sale, Ortgies, New York, Mar. 19–20, 1889, no. 141, bought in).

GIFT OF ERWIN DAVIS, 1889.

Mademoiselle Victorine in the Costume of an Espada   29.100.53

Victorine Meurend was a favorite model of Manet, who abhorred ordinary studio models with their conventional poses. He is said to have noticed her first in a crowd at the Palais de Justice, though according to some it was in the Latin Quarter or the Batignolles neighborhood. She posed for him during more than a decade, serving as his model for this picture and for a portrait in 1862 and continuing until 1873, when he used her for the picture called The Railway now in the National Gallery, Washington. Three other famous paintings by Manet in which Victorine appears are Olympia and the Déjeuner sur l'Herbe in the Louvre and A Woman with a Parrot (see below). Victorine also posed for Alfred Stevens, and she became a painter herself, managing to get a self-portrait into the Salon of 1876. She made a trip to America and did not return to France until after Manet's death. She is said to have come to a sordid and distressing end, described, and probably romanticized, by George Moore in *Memoirs of my Dead Life* (she appears as "La Glue" in the chapter "The End of Marie Pellegrin").

This is one of the paintings of Spanish subjects that Manet made in his studio on the Rue Guyot, well before his visit to Spain.

Although in its background it reflects Goya's prints, the point of view is romantic and characteristically French rather than Spanish. The young woman, costumed as an *espada*, or matador, is posed somewhat artificially, brandishing a sword and holding a pink cape unlike any ever seen in the bull ring.

This picture, along with the Young Man in the Costume of a Majo (see below) and the Déjeuner sur l'Herbe, was rejected by the Salon of 1863 and was shown in the famous Salon des Refusés of that year. Manet himself made an etching after it (Ref., Guérin, 1944, no. 70), and there is a water color by him, with the composition reversed, in the Rhode Island School of Design in Providence (ill. in *Bull. of the Rhode Island School of Design*, 1930, July cover).

A recent cleaning of the Museum's painting has reinforced the brilliance of the color and brought out the lively handling characteristic of Manet's work at this time.

29.100.53

Signed and dated (at lower left): *ed. Manet/ 1862.*

Oil on canvas. H. 65, w. 50¼ in. (165.1 x 127.7 cm.).

REFERENCES: Z. Astruc, *Le Salon de 1863* (May 20, 1863), expresses great admiration for the picture (see Moreau-Nélaton, 1926, I, p. 51) // J. Castagnary, *L'Artiste*, series 8, IV (1863), p. 76, reprinted in *Salons (1857–1870)* (1892), pp. 173f., criticizes it adversely, finding fault with the drawing and execution // T. Thoré [W. Bürger], *Le Salon de 1863: Les Réprouvés*, reprinted in *Salons de W. Bürger, 1861–1868* (1870), I, p. 424, comments on Manet's enthusiasm for Goya, praising the pictorial qualities of this painting, but complaining of a lack of psychological depth // E. Zola, *L'Artiste*, series 8, XIV (1867), pp. 53, 56, reprinted in *Salons* (1959), pp. 93, 95f., praises Manet's use of color // J. Péladan, *L'Artiste* (1884), I, pp. 106f., 116 // T. Duret, *Histoire d'Édouard Manet et de son oeuvre* (1902), p. 202, no. 37; *Manet and the French Impressionists* (1910), p. 215, no. 37 // E. Waldmann, *Kunst und Künstler*, IX (1910), pp. 134, 138, ill. p. 92, finds evidence in our picture of a new kind of artistic vision // J. Meier-Graefe, *Édouard Manet* (1912), pp. 64, 313, pl. 43, comments on the French spirit with which the artist interprets the Spanish subject matter // A. Tabarant, *Bull. de la vie artistique*, II (1921), p. 297, ill., discusses Victorine as Manet's model // E. Waldmann, *Édouard Manet* (1923), pp. 16f., 18, 29–32, 45f., ill. p. 43, praises this picture, discusses Manet's visit to Madrid // E. Moreau-Nélaton, *Manet* (1926), I, pp. 48, 51, 132, fig. 53, II, fig. 341, illustrates it hanging in the posthumous exhibition of 1884; publishes it in Manet's list of the pictures he was to sell to Durand-Ruel, with his asking price // P. Jamot, *Rev. de l'art*, LI (1927), pp. 36, 38 // L. E. Rowe, *Bull. of the Rhode Island School of Design*, XVIII (1930), pp. 26f., ill. (ill. of water color on cover, p. 25) // C. V. Wheeler, *Manet* (1930), pp. 14f., ill., 40, 42, gives a full account of Victorine's career // A. Tabarant, *La Renaissance*, XIII (1930), pp. 61–64,

ill. p. 58; *Manet, Histoire catalographique* (1931), pp. 84f., cat. no. 54 // P. Colin, *Édouard Manet* (1932), p. 73, pl. VII // P. Jamot and G. Wildenstein, *Manet* (1932), I, pp. 77, 89, 121, cat. no. 51; II, pl. 17, fig. 40 // P. Durand-Ruel, *Mémoires*, published in L. Venturi, *Les Archives de l'impressionnisme* (1939), II, p. 191, gives his record of this painting, calls it "Mademoiselle V. en toréador (portrait de V. Brin [?])" // G. Jedlicka, *Édouard Manet* (1941), pp. 78f. // M. Guérin, *L'Oeuvre gravé de Manet* (1944), no. 32, publishes Manet's etching of it in two states // J. Rewald, *The History of Impressionism* (1946), pp. 72, 225, ill. p. 75; (revised and enlarged edition, 1961), pp. 85, 272, ill. p. 83 // M. Florisoone, *Manet* (1947), pp. xxii, 116f., pl. 20 // A. Tabarant, *Manet et ses oeuvres* (1947), pp. 54, 73, 534, no. 55, and *passim* // J. C. Sloane, *French Painting between the Past and the Present* (1951), pp. 186, 194, note 10, fig. 60 // Metropolitan Museum, *Art Treasures* (1952), p. 233, no. 145, pl. 145 // G. H. Hamilton, *Manet and His Critics* (1954), pp. 43, 47, 50, 52, pl. 5 // J. L. Vaudoyer, *E. Manet* [c. 1955], no. 13, illustrates the painting and a large detail of the head // N. G. Sandblad, *Manet* (1954), p. 83 // J. Richardson, *Édouard Manet* (1958), pp. 14, 20f., 119, no. 10, pl. 10 // J. Lethève, *Impressionnistes et Symbolistes devant la presse* (1959), pp. 23f., quotes the critics of 1863 // H. Perruchot, *La Vie de Manet* (1959), pp. 118, 121, ill. in first section of plates // F. Daulte, *L'Oeil* (June 1960), p. 58, reproduces the page from Durand-Ruel's account book on which is recorded the purchase from Manet of this picture, called *Le Toréador*, in January 1872 // L. W. Havemeyer [Mrs. H. O.], *Sixteen to Sixty, Memoirs of a Collector* (1961), pp. 224f. // J. Canaday, *Horizon*, VI (Winter 1964), p. 92, ill. (the whole and a detail in color), analyzes Manet's method.

EXHIBITED: Paris, 1863, Salon des Refusés, no. 365; Avenue de l'Alma, Paris, 1867, *Exposition particulière de Manet*, no. 12; École des Beaux-Arts, Paris, 1884, *Exposition des oeuvres d'Édouard Manet*, no. 15; Metropolitan Museum, 1930, *The H. O. Havemeyer Collection*, no. 76; William Rockhill Nelson Gallery of Art, Kansas City, 1935, *One Hundred Years of French Painting*, no. 31; Stedelijk Museum, Amsterdam, 1938, *Honderd Jaar Fransche Kunst*, no. 139.

Ex coll.: [Durand-Ruel, Paris, from 1871/72]; Jean Baptiste Faure, Paris (until 1898); [Durand-Ruel, Paris, 1898]; H. O. Havemeyer, New York (1898–1929; Cat., 1931, p. 147).

The H. O. Havemeyer Collection. Bequest of Mrs. H. O. Havemeyer, 1929.

A Young Man in the Costume of a Majo   29.100.54

The painter's brother Gustave posed for this picture, dressed in the Andalusian costume affected by the young Spanish blades called *majos*. The painting, which was done in Manet's studio on the Rue Guyot, is inscribed very legibly with the date 1863, but books and catalogues have often erroneously given the date as 1862. Refused by the official Salon of 1863, it was exhibited at the Salon des Refusés.

Signed (at lower right): *éd. Manet 1863*.

Oil on canvas. H. 74, w. 49⅛ in. (188 x 124.8 cm.).

References: Z. Astruc, *Le Salon de 1863* (May 20, 1863), praises Manet, considers this picture frank and robust (see Moreau-Nélaton, 1926, I, p. 51) // J. Castagnary, *L'Artiste*, series 8, IV (1863), p. 76, reprinted in *Salons, 1857–1870* (1892), pp. 173f., criticizes it adversely, finds fault with the drawing and execution // T. Thoré [W. Bürger], *Le Salon de 1863: Les Réprouvés* (1863), in *Salons de W. Bürger, 1861–1868* (1870), I, p. 424, comments on Manet's enthusiasm for Goya, praising the pictorial qualities of this painting, but complains of a lack of psychological depth // E. Zola, *L'Artiste*, series 8, XIV (1867), pp. 53, 56, reprinted in *Salons* (1959), pp. 93, 95f., praises it highly, especially its color // J. Péladan, *L'Artiste* (1884), I, p. 106 // T. Duret,

Histoire d'Édouard Manet et de son oeuvre (1902), pp. 200f., no. 32, identifies the model as Manet's brother Eugène; *Manet and the French Impressionists* (1910), p. 214, no. 32 // J. Meier-Graefe, *Édouard Manet* (1912), pp. 64 (note 1), 312, pl. 42 // E. Waldmann, *Édouard Manet* (1923), pp. 16–18 // E. Moreau-Nélaton, *Manet* (1926), I, pp. 48, 51, 133, fig. 52; II, p. 47, fig. 341, illustrates it hanging in the 1884 posthumous exhibition, publishes it in Manet's list of the pictures he was to sell to Durand-Ruel, with his asking price // A. Tabarant, *La Renaissance*, XIII (1930), pp. 60f., ill. p. 57; *Manet, Histoire catalographique* (1931), pp. 83–85, cat. no. 53 // P. Jamot and G. Wildenstein, *Manet* (1932), I, pp. 25, 76, 121f., cat. no. 52; II, pl. 16, fig. 39, state that the model was Manet's brother

29.100.54

Gustave, not Eugène // R. Rey, *Manet* (1938), pp. 12, 26, 163, no. 116, ill. p. 116 // P. Durand-Ruel, *Mémoires*, published in L. Venturi, *Les Archives de l'impressionnisme* (1939), II, p. 190, gives his record of the painting // G. Jedlicka, *Édouard Manet* (1941), p. 85, compares this picture with Manet's Torero Saluting (see below) // J. Rewald, *The History of Impressionism* (1946), p. 72; (revised and enlarged edition, 1961), p. 85 // A. Tabarant, *Manet et ses oeuvres* (1947), pp. 62, 69, 136, 195, 491, 534, no. 54, and *passim*, accepts the identification of the model as Gustave rather than Eugène Manet // G. H. Hamilton, *Manet and His Critics* (1954), pp. 43, 47, 50, pl. 4 // N. G. Sandblad, *Manet* (1954), p. 83 // J. Lethève, *Impressionnistes et Symbolistes devant la presse* (1959), pp. 23ff., quotes the critics of 1863 // H. Perruchot, *La Vie de Manet* (1959), pp. 118, 121, ill. in first section of plates // F. Daulte, *L'Oeil* (June 1960), p. 58, reproduces the page from Durand-Ruel's account book on which is recorded the purchase from Manet of this picture, called l'Espagnol, in January 1872 // L. W. Havemeyer [Mrs. H. O.], *Sixteen to Sixty, Memoirs of a Collector* (1961), p. 224 // D. Rouart, in a letter (May 9, 1961), states that Gustave Manet was certainly the model.

EXHIBITED: Paris, 1863, Salon des Refusés, no. 364; Avenue de l'Alma, Paris, 1867, *Exposition particulière de Manet*, no. 13; École des Beaux-Arts, Paris, 1884, *Exposition des oeuvres d'Édouard Manet*, no. 11 (lent by Faure); Durand-Ruel, New York, 1913, *Loan Exhibition of Paintings by Manet*, no. 4, and 1928, *French Masterpieces of the Late XIX Century*, no. 9 (lent anonymously); Metropolitan Museum, 1930, *The H. O. Havemeyer Collection*, no. 77; Musée de l'Orangerie, Paris, 1932, *Exposition Manet*, no. 9; Toledo Museum of Art (Ohio), 1934, *French Impressionists and Post-Impressionists*, no. 6; George Walter Vincent Smith Art Gallery, Springfield (Mass.), 1935, *French Painting from David to Cézanne*; Wildenstein, New York, 1948, *Manet*, no. 11.

EX COLL.: [Durand-Ruel, Paris, from 1871/72]; Ernest Hoschedé, Paris (sale, Hôtel Drouot, Paris, June 5–6, 1878, no. 43, as Le Toréador); Jean Baptiste Faure, Paris (1878–1898); [Durand-Ruel, Paris, 1898–1899]; H. O. Havemeyer, New York (1899–1929; Cat., 1931, no. 143).

THE H. O. HAVEMEYER COLLECTION. BEQUEST OF MRS. H. O. HAVEMEYER, 1929.

The Dead Christ with Angels

29.100.51

Religious subject matter was seldom treated by the Impressionists. This painting and the Mocking of Christ (1865) in the Art Institute of Chicago are the most important of the rare religious pictures by Manet. Although he once told Antonin Proust that he would like to paint a Crucifixion, there is no extant painting by him with this subject (Ref., Courthion, 1961, p. 78). In the late fall of 1863 Manet told his friend the Abbé Hurel that he proposed to paint a Dead Christ with Angels. He probably began the picture soon after, finishing it in March of 1864, in time to send it to the Salon of that year. The jury of 1864, more liberal than its predecessors, accepted from Manet this picture and a bullfight scene. The Dead Christ showing his wounds, and often held upright by a pair of angels, is an old devotional theme that goes back to the fourteenth century. But the title of Manet's painting when it appeared at the Salon, Les Anges au Tombeau du Christ, suggests that Manet did not intend to treat this traditional mystical theme of the Man of Sorrows. He has, in fact, inscribed on the painting a reference to the Gospel of St. John, citing chapter XX, verses 5 to 12. The allusion to the text of St. John is puzzling, for the passage describes the two angels and the deserted tomb, whereas in the picture the emphasis is laid on Christ himself. Manet was so little versed in traditional iconography that he painted Christ's wound on his left side rather than his right, and it also appears on the left in his etching of the same composition (ill. in Ref. Guérin, 1944). Baudelaire pointed out the error after the painting had already been sent off to the Salon. A water color probably made in preparation for the etching shows the entire composition in reverse and the wound therefore on the right side of Christ. This water color, now in the Louvre, was presented by Manet to Zola, who had praised the original painting (ill. in color in Ref. Martin, 1958).

Whenever Manet painted from imagination rather than from places and people he actually knew, he looked for sources not in texts but, as here, in paintings and old engravings. The arrangement recalls compositions by several artists of the Italian Renaissance, especially Veronese's paintings of the Dead Christ in the Hermitage and in the Museums at Lille and Ottawa. There is also some similarity to a

29.100.51

picture in the Louvre formerly attributed to Tintoretto and an even more direct connection with the Dead Christ with Angels by Mantegna at Copenhagen, which was well known through two engravings. A striking formal relationship seems to exist between our painting and the Jupiter and Thetis by Ingres (1811; Musée Granet, Aix), which also has for central theme a large frontal male figure, similarly posed and lit.

When Manet's Dead Christ with Angels was shown at the Salon it set off a barrage of criticism. Courbet and others subjected it to crude ridicule, but Thoré-Bürger, the famous "discoverer" of Vermeer, spoke out loudly in its praise, though he thought it a pastiche, assuming Manet had borrowed from a number of painters, Greco in particular. Baudelaire, who considered himself a friend of Manet's, wrote a warm acknowledgment of Thoré-Bürger's praise but denied that the painter had ever seen works by Greco or Goya, or even the Spanish pictures belonging to Louis Philippe, which were on exhibition in the Louvre in the years between 1838 and 1848 (quoted in Ref. Moreau-Nélaton, 1926).

The painting has been sharply criticized as completely lacking in religious feeling. Actually the grandeur of the monumental body, frontal and so dramatically lit, and the expression of rapt devotion in the pose and on the faces of the attendant angels combine to give an effect of solemn dignity that belongs completely to the French tradition. This effect has been much heightened by a recent cleaning.

Signed (at lower left): *Manet*; inscribed (on stone): *évang*[ile] *sel*[on] *St. Jean/ Chap*[itre] *XX v-xii* (gospel according to St. John, Chapter xx v-xii).

Oil on canvas. H. 70⅝, w. 59 in. (179.4 x 149.9 cm.).

REFERENCES: E. About, *Le Petit Journal* (June 3, 1864) // H. de Callias, *L'Artiste*, series 8, v (1864), p. 242, finds fault with its color // T. Thoré, *L'Indépendance belge* (1864), considers Greco Manet's source for this painting (quoted in Moreau-Nélaton, 1926, I, p. 57) // C. Baudelaire, *Lettres . . .* (1907), pp. 361f.,

retorts in a letter to Thoré, 1864, that Manet had never seen the work of Greco, though he was familiar with that of Velazquez // T. Thoré [W. Bürger], *Salon de 1864*, reprinted in *Salons de W. Bürger, 1861–1868* (1870), II, pp. 137f., gives credit to some of Baudelaire's contentions // E. Zola, *L'Artiste*, series 8, XIV (1867), p. 57, reprinted in *Salons* (1959), pp. 96f., praises the picture for its freedom and vigor // E. Bazire, *Manet* (1884), pp. 40f., gives some account of contemporary criticism of this painting, states wrongly that Manet corrected the error in the placing of Christ's wound // G. Moore, *Modern Painting* (1898), pp. 35, 41, considers this one of Manet's finest works, comments on its lack of religious intention // T. Duret, *Histoire d'Édouard Manet et de son oeuvre* (1902), pp. 27, 206, no. 56 // H. v. Tschudi, *Édouard Manet* (1902), p. 19, says that Manet relied on Venetian prototypes // T. Duret, *Manet and the French Impressionists* (1910), pp. 23, 218, no. 56 // J. Laran and G. Le Bas, *Manet* [c. 1912], pp. 37f., pl. XI // J. Meier-Graefe, *Édouard Manet* (1912), pp. 71–76, 312, pl. 39, suggests that this picture shows the influence of Greco, supplies information about ownership of the picture // W. H. Wright, *Modern Painting* (1915), p. 79, suggests that in its arrangement and lighting it recalls the Jupiter and Thetis by Ingres // E. Waldmann, *Édouard Manet* (1923), p. 37, ill. p. 27, mentions this painting as an example of Manet's dependence on Titian // A. Tabarant, *Bull. de la vie artistique*, IV (1923), pp. 247–250, ill. // J. E. Blanche, *Manet* (1925), pp. 35f., pl. 12, finds the robes of the angels similar to those in Velazquez's Christ and the Christian Soul in the National Gallery, London // A. Vollard, *Renoir* (1925), p. 46, and *Degas* (1927), pp. 99f., confuses the comments of Renoir and Degas about this picture and their allusion to Courbet's ridicule of it // E. Moreau-Nélaton, *Manet* (1926), I, pp. 57–59, 133, fig. 58, quotes exchange of opinions between Thoré-Bürger and Baudelaire about Manet's sources for this painting, publishes it in Manet's list of the pictures he was to sell to Durand-Ruel, with his asking price // A. Tabarant, *La Renaissance*, XIII

(1930), pp. 64–66, ill. p. 59, states that the painting was begun at the end of 1863 and finished in March 1864; and *Manet, Histoire catalographique* (1931), pp. 116–119, cat. no. 72, quotes contemporary press accounts concerning this painting in the 1864 Salon; p. 524, no. 31 (the water color) // P. Colin, *Édouard Manet* (1932), pp. 24, 28, 74, reports Courbet's derision of the painting // P. Jamot and G. Wildenstein, *Manet* (1932), I, pp. 27, 126, cat. no. 85; II, pl. 6, fig. 22, date it 1864 // D. C. Rich, *Parnassus*, IV (Feb. 1932), p. 4 // M. Florisoone, *L'Amour de l'art*, XVIII (1937), pp. 26f., agrees with Charles Sterling in seeing a connection with Veronese, relates the painting also to one by Tintoretto in the Louvre (now attributed to the school of Tintoretto) // P. Durand-Ruel, *Mémoires*, published in L. Venturi, *Les Archives de l'impressionnisme* (1939), II, p. 191, gives his record of the picture // G. Jedlicka, *Édouard Manet* (1941), pp. 86f., 397, note 9, observes similarities to religious paintings by Velazquez, comments on the lack of religious emotion // M. Guérin, *L'Oeuvre gravé de Manet* (1944), no. 34, illustrates first and third states of Manet's etching after this painting and his water color, discusses iconography of misplaced wound // A. Tabarant, *La Vie artistique au temps de Baudelaire* (1942), pp. 393f., 405, quotes many adverse criticisms of it in the contemporary press when it was shown at the Salon of 1864 // L. Piérard, *Manet l'incompris* (1944), pp. 75f., quotes Courbet's adverse criticism // I. N. Ebin, *Gaz. des B.-A.*, XXVII (1945), p. 362, ill. p. 359 // *Manet raconté par lui-même et par ses amis* (1945), pp. 69, 95, 126–129, quotes Zola, Thoré, and Baudelaire // H. Huth, *Gaz. des B.-A.*, XXIX (1946), pp. 230f., fig. 5, discusses the Foreign Exhibition in Boston in 1883, in which this painting was shown // J. Rewald, *The History of Impressionism* (1946), pp. 92, 118, notes 21, 22 // M. Florisoone, *Manet* (1947), pp. xv, XXXI, note 6, pl. 28, notes Jean Feidel's suggestion that there is a relationship here with Mantegna's Dead Christ in Copenhagen // A. Tabarant, *Manet et ses oeuvres* (1947), pp. 80–84, 87, 173, 535, no. 71 // J. C. Sloane,

French Painting between the Past and the Present (1951), p. 192, fig. 65 // E. Wind, *Art News*, LII (1953), pp. 19f., ill., studies the picture in relation to modern attitudes toward religious themes // D. Cooper, introduction to *The Courtauld Collection* (1954), p. 22, note 1, identifies the Christ in the Sepulchre exhibited by Durand-Ruel in London in 1872 as this picture // G. H. Hamilton, *Manet and His Critics* (1954), pp. 55–63, 98, pl. 12, quotes contemporary critics // J. L. Vaudoyer, *É. Manet* [c. 1955], no. 14, illustrates full page detail of head of angel at left // V. Gurewich, *Journal of the Warburg and Courtauld Institutes*, XX (1957), pp. 358–362, pl. 26a, publishes this picture in a detailed study of the iconography of the wound in Christ's side // [K. Martin], *Édouard Manet: Aquarelle und Pastelle* (1958), p. 11 and no. 6, illustrates the water color // J. Richardson, *Édouard Manet* (1958), p. 121, no. 22, pl. 22 // J. Lethève, *Impressionnistes et Symbolistes devant la presse* (1959), pp. 26, 28, quotes contemporary critics // H. Perruchot, *La Vie de Manet* (1959), pp. 149f., 153, 158, 160 // F. Daulte, *L'Oeil* (June 1960), p. 58, reproduces the page from Durand-Ruel's account book on which is recorded the purchase from Manet of this picture, called Le Christ, in January 1872 // P. Courthion, *Manet* (1961), pp. 34, 78, ill. p. 79 in color, quotes Manet's statement about wanting to paint a Crucifixion, finds the choice of colors Spanish // L. W. Havemeyer [Mrs. H. O.], *Sixteen to Sixty, Memoirs of a Collector* (1961), pp. 236f.

EXHIBITED: Paris, Salon of 1864, no. 1281; Avenue de l'Alma, Paris, 1867, *Exposition particulière de Manet*, no. 7; Durand-Ruel, London, 1872, *Fourth Exhibition of the Society of French Artists*, no. 91 (as Christ in the Sepulchre); Mechanics' Building, Boston, 1883, *American Exhibition of Foreign . . . Arts . . .*, no. 1 (as Entombment of Christ); Durand-Ruel, New York, 1895, no. 8; Carnegie Institute, Pittsburgh (Pa.), 1902, *Loan Exhibition of Paintings*, no. 94 (lent by Durand-Ruel); Metropolitan Museum, 1930, *The H. O. Havemeyer Collection*, no. 75; Musée de l'Orangerie,

Paris, 1932, *Exposition Manet*, no. 20; Cleveland Museum of Art, 1936, *Twentieth Anniversary Exhibition*, no. 285; World's Fair, New York, 1940, *Masterpieces of Art*, no. 281; Durand-Ruel, New York, 1949, *What They Said—Postscript to Art Criticism*, no. 2.

Ex coll.: [Durand-Ruel, Paris and New York, 1871/72–1903]; Mrs. H. O. Havemeyer, New York (1902–1929; Cat., 1931, pp. 140f.).

THE H. O. HAVEMEYER COLLECTION. BEQUEST OF MRS. H. O. HAVEMEYER, 1929.

Woman with a Parrot   89.21.3

Victorine Meurend was again Manet's model in this painting of 1866, made in his studio on the Rue Guyot (see Mademoiselle Victorine in the Costume of an Espada, above). The slender, elongated effect of her soft pink dress reflects the change in fashion that had taken place in France during the year it was painted, when the empress herself set a new style by appearing for the first time without a crinoline (Ref., Burnand, 1937). One of the old titles for the picture, La Femme en Rose, became meaningless during the many years when the brilliance of the painting was obscured by a heavy coat of yellowed varnish, which has recently been removed. Soon after completing the picture Manet showed it for two months in a private exhibition in his studio (Ref., Tabarant, 1947, p. 124). When it was admitted to the Salon of 1868 the opinions of the critics varied, Zola praising it for its elegance, grace, and charm and Gautier complaining that it lacked composition, drama, and poetry. In a letter to Bazille (June 25, 1867, in G. Poulain, *Bazille et ses amis*, 1932, p. 94) Claude Monet, who had seen it before the opening of the Salon, called it a bad picture and observed that Manet had painted better in the past. The violent attacks that this attractive and inoffensive painting provoked seem to have resulted from the presence of the parrot, which recalled to the indignant public Courbet's Woman with a Parrot, a picture that had caused a scandal at the Salon two years before (see Vol. II, p. 124).

Most Manet scholars have asserted that this picture was "Une jeune femme, 1867," lent by Gérard to the posthumous exhibition of Manet's works in 1884, but it had already been acquired by J. Alden Weir, probably in 1881, for the American collector Erwin Davis.

Signed (at lower left): *Manet*.

Oil on canvas. H. 72⅞, w. 50⅝ in. (185.1 x 128.6 cm.).

REFERENCES: T. Thoré [W. Bürger], *Salon de 1866*, part III, reprinted in *Salons de W. Bürger, 1861–1868* (1870), p. 318, praises the color of this painting, which he saw in Manet's studio as a sketch, but predicts that it will be refused by the Salon of 1867 // E. Zola, *L'Artiste (Revue du XIXe siècle)*, series 8, XIV (1867), p. 59, reprinted in *Salons* (1959), pp. 98f., speaks of the elegance of this picture; *L'Événement illustré* (May 10, 1868), reprinted in *Salons* (1959), p. 124, expresses admiration for the handling of the costume // L. Auvray, *Salon de 1868* (1868), pp. 73f., quotes adverse criticism of this picture // T. Gautier, *Le Moniteur universel* (May 11, 1868), writes an unfavorable criticism of it, pointing out many defects // P. Mantz, *L'Illustration* (June 6, 1868), p. 352, finds it unsuccessful in its treatment of flesh tones and untrue to nature // *Le Salon pour rire* (1868), p. 11, publishes a cartoon of it by André Gill [Louis Alexandre Gosset de Guignes] // P. Véron, *Le Monde illustré* (Aug. 1, 1868), p. 67, alludes to this picture in expounding the theme that Manet exploited ugliness // T. Duret, *Histoire d'Édouard Manet et de son oeuvre* (1902), pp. 55f., 214, no. 88; *Manet and the French Impressionists* (1910), pp. 46, 223, no. 88, ill. opp. p. 46 // E. Hancke, *Kunst und Künstler*, VIII (1910), pp. 247f., ill., finds many praiseworthy elements in it // J. Laran and G. Le Bas, *Manet* [c. 1912], pp. 51f., pl. XVIII // J. Meier-Graefe, *Édouard Manet* (1912), p. 312, pl. 91 // K. M. Roof, *Life and Art of Chase* (1917), p. 94, supposes that William Merritt Chase advised J. Alden Weir to buy this picture from Durand-Ruel for Erwin Davis in 1881 // D. Phillips, in *Julian Alden Weir, an Appreciation*

(1921), pp. 20f., gives 1883 as the date of Weir's purchase of this picture for Davis // E. Waldmann, *Édouard Manet* (1923), pp. 46f., 72, ill. // P. Jamot, *Burl. Mag.*, XLIX (1926), pp. 302–309, fig. A on p. 306, declares this portrait a masterpiece, comments on its delicacy, subtlety, and grandeur // E. Moreau-Nélaton, *Manet* (1926), I, pp. 88, 97f., 132, fig. 91, publishes it in Manet's list of the pictures he was to sell Durand-Ruel, with his asking price // P. Jamot, *Rev. de l'art*, LI (1927), pp. 39f., ill. opp. p. 38, detail p. 41, says that Victorine Meurend was the model in this painting but that her proportions have been elongated // C. V. Wheeler, *Manet* (1930), pp. 39f., ill., mentions this picture in an account of Victorine Meurend as Manet's model // P. Colin, *Édouard Manet* (1932), pp. 33, 74, pl. XX // A. Tabarant, *Manet, Histoire catalographique* (1931), pp. 149–151, cat. no. 111, quotes Gautier, Mantz, and Zola // P. Jamot and G. Wildenstein, *Manet* (1932), I, pp. 37f., 42f., 83, 133, cat. no. 132, II, pl. 15, fig. 38 // P. Jamot, *L'Amour de l'art*, XIII (1932), p. 151 // P. Durand-Ruel, *Mémoires*, published in L. Venturi, *Les Archives de l'impressionnisme* (1939), II, pp. 190, 206, gives his record of the painting // [R. Burnand], in *Chefs-d'oeuvre de l'art français* (exhib. cat.), Éditions des Musées Nationaux (1937), I, p. 446, no. 171, ill. // E. Scheyer, *Art Quarterly*, VI (1943), p. 124, includes this among the works in which the Japanese influence upon Manet is at its climax // L. Piérard, *Manet l'incompris* (1944), p. 73, finds similarities in it to works by Alfred Stevens // H. Huth, *Gaz. des B.-A.*, XXIX (1946), p. 233, note 10, states that Weir bought this picture for Erwin Davis in 1881 // M. Florisoone, *Manet* (1947), p. xxi, pl. 38, includes it among the pictures reflecting Manet's study of Velazquez in the Prado // A. Tabarant, *Manet et ses oeuvres* (1947), pp. 119, 124, 146–150, 536, no. 115, quotes contemporary criticisms // D. Cooper, introduction to *The Courtauld Collection* (1954), p. 22, note 1, identifies the Lady in Pink exhibited by Durand-Ruel in London in 1872 as this picture // G. H. Hamilton, *Manet and His Critics* (1954), pp. 101, 114–116, 118–122, 124, 130, pl. 18 // J. L. Vaudoyer, *E. Manet* [c. 1955], no. 22, ill. and detail // J. S. Boggs, *Burl. Mag.*, C (1958), p. 243, note 6, and *Portraits by Degas* (1962), pp. 33, 91, note 3, suggests that while Manet was working on this picture (pl. 47), Degas may also have been using Victorine Meurent [*sic*] as a model for his painting Girl in a Red Peignoir (pl. 49) in the collection of the late Chester Dale // H. Perruchot, *La Vie de Manet* (1959), pp. 193f. // F. Daulte, *L'Oeil* (June 1960), p. 58, reproduces the page from Durand-Ruel's account book on which the purchase of this picture from Manet in January 1872 is recorded // J. Lethève, *Portfolio and Art News Annual*, no. 2 (1960), ill. p. 53, publishes the cartoon by A. Gill from *Le Salon pour rire* (Ref., 1868) // D. W. Young, *The Life and Letters of J. Alden Weir* (1960), p. 145, relates that J. Alden Weir bought this picture in Paris in 1881 for Erwin Davis // P. Courthion, *Manet* (1961), p. 88, ill. p. 89 in color, finds Manet returning in this picture to an earlier manner, praises the style and the modulations and sheen of the colors.

EXHIBITED: Avenue de l'Alma, Paris, 1867, *Exposition particulière de Manet*, no. 15 (as Jeune Dame en 1866); Paris, Salon of 1868, no. 1659 (as Une Jeune Femme); Durand-Ruel, London, 1872, *Fifth Exhibition of the Society of French Artists*, no. 49 (as Lady in Pink); National Academy of Design, New York, 1883, *Pedestal Fund Art Loan Exhibition*, no. 182 (as Portrait of a Lady, lent by Erwin Davis); Palais National des Arts, Paris, 1937, *Chefs-d'oeuvre de l'art français*, no. 356; Musée de l'Orangerie, Paris, 1955, *De David à Toulouse-Lautrec*, no. 38; Parrish Art Museum, Southampton (New York), 1957, *William Merritt Chase, a Retrospective Exhibition*, cat. p. 14; Haus der Kunst, Munich, 1965, *Französische Malerei des 19. Jahrhunderts von David bis Cézanne*, no. 161.

EX COLL.: [Durand-Ruel, Paris, from 1871/72]; Ernest Hoschedé, Paris (sale, Hôtel Drouot, Paris, June 5–6, 1878, no. 44); Albert Hecht, Paris (from 1878); [Durand-Ruel, Paris, in

1881]; Erwin Davis, New York (from 1881; sale, Ortgies, New York, Mar. 19–20, 1889, no. 99, as *Feeding the Parrot*; bought in).

GIFT OF ERWIN DAVIS, 1889.

A Torero Saluting   29.100.52

Manet painted this picture in his studio on the Rue Guyot in 1866, the year after his brief trip to Madrid. It seems to depict the moment in a bull fight when the matador salutes the president in his box, requesting his permission to kill. This is one of the very few paintings with Spanish subjects that Manet painted after his return from Spain. It shows the direct influence of Velazquez in the tone of the transparent ground, which makes the figure stand out in a setting of airy space. Although Eugène is said to have posed for the picture, descendants of the family assert that the model cannot have been either of the artist's brothers (Ref., Rouart, 1961). The well-known critic Théodore Duret, a friend of Manet's, bought it in 1870.

Signed (at lower left): *Manet*.

Oil on canvas. H. 67⅜, w. 44½ in. (171.1 x 113 cm.).

REFERENCES: E. Bazire, *Manet* (1884), p. 139, ill. p. 21, identifies the model for this painting as Manet's brother Gustave // L. Gonse, *Gaz. des B.-A.*, XXIX (1884), p. 142, dates it 1866 // J. Péladan, *L'Artiste* (1884), I, p. 110 // *Catalogue de la vente Théodore Duret* (Galerie Georges Petit, Paris, Mar. 19, 1894), no. 20, dates it 1867, suggests that the model was a member of a Spanish troupe performing in Paris // T. Duret, *Histoire d'Édouard Manet et de son oeuvre* (1902), pp. 179, 212, no. 78; *Manet and the French Impressionists* (1910), p. 222, no. 78 // E. Waldmann, *Kunst und Künstler*, IX (1910), p. 134, ill. p. 93, dates it 1866, after Manet had visited Madrid // J. Meier-Graefe, *Édouard Manet* (1912), pp. 154 (note 1), 316, pl. 72, dates it tentatively 1866 // E. Waldmann, *Édouard Manet* (1923), pp. 32, 46, ill. p. 39, dates it about 1865–1866, comments on the color // E. Moreau-Nélaton,

Manet (1926), I, pp. 76, 137, pl. 76; II, fig. 342, illustrates it hanging in the posthumous exhibition of 1884, identifies the model as Manet's brother Eugène // A. Tabarant, *La Renaissance*, XIII (1930), p. 69, ill. p. 61, dates it 1866, says the model was Eugène; *Manet, Histoire catalographique* (1931), pp. 152f., cat. no. 113 // P. Jamot and G. Wildenstein, *Manet* (1932), I, pp. 131f., cat. no. 124, II, pl. 21, fig. 44, say that the model was not Eugène Manet // G. Jedlicka, *Édouard Manet* (1941), pp. 85, 104, 397, note 7, dates it 1866 // A. Tabarant, *Manet et ses oeuvres* (1947), pp. 121, 124, 183, 512, 536, no. 121, dates it 1866, observes that Manet included it in a small private exhibition in his studio on the Rue Guyot, which Thoré-Bürger reviewed, July 5, 1866, in the *Indépendance belge* // M. Florisoone, *Manet* (1947), p. xxi, groups

29.100.52

this painting with the pictures that show the deep impression Velazquez made on Manet // H. Perruchot, *La Vie de Manet* (1959), pp. 188, 213 // D. Rouart (in a letter, 1961), states that neither Eugène nor Gustave Manet posed for this picture // L. W. Havemeyer [Mrs. H. O.], *Sixteen to Sixty, Memoirs of a Collector* (1961), pp. 223f., calls it El Espada.

EXHIBITED: Avenue de l'Alma, Paris, 1867, *Exposition particulière de Manet*, no. 16; École des Beaux-Arts, Paris, 1884, *Exposition des Oeuvres d'Édouard Manet*, no. 34 (lent by Théodore Duret); Durand-Ruel, New York, 1895, no. 24; Carnegie Institute, Pittsburgh (Pa.), 1897, *Second Annual Exhibition*, no. 139; Metropolitan Museum, 1930, *The H. O. Havemeyer Collection*, no. 78; Pennsylvania Museum of Art, Philadelphia, 1933, *Manet and Renoir* (*Pennsylvania Mus. Bull.*, XXIX, 1933, p. 17); Montreal Museum of Fine Arts, 1949, *Manet to Matisse*, no. 16; Detroit Institute of Arts and Art Gallery of Toronto, 1951, City Art Museum, St. Louis, and Seattle Art Museum, 1952, traveling exhibition from the Metropolitan Museum.

EX COLL.: Théodore Duret, Paris (from 1870; sale, Galerie Georges Petit, Paris, Mar. 19, 1894, no. 20); [Durand-Ruel, Paris, 1894–1898]; H. O. Havemeyer, New York (1898–1929; Cat., 1931, p. 144).

THE H. O. HAVEMEYER COLLECTION. BEQUEST OF MRS. H. O. HAVEMEYER, 1929.

The Funeral   10.36

This picture represents a modest funeral set against a vast, panoramic view of Paris. In the background at the left are the cupola of the Observatory and the church of Val-de-Grâce; at the right are the Pantheon, the belfry of Saint-Étienne-du-Mont, and the Tower of Clovis, now a part of the Lycée Henri IV. These buildings and their relationship to each other make it difficult to decide from what point Manet took the view of the city. It would appear to have been from the foot of the Montagne Sainte-Geneviève in the neighborhood of the Rue Monge, perhaps from the

little rise where, in 1869, they had begun to excavate the ruins of the old Roman amphitheater, called the Arena of Lutetia. This painting was one of those left in Manet's studio at his death and was described in the inventory as "Enterrement à la Glacière." If the Glacière really was the locale, Manet has shown the cupolas of the Observatory and the Val-de-Grâce closer together than they really are, no doubt in order to improve his composition. He probably painted the picture in 1870 on the eve of the Franco-Prussian War, as it bears a strong resemblance in style to a landscape made in February of 1871 at Oloron-Sainte-Marie, in the Basses-Pyrénées, where he had fled after the fall of Paris.[1] It is also very much like a painting by Manet of 1867 that shows a view of the Exposition Universelle.[2] This picture, now in the National Gallery of Oslo, like ours has a cluster of figures in the foreground and the architecture of Paris silhouetted against the horizon. Neither the Oslo painting nor our Funeral is signed, and it is possible that the artist regarded them both as studies or hesitant experiments in out-of-door painting. Our picture is unfinished, but like all sketches by great artists, it has been carried through to a point of harmony and unity which makes it a most interesting work of art.

The suggestion has been made that the funeral represented was that of Daumier, but Daumier did not die until 1879, and by this time Manet's style had become very different. The white pall over the coffin and the white

10.36

horse, which are customary for the funeral of a child or a young girl, also contradict this identification, though Manet may well have introduced these light accents in order to break the monotony of the dark tones of the procession. Before coming to America the painting belonged for a time to Camille Pissarro.

Oil on canvas. H. 28⅝, w. 35⅝ in. (72.7 x 90.4 cm.).

Notes: 1. Ref., Jamot and Wildenstein (1932), II, pl. 145, fig. 286. 2. E. Moreau-Nélaton, *Manet* (1926), I, fig. 107.

REFERENCES: T. Duret, *Histoire d'Édouard Manet et de son oeuvre* (1902), pp. 223f., no. 126, dates this painting 1869–1870, lists it as in the possession of Camille Pissarro, Paris; *Manet and the French Impressionists* (1910), p. 229, no. 126 // B. B[urroughs], *Met. Mus. Bull.*, v (1910), pp. 123, 127, ill., states that the Museum acquired it from Vollard, who had got it from the family of Pissarro; regards it as unfinished because there is no signature; believes that it was painted after 1870, when Manet gave up his dependence on older painters // C. L. Borgmeyer, *The Master Impressionists* (1913), pp. 115, 119, ill. p. 109 // B. B[urroughs], *Met. Mus. Bull.*, XIII (1918), pp. 177f., ill., considers it as marking the beginning of the period when Manet painted out of doors // A. Tabarant, *Manet, Histoire catalographique* (1931), pp. 202f., cat. no. 153, dates it 1870 and feels that the presence of a grenadier of the imperial guard proves that it was painted before the end of the second Empire in that year, believes that the scene was viewed from the Rue de l'Estrapade // P. Jamot and G. Wildenstein, *Manet* (1932), I, p. 140, cat. no. 184, note that in the inventory of the works that Manet left at his death it is listed as l'Enterrement à la Glacière; II, pl. 145, fig. 288 // A. Tabarant, *Manet et ses oeuvres* (1947), pp. 171, 537, no. 158, dates it 1870, possibly January or February; reports that Pissarro bought it from the dealer Portier, who had got it from Mme Manet on April 10, 1894, according to her account book // J. Richardson, *Édouard Manet* (1958), p. 124,

no. 37, pl. 37, argues that it was painted in the winter of 1870–1871 by relating it to two snow scenes done at this time; (in a letter, 1960) agrees that it is not a winter scene.

EXHIBITED: Carnegie Institute, Pittsburgh (Pa.), 1924, *Exhibition of Paintings, Édouard Manet, Pierre Renoir, Berthe Morisot*, no. 41; Boston Museum of Fine Arts, 1935, *Independent Painters of Nineteenth-Century Paris*, no. 27; Metropolitan Museum, 1934, *Landscape Paintings*, no. 46; Montreal Museum of Fine Arts, 1952, *Six Centuries of Landscape*, no. 49.

EX COLL.: Madame Manet, Paris (until 1894); [Portier, Paris, 1894]; Camille Pissarro, Paris (probably from 1894–d. 1903); the Pissarro family, Paris; [Ambroise Vollard, Paris, until 1909].

PURCHASE, WOLFE FUND, 1909.

Boating   29.100.115

In the summer of 1874 both Manet and Renoir joined Monet at Argenteuil on the Seine. Manet painted at this time the picture called Argenteuil, now in the Museum of Tournai, and shortly afterwards this Boating. He probably used his brother-in-law, the Dutch painter Rodolphe Leenhoff, as the model for the male figure in both paintings, though a certain Baron Barbier has also been mentioned as the model.[1] In spite of various conjectures the young woman has not been definitely identified. Manet made charming pen drawings of her in preparation for the painting.[2] Like the Argenteuil our picture is of considerable importance in Manet's development, for it shows him adopting completely the aesthetic approach of the Impressionists and, at Monet's enthusiastic urging, their practice of painting out of doors. Unlike the finished paintings Monet and Renoir were making, Boating retains the character of a sketch. It is said to have been painted very rapidly, and it shows Manet's characteristic simplification of form. The composition clearly reflects the influence of Japanese prints in the surprising abruptness with which forms are cut at the edges of the

picture. Boating seems to be the only one of
Manet's works that found a purchaser while
it was in the Salon.

Signed (at lower right): *Manet.*

Oil on canvas. H. 38¼, w. 51¼ in. (97.1 x
130.2 cm.).

Notes: 1. Ref., Blanche, 1937; about Barbier,
see J. Renoir, *Renoir, My Father*, 1962, p. 208.
2. Ill. in T. Duret, *Manet, Sein Leben und
seine Kunst* (1910), p. 135; another in coll. of
A. Strölin, Paris, ill. in J. Mathey, *Graphisme
de Manet* (1961), p. 33, no. 135.

REFERENCES: J. K. Huysmans, *Salon de 1879*,
reprinted in *L'Art moderne* (1883), pp. 35f.,
praises this picture for its freedom from convention and tradition, especially in regard to
color // J. Péladan, *L'Artiste* (1884), 1, p. 114
// T. Duret, *Histoire d'Édouard Manet et de
son oeuvre* (1902), pp. 117, 237, no. 181, dates
it 1874; *Manet and the French Impressionists*
(1910), pp. 85, 238, no. 181, ill. // J. Laran

and G. Le Bas, *Manet* [c. 1912], pp. 95f., pl.
XL, quotes contemporary critics // J. Meier-
Graefe, *Édouard Manet* (1912), p. 231, note 3,
p. 232, pl. 133, identifies the man as Manet's
brother-in-law, Rodolphe Leenhoff; discusses
the coloring in the pictures painted at Argenteuil // A. Ségard, *Mary Cassatt* (1913), pp.
61f., comments on its influence on Mary Cassatt, who admired it and recommended Mrs.
Havemeyer's purchase of it // E. Moreau-
Nélaton, *Manet* (1926), II, pp. 24, 57, figs.
195, 352, illustrates it in the 1884 posthumous
exhibition // A. Tabarant, *La Renaissance*,
XIII (1930), pp. 68, 72, ill., identifies the man
as Rodolphe Leenhoff; *Manet, Histoire catalographique* (1931), pp. 264f., cat. no. 215 //
P. Jamot and G. Wildenstein, *Manet* (1932),
I, p. 149, cat. no. 244; II, pl. 87, fig. 176,
identifies the man as Rodolphe Leenhoff //
J. E. Blanche, *Portraits of a Lifetime* (1937),
p. 39, identifies the man as Baron Barbier, a
"bosom friend" of Guy de Maupassant //
G. Jedlicka, *Édouard Manet* (1941), pp. 173f.,

29.100

404, note 5, regards this picture as a kind of preparation for Argenteuil and The Atelier of Claude Monet // J. Rewald, *The History of Impressionism* (1946), ill. p. 288; (revised and enlarged edition, 1961), ill. p. 360 // M. S[alinger], *Met. Mus. Bull.*, v (1946), p. 172, ill. on cover (detail), identifies the man as Leenhoff and the woman as possibly Manet's wife // A. Tabarant, *Manet et ses oeuvres* (1947), pp. 247, 345–349, 539, no. 226, states that it was painted a few days after Argenteuil, quotes contemporary critics // F. Kimball and L. Venturi, *Great Paintings in America* [c. 1948], pp. 180f., color pl. 83, analyze the picture // L. Venturi, *Impressionists and Symbolists* (1950), pp. 23f., fig. 20 // G. H. Hamilton, *Manet and His Critics* (1954), pp. 211, 216f., pl. 31 // J. Leymarie, *Impressionism* (1955), II, p. 35 // L. Venturi, *Four Steps toward Modern Art* (1956), p. 57, pl. 23 // J. Richardson, *Édouard Manet* (1958), p. 126, no. 48, pl. 48, discusses the identification of the male figure // H. Perruchot, *La Vie de Manet* (1959), pp. 250f., 280 // L. W. Havemeyer [Mrs. H. O.], *Sixteen to Sixty, Memoirs of a Collector* (1961), p. 225, without naming the picture, states that Mary Cassatt called it "the last word in painting," and that Manet painted it in a couple of days, just after he had finished his prolonged work on the Argenteuil.

EXHIBITED: Paris, Salon of 1879, no. 2011; École des Beaux-Arts, Paris, 1884, *Exposition des oeuvres d'Édouard Manet*, no. 76 (lent by Desfossés); Paris, 1889, *Exposition centennale de l'art français*, no. 498 (lent by V. Desfossés); Durand-Ruel, New York, 1913, *Loan Exhibition of Paintings by Édouard Manet*, no. 13; Metropolitan Museum, 1930, *The H. O. Havemeyer Collection*, no. 79; Pennsylvania Museum of Art, Philadelphia, 1933, *Manet and Renoir* (*Pennsylvania Mus. Bull.*, XXIX, 1933, p. 17); Art Gallery of Toronto, 1935, *Loan Exhibition of Paintings Celebrating the Opening of the Margaret Eaton Gallery and the East Gallery*, no. 181; Art Institute of Chicago, 1955, *Great French Paintings in Memory of Chauncey McCormick*, no. 23.

EX COLL.: V. Desfossés, Paris (acquired at the Salon of 1879; still in his possession in 1889); [Durand-Ruel, Paris]; H. O. Havemeyer, New York (before 1902–1929; Cat., 1931, p. 139).

THE H. O. HAVEMEYER COLLECTION. BEQUEST OF MRS. H. O. HAVEMEYER, 1929.

Mademoiselle Isabelle Lemonnier

29.100.56

The subject of this portrait was the sister of Madame Charpentier, whom Renoir immortalized in the great portrait with her children in this Museum (see p. 149). Mademoiselle Lemonnier seems to have made a strong impression on Manet, who offered her a great deal of complimentary attention, to which she was apparently indifferent. During the summer of 1880, which he spent in the Parisian suburb of Bellevue, he wrote her a series of brief notes (most of them preserved in the Louvre), enchantingly decorated with watercolor drawings of the flowers and fruits of the season and with occasional amusing sketches of her done from imagination (*Letters with Aquarelles*, Pantheon, New York, n.d., facsimiles). Beside making this pastel, which he called the "Lady with a Rose," Manet did several other portraits of Mademoiselle Lemonnier. It is reported that although this was the only one of the likenesses that she ever owned, she sold it when she wanted money to buy a house near Paris (Ref., Robida, 1955).

Pastel on fine canvas. H. 22, w. 18¼ in. (55.9 x 46.4 cm.).

REFERENCES: T. Duret, *Histoire d'Édouard Manet et de son oeuvre* (1902), pp. 251, 281, no. 10, lists ours and six other portraits of Mlle Lemonnier made in the years 1876–1878, says Manet called our portrait Jeune Fille à la Rose, believes he sees the initial M in blue at the lower right; *Manet and the French Impressionists* (1910), pp. 246f., 264, no. 10 // E. Moreau-Nélaton, *Manet* (1926), II, pp. 70f., publishes some of Manet's letters to Mlle Lemonnier // A. Tabarant, *Manet, Histoire catalographique* (1931), p. 466, cat. no. 27,

29.100.56

includes the portrait among pastels done in 1879 // P. Jamot and G. Wildenstein, *Manet* (1932), I, p. 164, cat. no. 358, include it among works painted in 1879 // J. Rewald, *Édouard Manet Pastels* (1947), no. 29, fig. 29, dates it 1878 // A. Tabarant, *Manet et ses oeuvres* (1947), pp. 369, 546, no. 482 // M. Robida, *Ces Bourgeois de Paris* (1955), pp. 142f., ill. opp. p. 145, states that Manet made six portraits of Mlle Lemonnier [grandmother of the author], that this pastel was the only one of them that she owned, and that she sold it to Georges Bernheim in order to buy a house outside of Paris; states that Th[éophile] Poilpot made a perfect copy of it, and inscribed it accordingly; *Le Salon Charpentier* (1958), pp. 117, 119, repeats the information above but says that the purchaser of the pastel was Gaston, not Georges, Bernheim (see Ref., Dauberville, 1962) // H. Perruchot, *La Vie de Manet* (1959), p. 282 // L. W. Havemeyer [Mrs. H. O.], *Sixteen to Sixty, Memoirs of a Collector* (1961), p. 232 // J. Dauberville, of Bernheim-Jeune et Cie., Paris (in a letter,

1962), cannot confirm that Gaston Bernheim bought this pastel.

EXHIBITED: Galerie de la Vie Moderne, Paris, 1880, *Exposition d'oeuvres nouvelles d'Édouard Manet*, no. 19 (as Tête de Femme); Metropolitan Museum, 1930, *The H. O. Havemeyer Collection*, no. 183.

Ex coll.: Mademoiselle Lemonnier, Paris; H. O. Havemeyer, New York (Cat., 1931, pp. 148f., ill.).

THE H. O. HAVEMEYER COLLECTION. BEQUEST OF MRS. H. O. HAVEMEYER, 1929

George Moore   29.100.55

The Irish writer George Moore (1853–1933) spent the greater part of the years between 1873 and 1880 in Paris. He went there to study art, but after he had given up his ambition to become a painter and begun to write, he stayed on, enjoying the company of the Impressionist painters. The artists did not take him seriously, but they were entertained by his poor command of French and with good-natured amusement admitted him to their circle at the café Nouvelle Athènes.

Moore always had a special admiration for Manet and in various passages in his autobiographical writings described their first meeting and the painter's appearance. Manet made at least three portraits of George Moore, this one, the oil sketch called Au Café (see below), and another sketch painted in the garden of Manet's studio in the Rue d'Amsterdam.[1]

This sharply characterized pastel was probably done in 1879, at the end of Moore's stay in Paris. Moore's writings reveal quite clearly his vanity, self-consciousness, and angularity, and Manet has captured these qualities with sympathy and skill in the pastel. It is the most finished of the three portraits and is usually regarded as the definitive one. It was used by Moore as the frontispiece for his volume of collected essays entitled *Modern Painting*, though many people are said to have thought that the artist had made him appear a little ridiculous. It was known as "le noyé repêché" (the drowned man fished out of the water). Moore himself, in a letter written to his brother in 1912, implied that he was embarrassed by the pastel (Ref., Cooper, 1945). Other portraits of himself were also subject to acrid criticism. He found that one by J. E. Blanche made him look like a drunken cabby, and another, by Sickert, was called "an intoxicated mummy," "a boiled ghost," or a "leprous portrait." Another artist who was friendly with Moore, Degas, recorded his appearance in a drawing, a standing full-length, in the Ashmolean Museum, Oxford (Ref., Pickvance, 1963).

Signed (at lower left): *Manet.*

Pastel on fine canvas. H. 21¾, w. 13⅞ in. (55.3 x 35.3 cm.).

Note 1. In a private collection, New York; Jamot and Wildenstein, 1932, II, pl. 108, fig. 201.

REFERENCES: T. Duret, *Histoire d'Édouard Manet et de son oeuvre* (1902), pp. 136, 298, no. 67, ill. p. 159, analyzes Manet's characterization of Moore in this pastel; *Manet and the French Impressionists* (1910), p. 275, no. 67 // J. Meier-Graefe, *Édouard Manet* (1912), pp. 272, 326 // E. Moreau-Nélaton, *Manet* (1926), II, p. 65, fig. 259, fig. 347, illustrates this portrait hanging in the 1884 posthumous exhibition // A. Tabarant, *La Renaissance*, XIII (1930), pp. 73f., ill.; *Manet, Histoire catalographique* (1931), p. 468, cat. no. 30, dates it 1879 // P. Jamot and G. Wildenstein, *Manet* (1932), I, p. 164, cat. no. 365; II, pl. 112, fig. 207, date it 1879 // A. Tabarant, *Oeuvre* (Oct. 9, 1932), ill., dates it 1879 // G. Jedlicka, *Édouard Manet* (1941), pp. 117–120, 281, ill. opp. p. 289, dates it 1879 // D. Cooper, *Horizon*, 11 (1945), p. 120, infers from a letter Moore wrote in 1912 to his brother that Manet's pastel portrait distinctly embarrassed him because he felt it made him a figure of fun // J. Rewald, *Édouard Manet Pastels* (1947), p. 56, no. 1, fig. 1, frontispiece in color, dates it 1879; also fig. 17, another pastel portrait of Moore in the Fogg Museum // A. Tabarant, *Manet et ses oeuvres* (1947), pp. 36of., 546, no. 475, dates it 1879 // M. Salinger, *Met. Mus. Bull.*, XV (1957), pp. 117–119, ill. in color on cover // [K. Martin],

Édouard Manet: Aquarelle und Pastelle (1958), no. 21, ill. in color // P. Courthion, *Manet* (1961), p. 138, ill. p. 139 in color, considers it one of Manet's best portraits of his male friends, finding it notably life-like // L. W. Havemeyer [Mrs. H. O.], *Sixteen to Sixty, Memoirs of a Collector* (1961), pp. 233–236, states that George Moore expressed to Mary Cassatt his dislike of this portrait; relates the circumstances of its purchase // J. Rewald, *The History of Impressionism* (revised and enlarged edition, 1961), p. 401, ill. p. 402, dates it 1879 // R. Pickvance, *Burl. Mag.*, XV (1963), p. 279, fig. 40, comments that Manet's portraits of Moore are "now generally agreed to have been executed in 1879," states that this portrait was known as Le Noyé Repêché.

29.100.55

EXHIBITED: Galerie de la Vie Moderne, Paris, 1880, *Exposition d'oeuvres nouvelles d'Édouard Manet*, no. 15; École des Beaux-Arts, Paris, 1884, *Exposition des oeuvres d'Édouard Manet*, no. 153; Metropolitan Museum, 1930, *The H. O. Havemeyer Collection*, no. 182.

EX COLL.: Estate of Manet (posthumous sale, Hôtel Drouot, Paris, Feb. 4–5, 1884, no. 96, to M. Jacob); private collection, Paris (until 1900/10); [Pottier, Paris, 1900/10]; H. O. Havemeyer, New York (from 1900/10, until 1929; Cat., 1931, pp. 148f., ill.).

THE H. O. HAVEMEYER COLLECTION. BEQUEST OF MRS. H. O. HAVEMEYER, 1929.

George Moore (Au Café)   55.193

In his book called *Modern Painting* (1893, p. 31) Moore stated that Manet's first intention was to paint him in a café: "... he had met me in a café, and he thought he could realize his impression of me in the first surrounding he had seen me in. The portrait did not come right; ultimately it was destroyed...." Moore went on to describe that picture, which must have been carried considerably farther than this oil sketch, which is the beginning of another portrait of Moore that Manet never finished. It was made about the same time as the pastel above and it is especially interesting because it reveals his method of working directly on the canvas in oil paint, without preliminary drawing. The figure is outlined

55.193

with simple linear strokes of the brush and only the areas in shadow can be described as painted. It is perhaps the rapid and casual statement that gives so much verve and flavor to the characterization of Moore—not as the inspired writer and poet of the pastel above but as the habitué of the café, the Anglo-Saxon infatuated with the Parisian world of art who wrote enthusiastically, "Everyone must go to France."

Oil on canvas. H. 25¾, w. 32 in. (65.4 x 81.3 cm.).

REFERENCES: J. Meier-Graefe and E. Klossowski, *La Collection Chéramy* (1908), p. 110, no. 249, pl. 249 // E. Moreau-Nélaton, *Manet* (1926), II, pp. 54f., fig. 248, observes that Manet was dissatisfied with this sketch and left it unfinished, dates it about 1879 // L. Gillet, *Le Trésor de cent ans de vie française* (1930), Notes, p. 10, pl. XL, calls this the earliest of three portraits of Moore by Manet; *Gaz. des B.-A.*, III (1930), pp. 109–111, ill. // A. Tabarant, *Manet, Histoire catalographique* (1931), pp. 338f., cat. no. 290, dates it 1878 // P. Jamot and G. Wildenstein, *Manet* (1932), I, p. 161, cat. no. 337, date it 1879; II, pl. 39, fig. 103 // J. Rewald, *The History of Impressionism* (1946), p. 327, ill. p. 330, dates it about 1879; (revised and enlarged edition, 1961), p. 401, ill. p. 402; *Édouard Manet Pastels* (1947), p. 26, ill. // A. Tabarant, *Manet et ses oeuvres* (1947), pp. 331f., 541, no. 304, places it in 1878 // P. Courthion, *Montmartre* [c. 1956], p. 35, ill. in color // M. Salinger, *Met. Mus. Bull.*, XV (1957), pp. 117–119, ill. p. 118 // J. Richardson, *Édouard Manet* (1958), p. 128, no. 60, pl. 60.

EXHIBITED: Grand Palais des Champs-Élysées, Paris, 1905, *Oeuvres d'Édouard Manet, Salon d'Automne*, no. 31 (called a drawing, lent by M. Chéramy); Bernheim-Jeune, Paris, 1928, *Exposition d'oeuvres de Manet*, no. 35; Hôtel Jean Charpentier, Paris, 1929, *Cent Ans de vie française*, no. 676 (lent by Albert S. Henraux); Musée de l'Orangerie, Paris, 1932, *Exposition Manet*, no. 68 (lent by Henraux); Musée de Prince Paul, Belgrade, 1939, *La Peinture française au XIXe siècle*, no. 143 (lent by Henraux); Museo Nacional de Bellas Artes, Buenos Aires, 1939, *La Pintura Francesa de David a nuestros días*, no. 87 (lent by Henraux); Art Institute of Chicago, 1941, *Masterpieces of French Art*, no. 99a (lent by Henraux); Los Angeles County Museum, 1941, *The Painting of France since the French Revolution*, no. 85 (lent by Henraux); Des Moines Art Center, 1951, *Master Painters*, no. 25; Parke-Bernet Galleries, New York, 1955, *Art Treasures Exhibition*, no. 355 (lent by Mrs. Ralph J. Hines); Baltimore Museum of Art, 1962, *Manet, Degas, Berthe Morisot and Mary Cassatt*, no. 8.

Ex coll.: Estate of Manet (posthumous sale, Hôtel Drouot, Paris, Feb. 4–5, 1884, no. 58, as Au Café, *ébauche*); Alexis Emmanuel Chabrier, Paris (from 1884; sale, Hôtel Drouot, Paris, Mar. 26, 1896, no. 14, as Au Café, *ébauche*); P. A. Chéramy, Paris (from 1896; sale, Galerie Georges Petit, May 5–7, 1908, no. 218); [Ambroise Vollard, Paris, from 1908]; Albert S. Henraux, Paris (by 1929–1946 or later); [Knoedler, New York, 1951–1954]; Mrs. Ralph J. Hines, New York (1954–1955).

Gift of Mrs. Ralph J. Hines, 1955.

Countess Louise de la Bigne

29.100.561

It was Manet's idea to make the portrait of the young blonde countess who began life as Valtesse de la Bigne, an actress at the Bouffes Parisiennes, a famous music hall. Two letters from her to the painter display all the gracious charm that his portrait of her would lead us to expect.

Manet's many pastel portraits made toward the end of his life give evidence of his great skill in characterization and his keen aesthetic and sensuous awareness. They have traditionally been described simply as pastels. In a sense, however, they are paintings, since the color has been applied with a brush, the lively strokes of which are clearly visible and like those in his oils. This unusual technique accounts for the great freshness of effect and also for the surface, which is richer and smoother than that of conventional pastels. The use of

primed canvas instead of paper also contributes to the difference in appearance. Some of the color is applied in the conventional manner with chalk sticks, but for the more important and expressive passages Manet used a technique that consisted of dipping his brush in a mixture of color, possibly ground pastel chalks, and water.

Signed (at right of center): *Manet*.

Pastel on fine canvas. H. 21¾, w. 14 in. (55.3 x 35.6 cm.).

Formerly called Mademoiselle Valtesse de la Bigne.

References: T. Duret, *Histoire d'Édouard Manet et de son oeuvre* (1902), p. 284, no. 21, ill.; *Manet and the French Impressionists* (1910), p. 266, no. 21 // E. Moreau-Nélaton, *Manet* (1926), II, p. 64, fig. 250, dates the portrait about 1880, quotes part of Countess Louise's

29.100.561

letter to Manet thanking him for it; fig. 350, illustrates it in a gallery view of the 1884 posthumous exhibition // A. Tabarant, *La Renaissance*, XIII (1930), p. 74, ill. p. 71, dates it 1879; *Manet, Histoire catalographique* (1931), pp. 462f., cat. no. 23, quotes two letters from the sitter to the artist // P. Jamot and G. Wildenstein, *Manet* (1932), I, p. 164, cat. no. 359, date the portrait about 1879, II, pl. 115, fig. 210 // J. Rewald, *Édouard Manet Pastels* (1947), p. 59, no. 26, dates it 1879, fig. 26 // A. Tabarant, *Manet et ses oeuvres* (1947), pp. 368f., 546, no. 481 // L. W. Havemeyer [Mrs. H. O.], *Sixteen to Sixty, Memoirs of a Collector* (1961), p. 232, describes it without identifying the sitter.

EXHIBITED: Galerie de la Vie Moderne, Paris, 1880, *Exposition d'oeuvres nouvelles d'Édouard Manet*, no. 13; École des Beaux-Arts, Paris, 1884, *Exposition des oeuvres d'Édouard Manet*, no. 138 (lent by Mlle V.); Metropolitan Museum, 1930, *The H. O. Havemeyer Collection*, no. 184.

EX COLL.: Countess Valtesse de la Bigne, Paris (sale, Haro and Bloche, Paris, June 2–7, 1902, no. 78, as Portrait de Jeune Femme); Mrs. H. O. Havemeyer, New York (Cat., 1931, p. 150).

THE H. O. HAVEMEYER COLLECTION. BEQUEST OF MRS. H. O. HAVEMEYER, 1929.

Strawberries   56.230.1

In the last years of his life ill health forced Manet to spend long summers outside of Paris, in 1881 at Versailles and the following year at Rueil. He turned more and more to the painting of still life, with a technique that became increasingly concise and boldly suggestive, as in the forceful, heavily loaded brush strokes that form the basket in this picture.

Signed (at lower right): *Manet.*

Oil on canvas. H. 8⅜, w. 10½ in. (21.3 x 26.7 cm.).

REFERENCES: T. Duret, *Histoire d'Édouard Manet et de son oeuvre* (1902), p. 273, no. 311, lists this painting among pictures made at

56.230.1

Rueil in 1882; *Manet and the French Impressionists* (1910), p. 260, no. 311 // J. and G. Bernheim-Jeune, *L'Art moderne . . . d'après la collection privée de MM. J. and G. Bernheim-Jeune* (1919), I, pl. 78 // A. Tabarant, *Manet, Histoire catalographique* (1931), p. 424, cat. no. 386 // P. Colin, *Édouard Manet* (1932), p. 181, pl. XCVI // P. Jamot and G. Wildenstein, *Manet* (1932), I, p. 178, cat. no. 485; II, pl. 213, fig. 446 // A. Tabarant, *Manet et ses oeuvres* (1947), pp. 453f., 544, no. 412, says it was painted at Rueil in the summer of 1882.

EXHIBITED: Galerie Matthiesen, Berlin, 1928, *Ausstellung Édouard Manet*, no. 80 (lent from a private collection, Paris); Metropolitan Museum, 1960, *The Nate and Frances Spingold Collection*.

EX COLL.: Auguste Pellerin, Paris (by 1902); Gaston Bernheim de Villers, Paris (by 1919–c. 1951); [Sam Salz, New York, by c. 1951]; Mr. and Mrs. Nate B. Spingold, New York.

GIFT OF MR. AND MRS. NATE B. SPINGOLD, 1956.

Head of Jean Baptiste Faure   59.129

Jean Baptiste Faure (1830–1914) was a baritone at the Opera in Paris. He collected pictures by Manet and was painted by him more than once. In 1877 he posed as he appeared in the title role of Ambroise Thomas's opera, *Hamlet*, but he was hard to please and rejected the portrait, a full-length, which is now in the Folkwang Museum in Essen. Nevertheless, in December 1882, according to a letter that Manet wrote to Berthe Morisot,[1] he called upon the artist to order another portrait. This commission was apparently never completed, but at least three sketches seem to have been made in preparation for it, the two that belong to this Museum and a three-quarter length, whereabouts unknown,[2] which, except for the head, is little more than a line drawing in paint. After Manet died photographs of our half-length portrait of Faure (below) and of the three-quarter length were made by Fernand Lochard, who was called in to make a photographic record of the several hundred paintings left in the studio. He did not photograph this fine sketch of the head. It is puzzling to note that the inventory made at the same time as the photographs lists only one "esquisse de Faure." See also the half-length portrait of Jean Baptiste Faure, below.

Oil on canvas. H. 18⅛, w. 14⅞ in. (46 x 37.8 cm.).

Notes: 1. Quoted in E. Moreau-Nélaton, *Manet* (1926), II, p. 89. 2. Ref., Jamot and Wildenstein (1932), II, pl. 28, fig. 62.

59.129

REFERENCES: T. Duret, *Histoire d'Édouard Manet et de son oeuvre* (1926), pp. 122–124, 300, cat. suppl. no. 9, gives an account of Manet's portraits of Faure; describes this picture with some inaccuracies as one of the sketches for the second portrait // A. Tabarant, *Manet, Histoire catalographique* (1931), p. 439, cat. no. 413, considers this painting a fragment of an unfinished canvas, painted in the studio at 77 Rue d'Amsterdam about the end of 1882 // P. Jamot and G. Wildenstein, *Manet* (1932), I, pp. 103, 108, 181, cat. no. 518, II, pl. 30, fig. 70, assume that this is the sketch mentioned in the inventory of Manet's studio made after his death // A. Tabarant, *Manet et ses oeuvres* (1947), pp. 463f., 545, no. 441, considers that, except for the open eyes, the head is identical to that in the unfinished three-quarter length (no. 439), which is apparently lost.

EXHIBITED: Château de Bagatelle, Paris, 1912, *La Musique, la danse*, no. 86 (lent by J. B. Faure); Galerie Bernheim-Jeune, Paris, 1928, *Oeuvres de Manet*, no. 26 (lent by Maurice Faure, according to Tabarant), and 1938, *Cent Ans de théâtre, music-hall et cirque*, no. 64 (lent by Sacha Guitry).

Ex COLL.: Jean Baptiste Faure, Paris (1882/ 83–1914); Maurice Faure, Paris (from 1914); Jean and Pierre Faure, Paris; [Georges Bernheim, Paris]; Sacha Guitry, Paris (by 1931– 1957); [Van Diemen-Lilienfeld Galleries, New York, 1959]; Mrs. Ralph J. Hines, New York (1959).

GIFT OF MRS. RALPH J. HINES, 1959.

Jean Baptiste Faure (half-length)

50.71.1

This painting corresponds well with one of the two photographs made by Lochard. In the photograph, however, the eyes are less finished. Besides, more of the body is shown, and indeed an annotation on the reverse indicates that the picture Lochard photographed was larger than ours. Our painting, however, has been cut at the bottom and probably also at the sides, which accounts for the discrepancy

50.71.1

scribing the Lochard photograph (no. 102) and basing his information on material on the reverse of the photograph (see p. 22, statement that Koëlla-Leenhoff annotated fourteen albums of Lochard's photographs), assumes that this photographed portrait is Manet's last study of Faure and one of his last works // P. Jamot and G. Wildenstein, *Manet* (1932), I, p. 181, no. 519, II, pl. 218, fig. 473, illustrate the Lochard photograph, identify it as a portrait of Faure but erroneously associate it with the picture catalogued by Duret as Tête d'homme (1926, cat. suppl. no. 5) and wrongly state that it came from the collection of Faure // A. Tabarant, *Manet et ses oeuvres* (1947), pp. 463f., describes the Lochard photograph, says that he does not know the whereabouts of the painting.

EXHIBITED: Gump's Galleries, San Francisco, 1944, *Paintings from the Fifteenth Century to the Twentieth Century*, no. 53 (lent by Julius Weitzner).

in size. The difference in the eyes and other details could be the result of restoration. See Head of Jean Baptiste Faure, above.

Oil on canvas. H. 23¼, w. 19½ in. (59.1 x 49.5 cm.).

REFERENCES: A. J. Eddy, *Brush and Pencil*, I (1897–1898), ill. p. 139 (this picture before it was cut at the bottom) // A. Tabarant, *Manet, Histoire catalographique* (1931), p. 440, no. 415, catalogues a portrait of Faure by de-

EX COLL.: Estate of Manet, Paris (1883–1884); Arthur Jerome Eddy, Chicago (c. 1884–1920); Jerome Eddy, Chicago (1920–c. 1931); [William H. Thomson, Thomson Galleries, Detroit, from c. 1931]; [Julius Weitzner, New York, from c. 1936/37]; Mr. and Mrs. William B. Jaffe, New York.

GIFT OF MR. AND MRS. WILLIAM B. JAFFE, 1950.

Degas

Hilaire Germain Edgar Degas, called Edgar Degas. Also De Gas or de Gas. Born in Paris in 1834; died there in 1917. Degas was the son of a banker, and during the early part of his life he was free from financial care. Even as a boy he showed an interest in drawing. He received a careful general education, passing the baccalaureate examinations in 1853 and even beginning the study of law. He had already taken lessons for some months, however, with the painter Barrias and soon received the permission of his father, who had supplied him with a studio, to devote himself to becoming an artist. He now began to work under Louis Lamothe, a pupil of Ingres, and was directed by him toward the classic and linear tradition and introduced to the École des Beaux-Arts. He was deeply impressed by the style of Ingres, with whom he had one brief and memorable meeting. In 1854 Degas made the first of many trips to Italy, where he spent some time during each of the following five years. His paternal grandfather came from an old French family that had emigrated to Italy and lived in Naples; his aunt, the Baroness Bellelli, and cousins lived in Florence. In Italy, as well as in Paris, he assiduously copied the works of the old masters, especially the painters of the Italian Renaissance, and this discipline, combined with his admiration for the classicism of Ingres, determined his early style.

Returning to Paris in the spring of 1859, Degas settled down to serious work. He contributed regularly to the Salon from 1865 to 1870. During these years he became a friend of Manet, with whose aristocratic tastes he had much in common. In the war of 1870 they both served in the artillery of the National Guard. During the fall of 1872 and in the spring of the following year Degas was in America, visiting his brothers, who were cotton merchants in New Orleans. It was at this time that he painted the famous picture of The Cotton Market, which as early as 1878 was acquired by the Museum in Pau.

Back in France, Degas resumed his old associations with the courageous young experimenting artists, who were meeting then at the Café de la Nouvelle Athènes. He was an active member of the group that organized the Société Anonyme and contributed ten paintings to the famous first Impressionist exhibition in the spring of 1874. He showed steadily with them through the eighth and final exhibition, abstaining only in 1882, along with his friend and disciple Mary Cassatt. Always strong and independent in character, Degas was never completely at one with the Impressionists and indeed voiced bitter criticism of them. He never felt their predilection for working out of doors, and landscape was not his favorite subject matter as it was with Monet and Pissarro. He did, however, share with the Impressionists a tendency to use light colors and a deep interest in the effects of light and movement. Like them also he was attracted to themes drawn from daily life.

In the early sixties, at the beginning of his career, Degas had painted a few pictures with historical and mythological subjects, such as Semiramis Founding a City, Young Spartans Exercising, and The Misfortunes of the City of Orléans, which he showed at the Salon of 1865. He abandoned these ambitious, many-figured compositions, however, and concentrated henceforth on portraits, marvelously well-observed studies of horses and jockeys, dancers, laundresses, and women bathing and dressing. From the youthful studies of relatives, made on his visits in Italy, to the countless likenesses of his friends in Paris, his numerous portraits are all distinguished by their acuity and perceptiveness and by the unique mastery with which he adapted the setting to the personality of the sitter. He succeeded always in stirring the spectator's curiosity about the inner life of the subject.

Although Degas was an indefatigable workman, the world into which he was born and the attraction of his elegant and astringent personality combined to provide him with a rich and varied social life. Besides traveling widely he paid repeated visits to his many friends in Paris and in the country and wrote them witty and poignantly revealing letters. He assembled a varied collection of pictures by such old masters as Greco, by Delacroix and Ingres, and by his contemporaries Manet, Cézanne, Gauguin, Renoir, Pissarro, and Sisley. Degas cared deeply for music and through his cultivated father made the acquaintance of many professional musicians. Opera, theater, and ballet he knew intimately; he attended performances constantly and obtained permission to go behind the scenes to study and make drawings at close range. Degas was not yet forty when he began to suffer from serious eye trouble, which increased steadily, until by 1898 he had become almost totally blind. Parallel to his failing vision there was a modification of the precise, Ingres-like technique with which he had started. Probably both his blindness and his mature pursuit of a broader style explain his adoption in the mid-eighties of the medium of pastel.

The miseries and loneliness of the last two decades of his life, in a world that had become strange and difficult, were mitigated by his practice of the art of sculpture. When he could no longer see well enough to paint or draw, he modeled. The only statuette Degas had ever shown in public was the dancer dressed in a gauze skirt that he exhibited in 1881. He was extremely reticent about his sculpture and so inexpert that many of his works crumbled and were lost. At his death, however, he left about a hundred and fifty small pieces, seventy-four of which, subsequently cast in bronze by the founder A. A. Hébrard, bear witness to the remarkable importance and beauty of his achievement in this medium.

In developing his complicated style Degas combined rigid discipline with unfettered experiment. He excelled in the art of drawing, and quantities of preparatory studies preceded his finished paintings and pastels. Like many of his contemporaries he came early under the influence of Japanese prints, with their artful and deceptive appearance of casualness, which he adopted with infinite success for his own purposes. Degas himself was a skilled and successful innovator in the field of print-making. He was interested in the new art of the camera, taking photographs himself and using them in planning pictures and in his efforts to produce instantaneous effects. His bold and effective use of color had a significant influence on Toulouse-Lautrec, the Fauves, and the young Picasso. Perhaps Degas's most salient talent lay in his exhaustive knowledge of the human body and in his exquisitely truthful renderings of the body in delicate and complicated movement.

Self-Portrait   61.101.6

In his early years Degas painted many self-portraits. Although none is dated, a similarity to a datable sketch in Degas's notebooks places one that is in the Ganay collection in Paris (Lemoisne no. 2) between September and December of 1854 (see J. S. Boggs, *Burl. Mag.*, c, 1958, p. 166, Notebook A III). Ours resembles it closely, both showing him as an earnest, deeply introspective young artist. In ours he wears an artist's smock, and in the Ganay version he holds a palette. Although Lemoisne dates the Museum's picture about 1856, the pose of the head, the expression of the face, the hint of moustache, and the distribution of light and shadow in the two paintings are so similar that we may suppose ours, like the Ganay picture, was probably made toward the end of 1854, when Degas was twenty.

This likeness of himself is, in any case, the earliest of the Museum's series of portraits by this artist and is the only one of them that is solidly rooted in the conventional artistic tradition of the French nineteenth century. It recalls figure paintings and portraits by Courbet, Corot, and Chassériau, and like them reveals the influence of seventeenth-century pictures, especially Dutch ones.

61.101.6

Oil on paper mounted on canvas. H. 16, w. 13½ in. (40.6 x 34.3 cm.).

References: P. A. Lemoisne, *Degas* (1946), I, pp. 14, 20, II, pp. 6f., no. 12, ill., calls this picture Degas en blouse d'atelier, dates it about 1856, finds the color and drawing reminiscent of Ingres, suggests comparison to cat. nos. 2–5, 11–14, 31, 32, 37, 51, 103–105, and 116 // J. S. Boggs, *Portraits by Degas* (1962), pp. 9, 87 (note 36), 105, dates it 1855–1856, groups it with Lemoisne nos. 11 and 13, done after Degas's return to his family home after quarreling with his father about his future as a painter.

Exhibited: Musée de l'Orangerie, Paris, 1931, *Degas, portraitiste et graveur*, no. 1; Galerie Charpentier, Paris, 1943, *Scènes et figures parisiennes*, no. 70; Knoedler, New York, 1954, *A Collector's Taste: Selections from the Collection of Mr. and Mrs. Stephen C. Clark*, no. 7 (catalogue material completely erroneous); Metropolitan Museum, *Paintings from Private Collections*, 1959, no. 28, 1960, no. 30 (lent by Stephen C. Clark); Yale University Art Gallery, New Haven (Conn.), 1960, *Paintings, Drawings and Sculpture Collected by Yale Alumni*, no. 49 (lent by Stephen C. Clark).

Ex coll.: R. Nepveu de Gas, Paris (until after 1946); [Sam Salz, New York, until 1950]; Stephen C. Clark, New York (from 1950).

Bequest of Stephen C. Clark, 1960.

A Woman with Chrysanthemums
29.100.128

This famous painting is an extraordinarily acute study of the personality and the mood of the subject. Its strangely asymmetrical composition, with the sitter at the edge of the painting and three quarters of the picture space allotted to still life, was commented upon well into this century by critics who thought that Degas lacked respect for the human figure or had used the device in order to startle the public. Actually the powerful effect of the portrait is paradoxically due in large part to the unusual location of the subject. The treatment also contributes to the strong impression of the personality of the sitter, who is rendered with subtlety and understatement in contrast to the boldness with which the huge bouquet is painted. Courbet in 1863, in a picture called The Trellis, in the Toledo Museum of Art, had also used an off-center arrangement for a portrait of a young girl, who shares the picture space with a great mass of flowers. Millet, somewhat after Degas, used the same device, bringing the still life forward in the composition and painting a young girl in the right background, in shadow and partly concealed by the flowers (Ref., Bazin, 1931, fig. 96).

In the Fogg Museum in Cambridge there is a drawing by Degas for the figure of the woman (Ref., Mongan and Sachs, 1940). It is difficult to explain why this woman, represented in our painting and in the Fogg drawing, has been identified with Madame Hertel.[1] A three-quarter-length drawing in the Louvre (third Degas sale, no. 159) is labeled, apparently in Degas's own handwriting, "M\^e Hertel vers 1860" (Mme Hertel about 1860),[2] but it shows a woman seated on a sofa who bears little if any resemblance to the Woman with Chrysanthemums. Another drawing in the Louvre of a younger woman was designated in the first Degas sale (no. 313) as a likeness of one Mademoiselle Hélène Hertel who became Countess Felzacappa;[3] it is signed by the artist and dated 1865, like our painting.

The form in which our picture is signed, Degas, is uncommon for this artist in the years around 1865, a period when he usually separated his name into two words, De Gas. Ronald Pickvance suggests that he added the signature some time after the painting was finished, a frequent practice of Degas's. In the lower left corner of our picture, partly covered with paint, are the remnants of a second Degas signature and the last two digits of a date that was apparently 1858.

Signed and dated (at lower left): *1865/Degas.*

Oil on canvas. H. 29, w. 36½ in. (73.7 x 92.7 cm.).

Notes: 1. Lafond (Ref., 1919), writing two years after Degas's death, was apparently the first critic to make this identification. 2. Degas uses M\^e for Madame in his inscription on a drawing in pastel and charcoal of Madame Loubens in the Metropolitan Museum (Lemoisne no. 267). 3. A note in one of Degas's notebooks proves that both a Mademoiselle

and a Madame Hertel existed and, indeed, in 1872 were living at the same address in Rome (Ref., Boggs, 1962, p. 119).

REFERENCES: L. Hourticq, *Art et Décoration,* XXXII (1912), p. 109, finds the off-center composition of this picture disturbing and accuses Degas of disregarding the human figure // P. A. Lemoisne, *Degas* [1912], pp. 33f., pl. IX, comments on the advanced character of this picture of 1865 in comparison with the Ingres-like Malheurs de la Ville d'Orléans that Degas sent to the Salon of the same year (painted in 1865, according to Lemoisne, 1946, II, no. 124) // J. Meier-Graefe, *Entwicklungsgeschichte der modernen Kunst* (1915), II, p. 278, suggests that Degas could here have been influenced by the Pre-Raphaelites // P. Jamot, *Gaz. des B.-A.,* XIV (1918), pp. 152, 156, ill. p. 153, observes that it is the first example in Degas's work and indeed in nineteenth-century painting of an off-center composition, suggests that Degas may have been inspired by Van Dyck's Self Portrait with a Sunflower // P. Lafond, *Degas,* II (1919), p. 11, identifies the sitter as Mme Hertel, sees in the picture the influence of Japanese prints, erroneously locates it in the Camondo collection in the Louvre // *Art News,* XIX (Feb. 26, 1921), ill. p. 1 // J. Meier-Graefe, *Degas* (1923), p. 25, sees in it a compromise between the influence of Manet and the tradition of Ingres // P. Jamot, *Degas* (1924), pp. 23, 47f., 53f., 90, 133, pl. 11, identifies the sitter as Mme Hertel // H. Focillon, *La Peinture au XIX\^e et XX\^e siècles* (1928), II, p. 182, mentions it as an example of a new development in portraiture // G. Bazin, *L'Amour de l'art,* XII (1931), p. 304, fig. 94, compares the off-center composition with the conventions of modern film-makers and photographers in the effort to suggest momentary action // L. Burroughs, *Met. Mus. Bull.,* XXVII (1932), pp. 143ff., ill., compares it with the drawing in the Fogg Museum // V. Nirdlinger, *Parnassus,* IX (Mar. 1937), p. 19 // A. Mongan and P. J. Sachs, *Drawings in the Fogg Museum of Art* (1940), p. 359, find a greater likeness to this subject in the drawing entitled Mlle Hélène Hertel (first Degas sale, no. 313) than in the one inscribed Mme Hertel (third Degas sale, no. 159) // M. Rebatet, *Degas* (1944), p. 31, pl. 14 // J. Rewald, *Edgar Degas* [before 1945], fig. 3, gives the date of the picture wrongly as 1863 // D. Rouart, *Degas à la recherche de sa technique* (1945), pp. 13–15, note 24, wrongly assumes that this is one of the examples of finished paintings by Degas done in the *essence* technique on paper // P. A. Lemoisne, *Degas* (1946), I, pp. 55f., 239 (note 117), ill. opp. p. 56, II, pp. 62f., cat. no. 125, ill., calls the sitter Mme Hertel // J. Rewald, *Mag. of Art*, XXXIX (1946), p. 13, cites the gloves on the table as an example of the resolution Degas made in 1859 to render objects in close relation to the lives of their owners // G. Bazin, *L'Époque impressionniste* (1947), p. 67 // F. Fosca, *Degas* (1954), p. 29, ill. in color p. 28, states that photographs have been found that were used by Degas in composing this picture (whereabouts unknown) // P. Cabanne, *Edgar*

Degas (1957), pp. 23f., 29, 96, 106, no. 22, pl. 22, like Fosca, makes assertion that in London some years ago photographs were found which served Degas for this portrait // G. Bazin, *French Impressionists in the Louvre* (1958), p. 126 // I. Elles, *Das Stilleben in der französischen Malerei des 19. Jahrhunderts* (1958), p. 75 // J. Rosenberg, *Great Draughtsmen from Pisanello to Picasso* (1959), p. 109 // J. S. Boggs, *Portraits by Degas* (1962), pp. 31f., 37, 41, 59, 119, pl. 44, accepts the identification of the sitter as Mme Hertel, and identifies the sitter for the drawing in the third Degas sale (no. 159) as Mlle Hélène Hertel rather than Mme Hertel (see footnote 2, p. 58) // G. Gottlieb, *Journal of Aesthetics and Art Criticism*, XXII (Summer 1964), p. 418, suggests that this picture inspired certain paintings by Matisse // P. Poole, *Degas* (1964), p. 39, pl. x, calls it probably the first example of decentralized composition in Degas's work,

29.100.128

comments on the color as a result of Degas's emancipation from the school of Ingres.

EXHIBITED: Metropolitan Museum, 1930, *The H. O. Havemeyer Collection*, no. 45; Pennsylvania Museum of Art, Philadelphia, 1936, *Degas*, no. 8; Musée de l'Orangerie, Paris, 1937, *Degas*, no. 6; Wadsworth Atheneum, Hartford (Conn.), 1938, *The Painters of Still Life*, no. 55; Cleveland Museum, 1947, *Works by Edgar Degas*, no. 8; Philadelphia Museum, 1951, *Diamond Jubilee Exhibition*, no. 72.

Ex COLL.: Mme Boivin, Paris; [Boussod-Valadon, Paris]; [Durand-Ruel, until 1921]; H. O. Havemeyer, New York (from 1921; Cat., 1931, pp. 108f., ill.).

THE H. O. HAVEMEYER COLLECTION. BEQUEST OF MRS. H. O. HAVEMEYER, 1929.

Portrait of a Lady in Gray   57.171

This is an unusual portrait by Degas because he rarely painted a face that reflects so much good humor and calm.

57.171

The subject is not comfortably settled on her sofa, and seems on the verge of rising from it. The color scheme is carefully carried out, low-keyed in the costume but in the background warm with rose tones that repeat the clear color of the flower in the hat and the healthy flesh. The broad, rapid brush strokes of the gray dress and even more those of the black lace scarf recall Manet's style in such paintings as Mademoiselle Victorine as an Espada of 1862.

Lemoisne dates The Lady in Gray about 1865.

Stamped (at lower right): *Degas*.

Oil on canvas. H. 36, w. 28½ in. (91.5 x 72.4 cm.).

REFERENCES: P. Jamot, *Degas* (1924), pp. 49f., 52, 133, pl. 9, discusses the subtlety with which movement is suggested in this portrait, dates it 1863–1865 // R. Bouyer, *Gaz. des B.-A.*, XI (1925), p. 49, ill. opp. p. 46, dates it 1863–1865 // W. George, *L'Amour de l'art*, VI (1925), p. 362, ill. p. 370, dates it about 1865–1868, discusses its relationship to the work of Ingres // P. A. Lemoisne, *Degas et son oeuvre* (1946), II, pp. 64f., no. 128, ill., dates it about 1865 // T. Rousseau Jr., *Art News*, XLVIII (April 1949), p. 21, ill., sees in its cool colors the influence of Velazquez.

EXHIBITED: Galerie Georges Petit, Paris, 1924, *Degas*, no. 49 (lent by Dr. Viau); Musée de l'Orangerie, Paris, 1931, *Degas, portraitiste et sculpteur*, no. 34 (lent by Dr. Georges Viau); Royal Academy of Art, Burlington House, London, 1932, *French Art, 1200–1900*, no. 390, commemorative catalogue, no. 350 (lent by Dr. Georges Viau); French Pavilion, World's Fair, New York, 1939, *Five Centuries of History Mirrored in Five Centuries of French Art*, no. 373 (lent by Dr. Georges Viau); Wildenstein, New York, 1949, *Degas*, no. 9 (lent by Mr. and Mrs. Edwin C. Vogel), and 1960, *Degas*, no. 10.

Ex COLL.: Estate of Degas (first sale, Galerie Georges Petit, Paris, May 6–8, 1918, no. 75); Dr. Georges Viau, Paris (by 1924; sale, Galerie

Charpentier, Paris, June 22, 1948, no. 2);
[Durand-Ruel, Paris and New York, 1948];
Mr. and Mrs. Edwin C. Vogel, New York
(from 1948).

GIFT OF MR. AND MRS. EDWIN C. VOGEL,
1957.

The Collector of Prints   29.100.44

Although the model who posed for this painting of a man looking through a portfolio of
prints has highly individualized features, he
has not been identified. Degas did a rather
carefully finished preparatory study for the
head (formerly in the collection of Marcel
Guérin; Lemoisne no. 139). He probably
drew the idea for the picture from Daumier's
many paintings and drawings of amateurs absorbed in examining the contents of large
portfolios.

Mrs. Havemeyer relates in her memoirs
(Ref. 1961) that after agreeing to sell this
picture to the Havemeyers for one thousand
dollars Degas asked them to leave it with him
briefly as he characteristically wanted to make
some minor improvements. After two years
he exacted from them three times the original
price, explaining that his pictures had meanwhile increased in value.

Signed and dated (at lower left): *Degas / 1866.*

Oil on canvas. H. 20⅞, w. 15¾ in. (53 x 40
cm.).

REFERENCES: P. A. Lemoisne, *Degas* (1946),
II, pp. 70f., no. 138, ill., calls this picture
L'Amateur, connects it with the study (no.
139) formerly in the collection of Marcel
Guérin // P. Cabanne, *Edgar Degas* (1957),
p. 106, no. 25, color plate 25 // L. W. Havemeyer [Mrs. H. O.], *Sixteen to Sixty, Memoirs
of a Collector* (1961), p. 252, gives an account
of Degas's raising the original price of $1000
to $3000 after keeping the picture for nearly
two years to retouch it.

EXHIBITED: Metropolitan Museum, 1930,
The H. O. Havemeyer Collection, no. 47; De-
troit Institute of Arts and Art Gallery of
Toronto, 1951, City Art Museum, St. Louis,

29.100.44

and Seattle Museum, 1952, traveling exhibition from the Metropolitan Museum.

EX COLL. H. O. Havemeyer, New York (from
1895; Cat., 1931, pp. 112f.).

THE H. O. HAVEMEYER COLLECTION. BE-
QUEST OF MRS. H. O. HAVEMEYER, 1929.

Mademoiselle Marie Dihau
29.100.182

The subject of this picture was a talented
pianist and singer who often performed in
Paris at the Colonne and the Lamoureux con-
certs. With her brother Désiré, who played
the bassoon in the orchestra of the opera, she
belonged to the music-loving circle of Degas
and his father. Around 1867–1868, when this
portrait is thought to have been painted, she
was dividing her time between Lille and Paris.
Mademoiselle Dihau, who lived until 1935,

29.100.182

Dallas Museum of Fine Arts (Texas), 1955; Marion Koogler McNay Art Institute, San Antonio (Texas), 1955.

Ex coll.: Mlle Dihau, Paris (until 1922); [Durand-Ruel, Paris, 1922–1923]; H. O. Havemeyer, New York (from 1923; Cat., 1931, p. 115).

The H. O. Havemeyer Collection. Bequest of Mrs. H. O. Havemeyer, 1929.

Jacques Joseph Tissot (1836–1902)

39.161

used to tell how Degas made this picture of her with her traveling bag as a consolation gift on one of her departures from Paris. It was done rapidly, its background left unfinished, in the restaurant of Mère Lefebvre in the Rue de la Tour d'Auvergne. A few years later Degas painted her again, seated at the piano (Lemoisne no. 263).

After the war of 1870 Mademoiselle Dihau settled in Paris with her brother Désiré, and it was at their house that Toulouse-Lautrec, their cousin, was introduced to Degas. In 1890 he too painted her portrait at the piano (D. Cooper, *Toulouse-Lautrec*, 1956, pp. 86f., ill.).

Oil on canvas. H. 8¾, w. 10¾ in. (22.2 x 27.3 cm.).

References: A. Mongan, *Burl. Mag.*, LXXII (1938), p. 296 // P. A. Lemoisne, *Degas* (1946), II, pp. 88f., no. 172, dates the picture about 1867–1868, gives information about the circumstances of the painting of the portrait and about the life of the sitter, suggests comparison with a later portrait (no. 263) // *Degas Letters* (English edition, M. Guérin editor) [1947], p. 260, comments on this picture and the sitter (in the notes to letter no. 2) // J. S. Boggs, *Portraits by Degas* (1962), p. 106, dates it 1868.

Exhibited: Metropolitan Museum, 1930, *The H. O. Havemeyer Collection*, no. 53; Institute of Modern Art, Boston, *France Forever*; Newark Museum (New Jersey), 1946, *19th Century French and American Paintings*, no. 14;

This portrait, which for many years was considered a likeness of the artist Jules Finot, surely represents Degas's friend the painter Jacques Joseph Tissot. Degas made at least three drawings of Tissot, identified as pictures of him in the third Degas sale (no. 158). Two of them are full-length and were certainly preparatory studies for our portrait.

Jacques Tissot, who, during a ten-year sojourn in London, called himself James, had been Degas's friend and fellow student in the atelier of Lamothe. In 1871 Tissot, perhaps in a self-centered effort to protect his personal property, allied himself with the Commune. Accordingly, in May of 1871 when it came to an end, he was obliged to flee, and went to London, where he remained until 1882. Letters indicate that the friendship between Degas and Tissot continued at least until 1874. It subsequently terminated, allegedly because of Degas's disapproval of Tissot's Communard activities.

The three sketches of Tissot were given a date of about 1861 in the catalogue of the third Degas sale. Two of them, both in charcoal, show him posed as in our portrait and resemble it in so many details that it is surprising to find an interval of seven years between the date assigned the drawings and the date of about 1868 generally given to the finished portrait.

The small picture on the wall behind Tissot is one of the numerous portraits by Cranach of Frederick the Wise, Elector of Saxony. The other paintings cannot be positively identified.

Oil on canvas. H. 59⅝, w. 44 in. (151.4 x 112.1 cm.).

Stamped (at lower right): *Degas*.

REFERENCES: *Renaissance de l'art français*, I (1918), p. 146, lists this picture as in the first Degas sale, calling it Portrait de Tissot dans son atelier // P. Lafond, *Degas*, II (1919), p. 15, identifies the subject as the painter Finot, states that it was exhibited at the Fourth Impressionist Exhibition in 1879 // S. Bourgeois, *The Adolph Lewisohn Collection of Modern French Paintings and Sculptures* (1928), pp. 98f., ill., calls it a portrait of Jules Finot, dates it 1868, discusses the paintings in the background // S. Bourgeois and W. George, *Formes* (1932), nos. 28–29, pp. 301, 304, ill. after p. 302 // A. M. Frankfurter, *Art News*, XXXV (Mar. 27, 1937), pp. 13, 24, ill. p. 15 // J. Laver, *Vulgar Society: The Romantic Career of James Tissot* (1938), pp. 11–13, credits Lemoisne with the re-identification of the subject as Tissot, suggests that Degas had deliberately suppressed Tissot's name in connection with the portrait, concludes from the date of 1861 given the drawings that the portrait was done in the early sixties // A. Mongan, *Burl. Mag.*, LXXII (1938), p. 296, pl. I A, identifies the sitter as Finot // A. Mongan and P. J. Sachs, *Drawings in the Fogg Museum of Art* (1940), p. 359, no. 668, fig. 344 (the crayon study), retains the identification of the sitter as Finot but discusses the problem involved // L. Burroughs, *Met. Mus. Bull.*, XXXVI (1941), pp. 35–38, ill. (on cover), justifies the identification of the sitter as Tissot, dates the picture about 1868 // J. Rewald, *Degas* [before 1945], fig. 21, dates it 1867–1870, calls the sitter Tissot // D. Rouart, *Degas à la recherche de sa technique* (1945), p. 51, observes that Degas later retouched the picture // J. Rewald, *The History of Impressionism* (1946), ill. p. 155, dates it c. 1868; (revised and enlarged edition, 1961), p. 207, ill. p. 176, dates it 1868 // P. A. Lemoisne, *Degas* (1946), I, pp. 56, 240 (note 117), II, pp. 90f., no. 175, ill., dates it 1868, identifies the sitter as Tissot on the basis of photographs made about that time, mentions three drawings for the portrait

in the third Degas sale (no. 158 in the sale cat.) // J. S. Boggs, *Burl. Mag.*, C (1958), p. 243, note 3, records a study for this portrait on p. 31 of one of Degas's notebooks in the Bibliothèque Nationale (B.N. carnet 327 d rés., 8, formerly E; Boggs no. C I), dates this notebook 1863–1867; mentions "studies" for this portrait in a privately owned notebook in Paris and gives 1866 as the "probable date" of this notebook, in which there is an entry for February of that year // J. Rosenberg, *Great Draughtsmen from Pisanello to Picasso* (1959), p. 109, agrees that the sitter was Tissot // J. S. Boggs, *Portraits by Degas* (1962), pp. 23, 32, 54, 57, 59, 106, 131, pl. 46, dates this portrait 1866, referring to a "study in [a] privately owned, dated notebook," compares this portrait with Manet's Zola of 1868 (pl. 45) and Degas's Diego Martelli (pl. 102).

EXHIBITED: 28 Avenue de l'Opéra, Paris, 1879, *La Quatrième Exposition de peinture*, no. 69 (Portrait d'un peintre dans son atelier; owned by M. H.-M. L.; possibly this picture); The Century Association, New York, 1931; Fogg Art Museum, Harvard University, Cambridge (Mass.), 1931, *Degas*, no. 3 (lent by Adolph Lewisohn); Marie Harriman Gallery, New York, 1934, *Degas*, no. 5 (lent by Adolph Lewisohn); Cleveland Museum of Art, 1936, *Twentieth Anniversary Exhibition*, no. 268 (lent by the Adolph Lewisohn collection); Durand-Ruel, New York, 1937, *Masterpieces by Degas*, no. 2 (lent by the Adolph Lewisohn collection); Wildenstein, New York, 1938, *Great Portraits from Impressionism and Modernism*, no. 9 (lent by the Adolph Lewisohn collection); Metropolitan Museum, 1941, *French Painting from David to Toulouse-Lautrec*, no. 34, and 1951, *The Lewisohn Collection*, no. 22; Wildenstein, New York, 1960, *Degas*, no. 14.

EX COLL.: Estate of Degas (first sale, Galerie Georges Petit, Paris, May 6–8, 1918, no. 37, as Portrait d'homme dans un atelier de peintre); [Jos Hessel, Paris, from 1918 until after 1921]; Adolph Lewisohn, New York (1922–1939; Cat., 1928, pp. 98f., ill.); [Jacques Seligmann, New York, 1939].

PURCHASE, ROGERS FUND, 1939.

Joseph Henri Altès   29.100.181

Altès (1826–1895) was a flutist who became concert master in the orchestra of the Paris Opera. He also taught at the Conservatory. Degas painted another portrait of him in the Louvre picture L'Orchestre de l'Opéra (Lemoisne no. 186), where he is shown between the bassoonist Dihau and Gouffé, who played the double bass. Lemoisne dates our head 1868, and the picture in the Louvre about the same time. In the Museum's portrait he has depicted the expressive eyes and the fine nose of the subject with extraordinary sensitiveness and delicacy.

Signed (at upper left): *Degas.*

Oil on canvas. Original size, h. 9⅞, w. 7⅞ in. (25 x 20 cm.); with added strips, h. 10⅝, w. 8½ in. (27 x 21.6 cm.).

REFERENCES: G. Grappe, *E. M. Degas* (1909), ill. p. 8 (upper right) // P. Lafond, *Degas,* I (1918), ill. p. 31, II (1919), p. 13 // A. Mongan, *Burl. Mag.,* LXXII (1938), p. 296 // P. A. Lemoisne, *Degas* (1946), I, p. 54, II, pp. 90f., no. 176, ill., dates this portrait 1868,

29.100.181

gives biographical information about Altès // P. Cabanne, *Edgar Degas* (1957), pp. 96, 109 // L. W. Havemeyer [Mrs. H. O.], *Sixteen to Sixty, Memoirs of a Collector* (1961), pp. 262f.

EXHIBITED: Metropolitan Museum, 1930, *The H. O. Havemeyer Collection,* no. 49; Minneapolis Institute of Arts, 1948, *Degas' Portraits of His Family and Friends;* Birmingham Museum of Art (Alabama), 1953.

EX COLL.: [Durand-Ruel, New York, 1903]; H. O. Havemeyer, New York (from 1903; Cat., 1931, p. 116).

THE H. O. HAVEMEYER COLLECTION. BEQUEST OF MRS. H. O. HAVEMEYER, 1929.

Madame Gobillard-Morisot
29.100.45

The model is Yves Gobillard, the eldest of the three Morisot daughters and a sister of the painter Berthe Morisot. Degas, who was fascinated by her appearance, made several studies and a pastel of her in her mother's house on the Rue Franklin in May and June of 1869. The Museum's oil was done in his studio in July. The pastel (Lemoisne no. 214), a head and shoulders that differs somewhat from this picture in the coiffure and the costume, belongs now to a daughter of the subject, Mademoiselle Paule Gobillard-Morisot. Another daughter, Madame Paul Valéry, owns two preparatory drawings, one of them identical to our picture and the other almost exactly like it in pose and setting, except that the face is turned toward the spectator (Ref., Burroughs, 1957, for ills. of both drawings and pastel). Although Lemoisne alludes to a third drawing as in the "Collection X," it has been impossible to acquire any further information about it.

Signed (at lower left): *Degas.*

Oil on canvas. H. 21¾, w. 25⅝ in. (54.3 x 65.1 cm.).

REFERENCES: P. A. Lemoisne, *Degas* (1946), I, pp. 57f., II, pp. 110f., no. 213, ill., dates this picture 1869, cites the letters of Mme Morisot of May 23 and June 24 of that year

29.100.45

in which she tells of the preparations for this portrait // J. Rewald, *The History of Impressionism* (1946), p. 188, ill. p. 182, dates it 1869; (revised and enlarged edition, 1961), p. 222, ill. p. 226 // *Correspondence of Berthe Morisot* (1957), pp. 33, 35f., ill. opp. p. 36 (one of the preparatory drawings), quotes letters of Mme Morisot and her daughters, Berthe and Yves, in which Degas's preparations for this portrait are discussed // L. W. Havemeyer [Mrs. H. O.], *Sixteen to Sixty, Memoirs of a Collector* (1961), pp. 264–267, states that this portrait was purchased upon Mary Cassatt's recommendation // J. S. Boggs, *Portraits by Degas* (1962), pp. 27, 31, 61, 119, pl. 64, quotes the Morisot letters, comments upon Degas's use of some of the squaring lines on the preparatory sketch (pl. 63) in the composition of the painting // L. Burroughs, *Met. Mus. Bull.*, XXI (1963), pp. 169–172, ill. inside

of cover, quotes from the Morisot letters, illustrates the two pencil sketches and the pastel head.

EXHIBITED: Metropolitan Museum, 1930, *The H. O. Havemeyer Collection*, no. 52; Minneapolis Institute of Arts, 1948, *Degas' Portraits of his Family and Friends;* Art Gallery of Toronto, 1952.

EX COLL.: [Manzi, Paris]; H. O. Havemeyer, New York (Cat., 1931, pp. 114f., ill.).

THE H. O. HAVEMEYER COLLECTION. BEQUEST OF MRS. H. O. HAVEMEYER, 1929.

The Ballet from Robert le Diable

29.100.552

Meyerbeer's first French opera, *Robert le Diable*, which had been steadily performed since its *première* in 1831, provided Degas with the subject of this picture. Lillian Browse, who has made a careful study of the ballet in Degas's time (Ref., 1949), suggests that he was inspired by the production of 1871 in which Madame Laure Fonta led the ballet of the nuns. He chose the scene when the spirits of the nuns, who have left their tombs by moonlight, circulate in the cloister. His unpublished notebooks include drawings for the composition and the following note about the setting: "In the recession of the arcades the moonlight barely touches the columns—on the ground the effect is rosier and warmer than I have made it. Vaults black, arches indefinite. The panel of footlights is reflected by the lamps (?).[1] Tree much grayer. Luminous blue around the arches in perspective. The second version. Men more in color—flannelly but more vague. In the front the arches are grayer and darker. The black and in the vaulting in perspective. . . . Slight reflection in the center" (Ref., Boggs, *Burl. Mag.*, c, 1958). Degas's customary interest in the effects of light on forms and shapes was extended in this picture to the dramatic contrast between the brilliantly lit action on the stage and the less illuminated areas of the musicians' pit and the floor of the orchestra. This contrast had already been treated by the German artist Adolf Menzel in his picture called At the Gymnase Theater, painted in 1856, now in the National Gallery, Berlin,[2] and also by Daumier in a lithograph of 1852[3] and in his painting The Melodrama of 1856–1858, now in the Neue Staatsgalerie, Munich.[4] Degas, a great admirer of the work of Daumier, must have known these two works and he probably knew the Menzel, since he copied one of Menzel's pictures while the German artist was working in Paris and very likely studied others. Furthermore, Menzel's painting includes two motifs that appear in Degas's work, the neck of a double bass silhouetted against the footlights as in the Museum's Rehearsal of the Ballet on the Stage (see above), and also the motif of spectators using their binoculars. In The Ballet from Robert le Diable the painter's friend Désiré Dihau, the bassoonist, can be recognized, and beside him is another friend, Albert Hecht, with opera glasses.

According to tradition Hecht was the first owner of the painting. By 1886 it seems to have come into the possession of Durand-Ruel, for in that year it was shown in New York along with many other pictures from his stock that made up a famous Impressionist exhibition. At some point after this it entered the collection of the singer and collector Jean Baptiste Faure in Paris (see Manet's portraits of Faure, pp. 52, 53, above). Faure sold it back to Durand-Ruel in 1894.

A larger and wider version of this subject, with more figures in the audience, was bequeathed by Constantine Ionides to the Victoria and Albert Museum in London. It is undated. Faure originally owned it, and some scholars have dated it 1876 because in a letter of that year Degas wrote to Faure that he was sending him "the Robert le Diable." Faure sold his picture in February 1881 to Durand-Ruel, from whom Constantine Ionides bought it some months later.[5]

A number of chalk drawings of the figures in the Ballet also belong to the Victoria and Albert Museum in London (Ref., Browse, 1949, pls. 6, 6A, 7).

29.100.552

See also Courbet, Louis Gueymard as Robert le Diable, Vol. II, p. 113.

Signed and dated (at lower right): *Degas/1872.*

Oil on canvas. H. 26, w. 21⅜ in. (66 x 54.3 cm.).

Notes: 1. "*Le panneau de la rampe est reflété par les lanternes.*" 2. E. Waldmann, *Der Maler Adolf Menzel* (1941), pls. 52 and 11 (detail in color). 3. L. Delteil, *Le Peintre-Graveur illustré*, 26 (1926), no. 2243. 4. J. Adhémar, *Honoré Daumier* (1954), pl. 103 (color). 5. R. Pickvance, *Burl. Mag.*, CV (1963), p. 266, note 86, says that Ionides did not acquire his Ballet of Robert le Diable (Lemoisne 391) until June 7, 1881 (information from gallery archives supplied by Charles Durand-Ruel).

REFERENCES: *The Critic*, 8 (1886), p. 195, refers to this picture's "two distinct planes of composition" and its "weirdness of color and light" // J. Meier-Graefe, *Entwicklungsgeschichte der modernen Kunst* (1903), II, pl. 254 (confuses this picture with the version in the Victoria and Albert Museum) // P. Jamot, *Gaz. des B.-A.*, XIV (1918), pp. 162f. // P. Lafond, *Degas*, I (1918), ill. p. 50, II, p. 25, discusses the London picture, dating it wrongly 1872, calls ours the "less well known variant," observes that this is one of the first representations by Degas of dancers on the stage // H. Hertz, *Degas* (1920), pp. 96f. // Y. [or Ia] Tugendkhol'd, *Edgar Degas* (1922), ill. p. 44 // P. Jamot, *Degas* (1924), pp. 98f. (note 1), 104, 138, finds ours "a little less advanced" in execution, believes it to be still in the collection of Mme Albert Hecht, claims it was the Victoria and Albert version that was shown in London (in 1872) by Durand-Ruel at the exhibition of the Society of French Artists // B. S. Long, in the *Catalogue of the Constantine Alexander Ionides Collection*, Victoria and Albert Museum, London (1925), p. 19, mentions ours in the entry for the London version // J. B. Manson, *Edgar Degas* (1927), p. 19, finds this version less satisfactory than the one in London // A. Alexandre, *La Renaissance*, XII (1929), p. 484, ill. p. 478 // L. Burroughs, *Met. Mus. Bull.*, XXVII (1932), p. 144, asserts

that Désiré Dihau inspired Degas to paint the London picture, calls ours a variant of it // A. Mongan, *Burl. Mag.*, LXXII (1938), p. 296 // H. Huth, *Gaz. des B.-A.*, XXIX (1946), p. 239, note 22, observes that either this version or the London one was exhibited in New York in 1886 // J. Rewald, *The History of Impressionism* (1946), ill. p. 231; (revised and enlarged edition, 1961), pp 274f., ill., observes that it must have been purchased by Durand-Ruel immediately after its completion in 1872, for it was exhibited by him that same winter in London // P. A. Lemoisne, *Degas* (1946), I, p. 68, II, pp. 144f., no. 294, ill., dates the London version (no. 391) 1876, calls it a replica, mentions studies and suggests comparisons // L. Browse, *Degas Dancers* [1949], pp. 22, 28, 52, 61, 66, 337, cat. no. 8, pl. 8, states that this ballet was revived at the end of 1871 with Laure Fonta, "a dancer of little renown," leading the "Ballet of the Nuns," gives further information on the ballet; discusses studies for the dancing figures // D. Cooper, in the introduction to the catalogue of *The Courtauld Collection* (1954), p. 60, associates the Museum's version with the one that was exhibited in London by Durand-Ruel in 1872, concluding from Degas's letter of 1876 to Faure that the London version was not finished until 1876 // F. Fosca, *Degas* (1954), p. 43 // P. Cabanne, *Edgar Degas* (1957), pp. 31, 97, 109, notes that Degas's Carnet no. 22 (Bibliothèque Nationale) contains many sketches of musicians for this composition and others // J. S. Boggs, *Degas* (exhib. cat.), Los Angeles County Museum (1958), p. 14; and *Burl. Mag.*, C (1958), p. 244, records studies for this painting and other theater scenes in one of Degas's notebooks in the Bibliothèque Nationale (B.N. carnet 327 d rés., 22, formerly S; Boggs no. C V), dates this notebook about 1872 and quotes from it Degas's description of this stage set and his color notations // L. W. Havemeyer [Mrs. H. O.], *Sixteen to Sixty, Memoirs of a Collector* (1961), p. 263 // G. Agnew, *The Listener*, LXXII (Dec. 10, 1964), pp. 944f., discusses the London version and related pictures.

EXHIBITED: 168 New Bond Street, London,

1872, *Fourth Exhibition of the Society of French Artists*, no. 95, marked for sale at 100 gns.; American Art Association and National Academy of Design, New York, 1886, *Works in Oil and Pastel by the Impressionists of Paris*, no. 17; Carnegie Institute, Pittsburgh (Pa.), 1897, *Second Annual Exhibition*, no. 65 (probably lent by Durand-Ruel); Metropolitan Museum, 1930, *The H. O. Havemeyer Collection*, no. 50; Boston Museum of Fine Arts, 1935, *Independent Painters of Nineteenth-Century Paris*, no. 12; Wildenstein Gallery, New York, 1944, *Five Centuries of Ballet*, no. 238; Columbus Gallery of Fine Arts (Ohio), 1948, *The Springtime of Impressionism*, no. 8; Wildenstein Gallery, New York, 1949, *Degas*, no. 23; Honolulu Academy of Arts (Hawaii), 1949–1950, *Four Centuries of European Painting*, no. 26; Art Gallery of Toronto, 1950, *Fifty Paintings by Old Masters*, no. 9; Kunstmuseum, Bern, 1952, *Degas*, no. 17; Stedelijk Museum, Amsterdam, 1952, *Edgar Degas*, no. 11; Metropolitan Museum, 1955, *The Comédie Française and the Theater in France*, cat. p. 6; Carnegie Institute, Pittsburgh (Pa.), 1959, *Retrospective Exhibition of Paintings from Previous Internationals*, no. 7; Arkansas Arts Center, Little Rock, 1963, *Five Centuries of European Painting*, cat. p. 46.

Ex coll.: Albert Hecht, Paris; [Durand-Ruel, Paris, 1886]; Jean Baptiste Faure, Paris (until 1894); [Durand-Ruel, Paris and New York, 1894–1898]; H. O. Havemeyer, New York (from 1898; Cat., 1931, pp. 106f., ill.).

The H. O. Havemeyer Collection. Bequest of Mrs. H. O. Havemeyer, 1929.

The Dancing Class   29.100.184

In 1871 and 1872 Degas began making his pictures of ballet dancers practicing or resting in their classrooms. This small painting and another larger one in the Camondo collection in the Louvre are generally agreed to be his first pictures of the subject. Both are said to have for setting practice rooms in the old opera house on the Rue Le Peletier, which

was burned in 1873; the Louvre painting shows a different salon, decorated with marble or stucco pilasters and a rich cornice.

Because of its very small size, the Museum's picture, rather than the one in the Camondo collection, can very probably be identified with the "Classe de Danse" by Degas that was lent by a M. Brandon to the First Impressionist Exhibition in 1874 and that Philippe Burty in his review of the Salon (Ref., 1874) described as being *tout petit*. Durand-Ruel had bought this picture from the artist in January 1872 at the same time as his first purchase of pictures from Manet. In February of the same year he sold it to someone named Brandon, but it is not known whether this was the painter Jacques Émile Édouard Brandon, who was a friend of Degas, or Brandon's son. A very small picture with the same dimensions as The Dancing Class, but called Pas de Deux, was acquired by Henry Hill of Brighton in 1876, or shortly before, and sold with his collection in 1889. Hill was a tailor in Brighton, who had the distinction of being perhaps the first English collector of Impressionist pictures, and the sale of his collection was the first auction of modern French paintings in London. Although the Museum's Dancing Class could never be called a Pas de Deux, its uniquely small size makes it almost certain that it is the picture that belonged to Hill (Hill also owned The Rehearsal on the Stage, above).

The dancer who posed alone in the middle of the floor in front of the mirror bears some resemblance to the dancer and actress Joséphine Gaugelin (or Gaujelin), whose appearance is preserved in an inscribed drawing dated 1872 or 1873, which shows her in a similar pose (Ref., Browse, 1949, pl. 12). There are several portraits of her, especially a beautiful oil painting in the Isabella Stewart Gardner Museum in Boston, which was painted in 1867.

Formerly called Le Foyer.

Signed (at lower right): *Degas*.

Oil on wood. H. 7¾, w. 10⅝ in. (19.7 x 27 cm.).

REFERENCES: [P. Burty], *La République fran-*
çaise (Apr. 25, 1874), reprinted in L. Venturi,
Les Archives de l'impressionnisme (1939), II,
p. 289, refers to a very small *(tout petit)* picture called Classe de Danse in the First Impressionist Exhibition of 1874 (probably this
picture, which is the only one of the subject
listed in Lemoisne that could be described as
tout petit) // M. de Montifaud, *L'Artiste*, series
9, XIX (1874), p. 309, describes this picture
(cf. Pickvance, 1963, pp. 257f., notes 18, 19)
// *Art Journal*, XXXVIII (1876), p. 211, comments on the great sense of space Degas con-
veys in this small picture, on exhibition in
London in 1876 // *The Athenaeum* (1876),
p. 571, praises its "breadth and softness of
effect" but finds it "slovenly in form" //
H. B. Wehle, *Met. Mus. Bull.*, XXV (1930),
p. 55, ill. p. 57 // L. Burroughs, *Met. Mus.
Bull.*, XXVII (1932), p. 144, quotes a letter in
which Mary Cassatt calls this picture "finely
executed, . . . a real *tour de force*" // J. Rewald,
The History of Impressionism (1946), ill. p. 232

and opp. p. 232 (detail in color), dates it about
1873, states that the Havemeyers bought it
through Mary Cassatt; (revised and enlarged
edition, 1961), ill. in color p. 279, dates it
about 1872 // P. A. Lemoisne, *Degas* (1946),
I, p. 69, II, pp. 148f., no. 297, ill., calls it Le
Foyer, dates it 1872, suggesting that it may
have been painted before the picture in the
Louvre (no. 298); because of its small size
connects it with the painting mentioned by
René de Gas in his letter of July 12, 1872
(p. 71), suggests comparing the central figure
to a drawing of a dancer (Fogg Museum, Ref.
Browse, pl. 10) // L. Browse, *Degas Dancers*
[1949], pp. 53f., 60, 341, cat. no. 17, pl. 17,
and color pl. II, calls it La Leçon de Danse,
identifies the setting as the opera house in the
Rue Le Peletier, suggests that Joséphine Gaugelin may have posed for the central figure //
T. Rousseau Jr., *Art News*, XLVIII (Apr. 1949),
p. 21, compares the arrangement of forms in
space to that of Vermeer and the cool colors
to those of Velazquez // P. Cabanne, *Edgar*

29.100.184

Degas (1957), pp. 32, 97, 107f., no. 26, color pl. 36 // L. W. Havemeyer [Mrs. H. O.], *Sixteen to Sixty, Memoirs of a Collector* (1961), pp. 265f. // R. Pickvance, *Burl. Mag.*, cv (1963), pp. 256–259, 265f., observes that Degas first took up the problem of "the organization of figure-groups in an interior" in this picture and the one in the Louvre (Lemoisne no. 298), and that he never repeated, as was his later practice, any of the many poses he invented in these two paintings; comments upon the absence of preliminary studies for this picture, the lack of *pentimenti*, and the sure handling; states that this picture cannot be identified with the small picture of a rehearsal mentioned by Degas's brother René in a letter dated July 1872, because it had already been bought by Durand-Ruel in January of that year and sold to Brandon in February; states that Henry Hill bought it at the exhibition in London in 1876 // P. Poole, *Degas* (1964), p. 40 (under catalogue entry for the Louvre picture, pl. xxii), states that this and the Camondo picture were painted in 1872.

EXHIBITED: 35 Boulevard des Capucines, Paris, 1874, *Société anonyme des artistes peintres, sculpteurs* . . . (First Impressionist Exhibition), no. 55 (Classe de danse, lent by M. Brandon; probably this picture, see Ref., Burty, 1874); Deschamps Gallery, 168 New Bond Street, London, 1876, *Twelfth Exhibition of Pictures by Modern French Artists*, no. 2 (as The Practising Room); Durand-Ruel, New York, 1928, *French Masterpieces of the XIX Century*, no. 6 (La Leçon de foyer, lent anonymously, probably this picture); Metropolitan Museum, 1930, *The H. O. Havemeyer Collection*, no. 48.

EX COLL.: [Durand-Ruel, Paris, Jan.-Feb., 1872]; Brandon, Paris (from Feb. 1872, until after April 1874); [Durand-Ruel, Paris, and 168 New Bond Street, London, until May 1875; and/or Charles W. Deschamps, 168 New Bond Street, London, until April-June, 1876]; Henry Hill, Brighton (1875/76–1889; sale, Christie's, London, May 25, 1889, no. 26, as A Pas de Deux, 7½ x 10 in., to Wallis for

41 guineas); [Wallis, French Gallery, London, in 1889]; [Manzi, Paris, until 1916/17]; H. O. Havemeyer, New York (from 1916/17; Cat., 1931, p. 117, ill.).

THE H. O. HAVEMEYER COLLECTION. BEQUEST OF MRS. H. O. HAVEMEYER, 1929.

Sulking (Bouderie)   29.100.43

The title Bouderie was given to this picture many years after it was painted, appearing in print, apparently for the first time, in 1910. Most observers read into the picture anger and fixed resolution, but the earliest known discussion of it interpreted the scene as one of affectionate and intellectual intimacy. The difficulty about the title is understandable considering the very unclear evidence presented by the scene. The setting is a room in which there are racks with ledgers at the upper right, and at the left a closed window of the type customary in banks, post offices, theater and other ticket offices. The man sits with crossed arms and an enigmatic facial expression at a table covered with documents, books, and writing materials. The young woman in an afternoon dress *(toilette de visite)*, who leans on the back of the chair in an informal pose, holds rolled-up papers in her hand. Lemoisne raises the possibility that the picture can be associated with one called The Banker, that was among several paintings that Degas managed in 1874 to get back from his dealer Durand-Ruel because he was dissatisfied with them.

The picture is painted in a style that marks a transition between the sharp clarity of most of Degas's earlier works and the sketchiness of those done after 1875. It shows distinct similarities in handling to The Cotton Market and The Pedicure, which were both painted in 1873, and was probably done about the same time. A painting called Conversation in the collection of Mr. and Mrs. Paul Mellon is a second version of Sulking with a more concentrated composition and in Degas's later, painterly style.

There are two sketches made in connection

with this painting in one of Degas's note-books, which is dated 1871–1872 by Jean Boggs (Ref., 1958).

Formerly called Pouting.

Signed (at lower right): *E. Degas.*

Oil on canvas. H. 12¾, w. 18¼ in. (32.4 x 46.4 cm.).

REFERENCES: *Revue Encyclopédique* (1896), p. 481, calls this picture a portrait, a scene of affectionate intimacy, observes that it shows Degas's admiration for Ingres // G. Moore, *Kunst und Künstler,* VI (1907–1908), ill. p. 142 (as Am Schreibtisch) // G. Lecomte, *L'Art et les Artistes,* XII (1910), ill. p. 27, calls it Bouderie // P. Jamot, *Gaz. des B.-A.,* XIV (1918), pp. 130, 132, ill., dates it about 1873, thinks it shows a husband and wife in his business office // P. Lafond, *Degas,* I (1918), ill. p. 37, II (1919), p. 5, concludes from the picture on the wall that the man is a bookmaker or a habitué of the track, finds it impossible to determine the exact nature of the subject;

mentions another picture *(un double)* with the same subject found unfinished in Degas's studio at his death (presumably Lemoisne no. 864, Causerie) // J. Meier-Graefe, *Degas* (1923), p. 28, pl. XVIII, dates the picture 1872, considers Causerie a sketch for it, supposes that it represents a husband angry with his wife // P. Jamot, *Degas* (1924), pp. 71f., 138f., pl. 26, dates it about 1872 or 1873, calls Causerie a sketch for it // J. B. Manson, *Edgar Degas* (1927), p. 19, considers it a "reversion to the Portrait de Famille of 1869" [the Bellelli Family, elsewhere in this text dated 1862 (p. 11) and c. 1866 (pl. 10)] // A. Alexandre, *La Renaissance,* XII (1929), p. 485, ill. // *L'Amour de l'art,* XII (1931), p. 268, fig. 7, locates it in the collection of Dr. Viau (confusing it with Causerie) // L. Burroughs, *Met. Mus. Bull.,* XXVII (1932), pp. 143f., ill. // C. Sterling, *Chefs-d'oeuvre de l'art français* (exhib. cat.), Palais National des Arts, Paris (1937), p. 149, no. 299, dates it about 1869; R. Burnand, in another catalogue of the same exhibition (Edition des Musées Na-

29.100.43

tionaux), i, p. 478, no. 185, ill., prefers Distraction as the title // J. Lassaigne, *Edgar Degas* (1945), pl. 40, dates it 1875–1876 // D. C. Rich, *Degas* (1951), pp. 62f., ill. in color, interprets the subject as a moment of domestic life, reminiscent in its realism of the Dutch seventeenth-century masters, analyses its composition // P. A. Lemoisne, *Degas* (1946), i, p. 83, ii, pp. 174f., cat. no. 335, ill., describes the woman's coiffure as a braid, concluding from this that she is still young and that the man is her father; dates it 1873–1875 and the variant (no. 864) 1885–1895 // P. Cabanne, *Edgar Degas* (1957), pp. 29, 97, 110, under entry no. 49 (for The Interior), states that in composing this picture the artist followed "very exactly" a photograph of himself with Mme Arthur Fontaine and M. Poujaud (presumably the photograph taken of the artist with Mme Fontaine and M. Poujaud ill. in Lemoisne, i, opp. p. 218, which can scarcely be the source Degas used for this picture, as it was almost certainly taken about twenty years later) // J. S. Boggs, *Burl. Mag.*, c (1958), p. 244, fig. 39 (study for the rack of ledgers), records two studies for this painting on pages 36 and 39 of a notebook by Degas in the Bibliothèque Nationale (B.N. carnet 327 d rés., 24, formerly U; Boggs no. C IV), dates the notebook 1871–1872 // R. Pickvance, *Burl. Mag.*, cvi (1964), p. 295, rejects the idea that the source of this painting could have been the photograph mentioned above // P. Poole, *Degas* (1964), p. 41, pl. xxvii, suggests that this is the picture called "The Banker" that Degas asked Faure to buy back for him, like Cabanne (above, 1957), states that it was probably based on a photograph posed by Mme Arthur Fontaine and M. Poujaud, which Degas followed closely.

EXHIBITED: Durand-Ruel, Paris, 1896, *Degas*; Knoedler, New York, 1915, *Masterpieces by Old and Modern Painters*, no. 25 (as The Dispute, 1876); Metropolitan Museum, 1930, *The H. O. Havemeyer Collection*, no. 46 (as Pouting); Pennsylvania Museum of Art, Philadelphia, 1936, *Degas*, no. 19; Musée de l'Orangerie, Paris, 1937, *Degas*, no. 11; Palais National des Arts, Paris, 1937, *Chefs-d'œuvre de l'art français*, no. 299; Minneapolis Institute of Arts, 1948, *Degas' Portraits of his Family and Friends* (unnumbered checklist); Springfield Museum of Fine Arts (Mass.), 1948, *Fifteen Fine Paintings* (unnumbered catalogue); Wildenstein Gallery, New York, 1949, *Degas*, no. 28; Seattle Art Museum, 1951.

EX COLL.: [Possibly Durand-Ruel, Paris]; H. O. Havemeyer, New York (by 1915; Cat., 1931, pp. 110f., ill.).

THE H. O. HAVEMEYER COLLECTION. BEQUEST OF MRS. H. O. HAVEMEYER, 1929.

The Rehearsal of the Ballet on the Stage   29.160.26

Degas, who so often studied the poses of dancers in their practice rooms, was interested also in the very different atmosphere and effect when they rehearsed on the stage. The artificial light, dramatic in its strong contrasts with the deep shadows between the coulisses, gives the dancers an unreal appearance that he took pleasure in depicting.

He made three closely similar pictures of a rehearsal on the stage: an oil and a pastel belonging to this Museum, and a painting in *camaïeu* in the Camondo collection of the Louvre. Ronald Pickvance convincingly dates all three 1873–1874. In a detailed study of Degas's pictures of dancers made in the years between 1872 and 1876 (Ref., 1963), he reveals the curious history of the Museum's oil painting, which is on paper mounted on canvas. It apparently began as a pen drawing that Degas submitted, according to Pickvance, in 1873, for publication in the *Illustrated London News*. The editor refused it because the ballet was not considered suitable subject matter for a prudish Victorian reading public.

Using as a basis the rejected pen drawing, which is still clearly visible, he then painted over it in the technique known as "peinture à l'essence," which means oil colors "thinned and freely mixed" with refined turpentine (See D. Cooper, *Pastels by Edgar Degas*, n.d.,

p. 13). There also seem to be traces of pastel and water color.

The Museum's pastel of the same composition (see following entry) also has as its foundation a careful drawing, this time done with brush and ink, that is still visible beneath the pastel. In the designing of this version Degas made changes that simplify the composition. The pattern of the dark necks of a pair of double basses rising from the pit and silhouetted against the stage in the left foreground becomes in the pastel one large, emphatic shape. The group of three performers at the front of the stage has been changed to two, and the four dancers at the left have been reduced to two, so that the one with her back turned to the spectator effectively closes the composition on that side. This pastel is the most developed and impressive of the three treatments of the theme.

It can be shown that the considerably larger *camaïeu* version in the Louvre (Lemoisne no. 340) that Degas sent to the First Impressionist Exhibition in April 1874 must have been made after the Museum's oil version. This painting differs significantly from the other two pictures, chiefly in terminating at the right with the curving edge of the stage and in omitting the ballet master and one of the spectators. Several tiny figures have been added in the wings, and the group at the front of the stage is made up of two performers, as in the pastel. Beneath the thinly applied paint, however, the figures of the ballet master and the second spectator may still be seen, and other *pentimenti* reveal that when Degas began this version he used the original design that he had submitted to the *Illustrated London News* and subsequently used as the foundation for the Museum's oil painting.

Degas prepared to paint these pictures by making his usual large number of careful studies of the individual figures (Ref., Lemoisne, 1946, and Browse, 1949). There is an oil in the Courtauld Collection in London of the two dancers (Lemoisne no. 425), which is directly related to the performers at the front of the stage in all three versions. It was exhibited in London in November 1874, reinforcing

the supposition that the whole group of pictures showing the rehearsal on the stage was made within the years 1873 and 1874.

Lillian Browse suggests that the setting of these pictures is the old opera house in the Rue Le Peletier, which, though probably still in use when Degas began the series, was destroyed by fire in October 1873. She believes that the ballet master was probably Eugène Caralli, but cannot identify the two seated male figures.

The Museum's oil painting of a rehearsal on the stage and a small group of other pictures by Degas were acquired soon after they were painted by Henry Hill (see The Dancing Class, p. 69, above). At the sale of Hill's collection in 1889 our oil was bought by the painter Walter Sickert, an enthusiastic admirer of Degas.

Signed (at upper left): *Degas.*

Oil colors freely mixed with turpentine, with traces of water color and pastel over pen-and-ink drawing on paper, mounted on canvas. H. 21⅜, w. 28¾ in. (54.3 x 73 cm.).

REFERENCES: A. Meynell, *Mag. of Art*, V (1882), p. 82, in discussing the pictures by Degas owned by Henry Hill, mentions one (this picture) showing "two dilettanti of the boulevard stretch[ing] themselves at ease to watch the work" // G. Moore, *Mag. of Art* (1890), ill. p. 420, as A Rehearsal // D. S. M[acColl], *The Spectator*, LXVII (1891), p. 809, calls this picture a masterpiece, "a demonstration against all pedantry of technique" // G. Moore, *The Speaker*, IV (1891), pp. 676–678, expresses his belief that the original drawing was done for the *Illustrated London News*, but rejected and returned to Degas, who then made it into a painting // L. Pissarro, in a letter to his father, Camille (May 1891), published in C. Pissarro, *Lettres à son fils Lucien* (1950), p. 239, mentions seeing an oil painting by Degas (which D. Cooper identifies with this picture, see below, 1954) hanging in the house of Walter Sickert, states that it had figured in a "famous sale" of which Theo van Gogh had spoken (the Hill sale) // J.

Meier-Graefe, *Entwicklungsgeschichte der modernen Kunst* (1903), ii, pl. 260 // *Brush and Pencil*, xv (1905), ill. p. 260 // P. Lafond, *Degas*, ii (1919), p. 26, states that this picture, which he calls a replica of the version in the Louvre, was lent by Madame Cobden-Sickert to the Exposition Centennale of 1900 // J. Meier-Graefe, *Degas* (1923), pp. 59f., finds this more lively than the picture in the Camondo collection because of its extraordinary angle of vision // P. Jamot, *Degas* (1924), p. 125 (note 6), 142f., confuses our oil version with the pastel, discusses the possibility that it was no. 61 of the Third Impressionist Exhibition // H. B. Wehle, *Met. Mus. Bull.*, xxv (1930), p. 55 // L. Burroughs, *Met. Mus. Bull.*, xxvii (1932), p. 144, compares the Museum's oil and pastel versions, finding the pastel more successful // W. R. Sickert, in the preface to the catalogue of the exhibition *Twentieth Century Art*, Leicester Galleries, London (Jan. 1932), quoted in *A Free House!* (1947), p. 294, states that Degas

did indeed paint this picture over the drawing submitted to the *Illustrated London News* // J. Bouchot-Saupique and M. Delaroche-Vernet, *Degas* (exhib. cat.), Musée de l'Orangerie, Paris (1937), pp. 31f., no. 22, pl. xiii, gives Lemoisne's as yet unpublished chronology for the three versions, which places this second, in 1876, and firmly identifies it with the version shown in the Third Impressionist Exhibition // P. Durand-Ruel, *Mémoires*, published in L. Venturi, *Les Archives de l'impressionnisme* (1939), ii, p. 195, states that he bought a Répétition de danse, possibly this picture, from Degas for 3000 francs and sold it for 200 pounds to a tailor in Brighton (D. Cooper, Ref., 1954, p. 61, note 1, identifies this picture as Lemoisne no. 341, and the tailor as Henry Hill) // L. Burroughs, *Met. Mus. Bull.*, iv (1946), note opp. p. 144, ill. and color detail on cover, compares the three versions in technique and composition // H. Huth, *Gaz. des B.-A.*, xxix (1946), p. 239, note 22, suggests that this may have been

29.160.26

one of the pictures called Dance Rehearsal by Degas exhibited in New York in 1886 by Durand-Ruel (impossible; see Ex coll.) // P. A. Lemoisne, *Degas* (1946), I, pp. 91f., II, pp. 218f., cat. no. 400, ill., dates it about 1876, lists related pictures and studies // F. Kimball and L. Venturi, *Great Paintings in America* [c. 1948], pp. 182f., color pl. 84 // L. Browse, *Degas Dancers* [1949], pp. 55f., 67, 345f., cat. no. 30, pl. 30, dates it about 1874–1875, identifies the theater as the stage of the Salle de la Rue Le Peletier, which had burnt (Oct. 28, 1873) before this and the pastel version were painted but not before the Louvre version; suggests that the ballet master was probably Eugène Coralli but finds it impossible to identify the two seated figures; does not recognize the ballet that is being performed; discusses the composition and the artist's use of the double-bass motif; mentions and illustrates related pictures and studies // D. Cooper, in the introduction to the catalogue *The Courtauld Collection* (1954), pp. 60–62, publishes new detailed information about the early ownership of the picture, finds that Henry Hill of Brighton must have bought it before 1875, and therefore concludes that it must have been painted somewhat earlier than is generally stated // P. Cabanne, *Edgar Degas* (1957), pp. 108, 112f., cat. no. 66, p. 130, pl. 66 // J. S. Boggs, *Degas* (exhib. cat.), Los Angeles County Museum (1958), p. 39, no. 26, ill. // L. W. Havemeyer [Mrs. H. O.], *Sixteen to Sixty, Memoirs of a Collector* (1961), pp. 259f., states that it was painted in gouache // R. Pickvance, *Burl. Mag.*, cv (1963), pp. 259–266, fig. 21, dates this picture 1873, comments on the related pictures and when they were painted, and on preliminary studies for this picture; brings to light Degas's original intention to publish the drawing beneath the oil in the *Illustrated London News*; gives information about the early owners, exhibitions, and critical opinions of the painting // P. Poole, *Degas* (1964), p. 41, entry for pl. XXVI (*camaïeu* in the Camondo collection), mentions it in a discussion of the Louvre picture.

EXHIBITED: Deschamps Gallery, 168 New Bond Street, London, 1876, *Twelfth Exhibition of Pictures by Modern French Artists*, no. 130 (as The Rehearsal); New English Art Club, London, 1891, *Seventh Exhibition*, no. 39 (as Répétition, lent by Mrs. Walter Sickert); The International Society of Sculptors, Painters, and Engravers, London, 1898, *Exhibition of International Art* (souvenir catalogue), no. 116 (as Dancers, ill., lent by Mrs. Unwin); Exposition Internationale Universelle, Paris, 1900, *Exposition centennale de l'art français*, no. 210 (as La Répétition, lent by Mme Cobden-Sickert); Knoedler, New York, 1915, *Masterpieces by Old and Modern Painters*, either no. 19 (Dancing Rehearsal) or no. 24 (The Rehearsal; probably lent by H. O. Havemeyer); Metropolitan Museum, 1930, *The H. O. Havemeyer Collection*, no. 58; Musée de l'Orangerie, Paris, 1937, *Degas*, no. 22; Cleveland Museum, 1947, *Works by Edgar Degas*, no. 23; Wildenstein, New York, 1949, *Degas*, no. 36; Philadelphia Museum of Art, 1951, *Diamond Jubilee Exhibition*, no. 73; William Rockhill Nelson Gallery, Kansas City, 1953, *Twentieth Anniversary Exhibition: 19th and 20th Century French Paintings*; Los Angeles County Museum, 1958, *Degas*, no. 26.

Ex COLL.: [Durand-Ruel, Paris, and 168 New Bond Street, London, until May 1875; and/or Charles W. Deschamps, 168 New Bond Street, London, until April–June, 1876]; Henry Hill, Brighton (1875/76–1889; sale, Christie's, London, May 25, 1889, no. 29, as A Rehearsal, 20½ x 28 in., to Sickert for 66 guineas); Walter Richard Sickert, London (from 1889); Ellen Cobden-Sickert, London (in 1900); [possibly Boussod-Valadon, Paris]; H. O. Havemeyer, New York (Cat., 1931, pp. 122f., ill.).

GIFT OF HORACE HAVEMEYER, 1929.

The Rehearsal on the Stage

29.100.39

This pastel is one of three versions of the subject. See comment under preceding entry.

Signed (at upper left): *Degas*.

Pastel over brush-and-ink drawing on paper.
H. 21, w. 28½ in. (53.3 x 72.3 cm.).

REFERENCES: G. Geffroy, *L'Art et les artistes*,
VII (1908), ill. p. 18, dates this picture 1874
// P. Lafond, *Degas*, II (1919), p. 26, dates
it 1874 // P. Jamot, *Degas* (1924), pp. 142f.,
pl. 36, dates it about 1874, confuses it with
the oil painting // A. Alexandre, *La Renaissance*, XII (Oct. 1929), p. 483, ill. p. 479 //
P. Jamot, in *La Peinture au Musée du Louvre*
(1929), I, *École Française, XIX siècle*, pt. 3,
p. 63, confuses it with the oil version, stating
that it is in America in the collection of Mme
Cobden-Sickert // L. Burroughs, *Met. Mus.
Bull.*, XXVII (1932), p. 144, compares the two
versions in this Museum, finding the pastel
"perhaps more successful" // J. Bouchot-
Saupique and M. Delaroche-Vernet, *Degas*
(exhib. cat.), Musée de l'Orangerie, Paris
(1937), pp. 31f., no. 22 (the Metropolitan's
oil version), quote Lemoisne's opinion that
this was done some years after 1876 // G.
Rivière, *M[onsieu]r. Degas* (1938), ill. p. 133,
dates it 1874 // M. Rebatet, *Degas* (1944),
pl. 75, dates it 1874–1875 // L. Burroughs,
Met. Mus. Bull., IV (1946), note opp. p. 144,
discusses the differences in composition of the
three versions // H. Huth, *Gaz. des B.-A.*,
XXIX (1946), p. 239, note 22, suggests that
this may have been one of the two pictures
by Degas called Dance Rehearsal exhibited by
Durand-Ruel at the National Academy of
Design, New York, in 1886 // P. A. Lemoisne,
Degas (1946), I, pp. 91f., II, pp. 276f., cat. no.
498, ill., dates it about 1878–1879, mentions
studies // L. Browse, *Degas Dancers* [1949],
pp. 55f., 67, 346, cat. no. 31, pl. 31, dates it
about 1876–1877 (see also in Refs. under preceding entry) // D. C. Rich, *Degas* (1951),
pp. 84f., ill. in color, finds it the best of the
three versions, discusses the composition and
the light // Metropolitan Museum, *Art Treasures* (1952), p. 233, cat. no. 147, pl. 147 //
R. Rey, *Degas* (1952), pl. 43, dates it about
1878 // D. C. Rich, *Degas* (1953), pl. 21, ill.
in color // P. Cabanne, *Edgar Degas* (1957),
p. 108 // L. W. Havemeyer [Mrs. H. O.],
Sixteen to Sixty, Memoirs of a Collector (1961),

29.100.39

pp. 259f. // R. Pickvance, *Burl. Mag.*, CV
(1963), p. 263, dates this picture 1874, grouping it with the others of the composition;
comments upon the minor modifications made
in its composition.

EXHIBITED: Knoedler, New York, 1915, *Loan
Exhibition of Masterpieces of Old and Modern
Painters*, no. 38 (as The Ballet Rehearsal,
1875); Metropolitan Museum, 1930, *The H. O.
Havemeyer Collection*, no. 143.

EX COLL.: Ernest May, Paris (sale, Galerie
Georges Petit, Paris, June 4, 1890, no. 75,
bought in); G. May, Paris (until 1899); [Du-
rand-Ruel, Paris and New York, 1899]; H. O.
Havemeyer, New York (from 1899; Cat.,
1931, pp. 124f., ill.).

THE H. O. HAVEMEYER COLLECTION. BE-
QUEST OF MRS. H. O. HAVEMEYER, 1929.

A Woman Ironing   29.100.46

Degas frequently used laundresses as subjects,
as Daumier also did, either at their work,
carrying baskets of wash, or resting. It has
been suggested that he knew the passage in
Goncourt's novel *Manette Salomon* (1867)
that describes the picturesque effects of a
laundry. To Degas, however, there would have
been incentive enough in the possibilities this
subject offered to study the exact motions and

29.100.46

gestures that always interested him and to experiment with lighting in the work room. As always with Degas's series of treatments of the same subject, it is difficult to determine the order in which the pictures were made. Most scholars agree that this series began in 1869 with the painting of a laundress (Lemoisne no. 216) shown from the front across the wide, pale expanse of her work table. He was still interested in the theme around 1902 when, according to Lemoisne, he did several pastels (no. 1418–1420 *bis*) of washerwomen.

Lemoisne dates our picture fairly early, about 1874, although he assigns a date eight years later to the closely similar but larger and more finished painting of the same subject in the collection of Madame Durand-Ruel at Neuilly (Lemoisne no. 685), for which ours could have been a preparatory study. Among the pictures Degas contributed to the Second Impressionist Exhibition of 1876 there was a "Blanchisseuse. Silhouette," and if the larger painting was indeed made as late as 1882, ours, although it is sketchy in character, was probably the one in the exhibition.

There was a charcoal drawing in the third

Degas sale (no. 269), which is very close to our painting, and a monotype that came up in the sale of prints by Degas (Galerie Manzi-Joyant, Paris, Nov. 22–23, 1918, no. 211) includes a very similar figure.

Signed (at lower left): *Degas*.

Oil on canvas. H. 21⅜, w. 15½ in. (54.3 x 39.4 cm.).

REFERENCES: L. Burroughs, *Met. Mus. Bull.*, XXVII (1932), p. 142, ill. // C. Mauclair, *Degas* (1937), p. 167, ill. p. 108, erroneously places this picture in a private collection // P. A. Lemoisne, *Degas* (1946), I, p. 87, II, pp. 188f., no. 356, ill., dates it about 1874, including it among Degas's second group of laundress pictures, painted after his trip to America; mentions a study; supposes that the painting appeared as "Blanchisseuse. Silhouette" in the Second Impressionist Exhibition in 1876.

EXHIBITED: 11 Rue Le Peletier, Paris, 1876, *La 2ᵉ Exposition de peinture* (Second Impressionist Exhibition) ("Blanchisseuse. Silhouette"; possibly this picture); Knoedler, New York, 1915, *Masterpieces by Old and Modern Painters*, no. 26 (as The Laundress, 1880); Metropolitan Museum, 1930, *The H. O. Havemeyer Collection*, no. 56; Virginia Museum of Fine Arts, Richmond, 1944, *Nineteenth Century French Paintings*, no. 22.

EX COLL.: [Durand-Ruel, Paris and New York, 1892–1894]; H. O. Havemeyer, New York (from 1894; Cat., 1931, pp. 112f., ill., dated c. 1880).

THE H. O. HAVEMEYER COLLECTION. BE-QUEST OF MRS. H. O. HAVEMEYER, 1929.

Dancers Practicing at the Bar

29.100.34

Lemoisne believes that this picture was painted in 1876–1877. Degas presented it to his friend Henri Rouart in exchange for a pastel he had reclaimed to improve and had ruined in the process. The watering can used to lay the dust on dance floors is a realistic touch that Degas later found offensive and wanted to remove, but Rouart refused to let this picture leave his house. His son Ernest Rouart, however, denies the legend that he secured it to his wall with a padlock (Ref., Valéry, 1960). In 1912, after Rouart's death, Mrs. Havemeyer bought the picture at auction, paying for it 478,000 francs ($95,700)—a record sum for an Impressionist painting at that time, comparable to the prices Impressionists have brought in the 1950's and 1960's. The aged painter, on hearing of the price, made the now famous remark that he understood the feelings of the horse who wins the Grand Prix and gets nothing for it but his oats.

Many critics have asserted that the picture was painted in tempera, but Degas himself stated that he had done it in his "usual" technique[1] (for discussion of this technique see The Rehearsal of the Ballet on the Stage, p. 73). He refrained from varnishing it in an effort to preserve its fresh effect, and that is why it is always protected by glass.

There is an oil sketch on paper of the two dancers (Lemoisne no. 409) and a pastel of the one on the right (Lemoisne no. 421), as well as a number of minor studies (Ref., Lemoisne, 1946, and Cooper, 1952).

Signed (at left center): *Degas.*

Oil colors freely mixed with turpentine on canvas. H. 29¾, w. 32 in. (75.6 x 81.3 cm.).

Note 1. G. Durand-Ruel, in an extract from a

29.100.34

letter of Dec. 24, 1912, pasted on the stretcher of the painting.

REFERENCES: G. Moore, *Mag. of Art* (1890), p. 423, describes this painting, considers it perhaps the finest of all of Degas's ballet pictures // A. Alexandre, *Les Arts*, I (June 1902), p. 10, ill. p. 5, tells that Rouart took measures to keep Degas from taking back the picture for corrections // J. Meier-Graefe, *Modern Art* (1908), I, p. 281, dates it 1878 // P. A. Lemoisne, *Degas* [1912], pp. 71f., pl. xxviii, dates it 1877; wrongly identifies the medium as tempera; mistakenly believes that two versions exist, one in the Rouart collection, and a "replica with variations" in the Havemeyer collection; erroneously associates it with a picture that was exhibited in 1877 at the Third Impressionist Exhibition // *American Art News*, xi (Dec. 28, 1912), p. 5, discusses the bidders for this picture at the Rouart sale, publishing the erroneous rumor that Mrs. Sears of Boston was the buyer // C. L. Borgmeyer, *The Master Impressionists* (1913), pp. 85, 87f., 219, ill. p. 83 // M. Cassatt, in letter to Durand-Ruel (Mar. 11 [1913], and Feb. 12 [1914]), published in L. Venturi, *Les Archives de l'impressionnisme* (1939), ii, pp. 131–133, mentions it // R. E. D[ell], *Burl. Mag.*, xxii (Jan. 1913), p. 240, repeats the rumor about Mrs. Sears // P. Lafond, *Degas*, I (1918), p. 150, ill. opp. p. 150, ii (1919), p. 27, repeats Lemoisne's errors; tells of Degas's reaction to the high price brought by the picture at the Rouart sale // J. E. Blanche, *De David à Degas* (1919), p. 305 // H. Hertz, *Degas* (1920), pp. 99f., 108, repeats Lemoisne's errors // L. Burroughs, *Met. Mus. Bull.*, xxvii (1932), p. 144 // G. Grappe, *Degas* (1936), pp. 60f., ill., tells anecdotes about the sale of the picture and Degas's reaction to it // A. Mongan, *Art News*, xxxv (Nov. 14, 1936), p. 12 // P. Poujaud, in a letter (1936), published in *Degas Letters* (1947, English ed.), p. 236, tells that Rouart was given this picture by Degas in exchange for one which the artist had taken away to retouch and had spoiled, and that Rouart then kept this one padlocked // A. Mongan, *Burl. Mag.*, lxxii (1938), p. 301 // E. Tietze-Conrat, *Gaz. des B.-A.*, xxvi

(1944), pp. 416f., fig. 4 // D. Rouart, *Degas à la recherche de sa technique* (1945), pp. 10f., ill., insists that the medium is tempera // P. A. Lemoisne, *Degas* (1946), i, pp. 93, 239, note 118, ii, pp. 224f., no. 408, ill., dates it about 1876–1877, suggests comparison with a drawing in the collection of Mme Jacques Doucet and catalogues a study (no. 409); states in vol. i (p. 239) that the Museum's painting was "without doubt" the picture shown as no. 41 in the Third Impressionist Exhibition, yet in vol. ii (p. 232) identifies a picture of a single dancer (no. 421) as the one probably in that exhibition // L. Browse, *Degas Dancers* [1949], pp. 32, 38, 353, cat. no. 46, pl. 46, wrongly asserts that the medium is tempera, repeats Paul Poujaud's story (above, 1936) adding that it was the watering can that Degas wanted to paint out, suggests comparison with other pictures // T. Rousseau Jr., *Art News*, xlviii (Apr. 1949), p. 21, finds the cool colors reminiscent of Velazquez's Las Meninas // D. C. Rich, *Degas* (1951), p. 30 // D. Cooper, *Pastels by Edgar Degas* [1952], p. 16, under no. 4, mentions this picture and related studies // R. Rey, *Degas* (1952), pp. xxiv f., pl. 32 // P. Cabanne, *Edgar Degas* (1957), pp. 108, 112, no. 63, pl. 63 // A. Frankfurter, *Art News Annual*, xxviii (1959), ill. p. 38 // D. Halévy, *Degas parle . . .* (1960), pp. 141–144, 148 // P. Valéry, *Degas, Manet, Morisot* (1960), p. 92, publishes the reminiscences of Ernest Rouart about this picture, in which he states that the story about the padlocking was "pure invention" // A. Frankfurter, *Horizon*, iv (Nov. 1961), p. 6 // L. W. Havemeyer [Mrs. H. O.], *Sixteen to Sixty, Memoirs of a Collector* (1961), pp. 252f., 257 (this passage is confusing; apparently the Havemeyers first acquired the pastel Dancers at the Bar that is now in the Electra Havemeyer Webb Museum in Shelburne, Vermont, and later, in 1912, got Dancers Practicing at the Bar from the Rouart sale).

EXHIBITED: Metropolitan Museum, 1930, *The H. O. Havemeyer Collection*, no. 57.

EX COLL.: Henri Rouart, Paris (sale, Galerie Manzi-Joyant, Paris, Dec. 9–11, 1912, no.

177); H. O. Havemeyer, New York (from 1912; Cat., 1931, pp. 120f., ill.).

THE H. O. HAVEMEYER COLLECTION. BE-QUEST OF MRS. H. O. HAVEMEYER, 1929.

At the Milliner's 29.100.38

Degas is said to have taken a great interest in fashion. He sometimes accompanied his women friends on visits to the dressmaker or milliner, which provided him with material for this and other pictures. In this one Mary Cassatt is said to have posed for him. With amusing effect half of the saleswoman's face and figure is concealed behind the cheval glass. The distribution of the lights and darks, the flat, even treatment of certain areas, and the cutting of the composition at the right, top, and bottom, are devices that recall the popular Japanese print.

George Moore, who seems certainly to have seen the Eighth Impressionist Exhibition in 1886, describes this pastel with characteristic incisiveness in the *Confessions of a Young Man* (see also Ref., Pickvance, 1963).

Signed and dated (at upper right): *1882 / Degas.*

Pastel on paper. H. 30, w. 34 in. (76.2 x 86.4 cm.).

REFERENCES: G. Moore, *Confessions of a Young Man* (1888; 1959 ed.), p. 45, describes this picture, finding the woman "as typical of the nineteenth century as Fragonard's ladies are of the Court of Louis XV"; *Mag. of Art* (1890), p. 424, recalls the picture but refers to "shop-women" // P. Lafond, *Degas*, II (1919), p. 46, ill. after p. 44 // P. A. Lemoisne, *Degas* (1946), I, ill. opp. p. 148 (detail), II, pp. 382f., no. 682, ill., states that Mary Cassatt was the model for this pastel // J. Rewald, *The History of Impressionism* (1946), ill. p. 391, says that it was probably exhibited at the Eighth Impressionist Exhibition in 1886; (revised and enlarged edition, 1961), ill. p. 524, states positively that it was in the 1886 exhibition // F. Fosca, *Degas* (1954), ill. p. 78 (detail, in color) // P. Cabanne, *Edgar Degas* (1957),

29.100.38

p. 118, no. 110, pl. 110 // L. W. Havemeyer [Mrs. H. O.], *Sixteen to Sixty, Memoirs of a Collector* (1961), pp. 257f., states that Mary Cassatt posed for this picture, which the Havemeyers secured through her // R. Pickvance, *Burl. Mag.*, CV (1963), p. 280, note 31, connects this pastel with one of two pictures of modistes described by George Moore; and in letters (March 17 and 25, 1966) states that it belonged to the dealer Alexander Reid, who sold it to T. G. Arthur, and that it was exhibited by Reid in London in 1891–92 and by Arthur in Glasgow in 1892, quotes press reviews.

EXHIBITED: 1 Rue Laffitte, Paris, 1886, *La 8ᵉ Exposition de peinture* (Eighth Impressionist Exhibition), no. 14 (as Femme essayant un chapeau chez sa modiste, pastel, lent by Mme A.; probably this picture; see J. Rewald, Ref., 1946); Mr. Collie's Rooms, 39B Old Bond St., London, 1891–92, *A Small Collection of Pictures by Degas and Others* (La Société des Beaux-Arts), no. 19 (lent by Alexander Reid); Glasgow Art Institute, 1892, 31st Annual Exhibition, no. 562 (lent by T. G. Arthur); Metropolitan Museum, 1930, *The H. O. Havemeyer Collection*, no. 145; Wildenstein, New York, 1949, *Degas*, no. 60.

Ex coll.: Possibly Mme A. (in 1886); [Alexander Reid, Glasgow, in 1891, until 1892]; T. G. Arthur, Glasgow (in 1892); Martin Camentron, Paris (until 1895); [Durand-Ruel, Paris and New York, 1895–1899]; H. O. Havemeyer, New York (from 1899; Cat., 1931, pp. 126f., ill.).

THE H. O. HAVEMEYER COLLECTION. BEQUEST OF MRS. H. O. HAVEMEYER, 1929.

The Singer in Green
(La Chanteuse Verte)   61.101.7

If, as Lemoisne suggests, this pastel dates from 1884, it is one of the latest of the group of paintings of cafés and singers that Degas did during the decade 1875–1885. The tipped-back head, the protruding collarbone, and the foreshortened face, with its eagerness to please, create an effect of youth and innocence quite different from Degas's other *chanteuses*. None

61.101.7

of his representations of women, however, is ever a caustic statement about personality like those of Toulouse-Lautrec.

There are two drawings by Degas that are clearly connected with this picture. One (third Degas sale, no. 393) gives the impression of reporting the appearance of a particular singer. Though the other (in a private collection in Switzerland[1]) shows certain marked differences in the costume and the pose of the arms, it is even more similar to our pastel in general appearance and treatment.

Signed (at lower right): *Degas*.

Pastel on paper. H. 23¾, w. 18¼ in. (60.3 x 46.3 cm.).

Note 1. Aargauischer Kunstverein, Aarau (Switzerland), 1960, *Jubiläums-Ausstellung aus Aargauischem Privatbesitz*, part 1, no. 100, ill.

REFERENCES: G. Grappe, *E. M. Degas* (1909), pp. 37f., describes a picture with this title, interpreting it as an example of cruel realism // P. A. Lemoisne, *Degas* [1912], pp. 101f., pl. XLIII, dates this pastel 1884 // P. Lafond, *Degas*, I (1918), ill. p. 7, II (1919), p. 38, mentions it // H. Hertz, *Degas* (1920), p. 102, places it in 1884 // Y. [or Ia] Tugendkhol'd, *Edgar Degas* (1922), ill. p. 8 // P. Jamot, *Degas* (1924), p. 153, pl. 66, dates it 1884 // Ternovietz, *L'Amour de l'art*, VI (1925), p. 464, ill. // H. A. Bull, *International Studio*, XCVII (1930), p. 25, ill. p. 23, contrasts it with Toulouse-Lautrec's first drawing for *Le Rire* showing Yvette Guilbert singing // J. Becker, *Creative Art*, X (1932), p. 199, ill. p. 196 // G. Rivière, *M[onsieu]r. Degas* (1935), ill. p. 137, with the date 1876 // A. M. Frankfurter, *Art News*, XXXIV (Feb. 1, 1936), p. 6 // A. Mongan, *Burl. Mag.*, LXXII (1938), pp. 296f. // J. W. Lane, *Art News* (Annual), XXXVII (Feb. 25, 1939), p. 132, ill. p. 139 // H. Huth, *Gaz. des B.-A.*, XXIX (1946), p. 239, note 22, suggests that this may be the picture of a café singer that was in the exhibition at the National Academy of Design, New York, 1886 (no. 57?) // P. A. Lemoisne, *Degas* (1946), III, pp. 440f., no. 772, ill., dates it 1884, suggests comparison with a drawing in the collection of Nepveu de Gas (third Degas sale, no. 393) // R. Schwabe, *Degas: the Draughtsman* (1948), fig. 37, briefly discusses it on the page (unnumbered) facing the illustration // L. Browse, *Degas Dancers* [1949], p. 42, observes that some of Toulouse-Lautrec's café subjects were derived directly from this picture and Degas's La Chanson du Chien // F. Fosca, *Degas* (1954), ill. in color p. 71.

EXHIBITED: American Art Association and National Academy of Design, New York, 1886, *Works in Oil and Pastel by the Impressionists of Paris*, no. 57 (Singer of the Concert Café; possibly this picture according to H. Huth, Ref., 1946); Grafton Galleries, London, 1905, *Pictures by Boudin, Cézanne, Degas . . .* (exhibition organized by Durand-Ruel, Paris), no. 69 (The Music Hall Singer in Green); The Century Association, New York, 1936, *French Masterpieces of the Nineteenth Century*, no. 16 (lent by Stephen C. Clark); Pennsylvania Museum of Art, Philadelphia, 1936, *Degas*, no. 44 (lent anonymously); Durand-Ruel, New York, 1937, *Masterpieces by Degas*, no. 3 (lent by Stephen C. Clark); Metropolitan Museum, 1941, *French Paintings from David to Toulouse-Lautrec*, no. 39 (lent by Stephen C. Clark); Rosenberg, New York, 1942, *Great French Masters of the Nineteenth Century*, no. 3 (lent by Mr. and Mrs. Stephen C. Clark); The Century Association, New York, 1946, *Paintings from the Stephen C. Clark Collection;* Knoedler Galleries, New York, 1954, *A Collector's Taste: Selections from the Collection of Mr. and Mrs. Stephen C. Clark*, no. 8; Museum of Modern Art, New York, 1955, *Paintings from Private Collections* (cat. p. 8; lent by Stephen C. Clark); Metropolitan Museum, *Paintings from Private Collections*, 1958, no. 41, 1959, no. 29, 1960, no. 31 (lent by Stephen C. Clark); Yale University Art Gallery, New Haven (Conn.), 1960, *Paintings, Drawings, and Sculpture Collected by Yale Alumni*, no. 188 (lent by Stephen C. Clark).

EX COLL.: [Possibly Durand-Ruel, Paris, 1886]; Laurent, Paris (sale, Dec. 1898, no. 4); [Durand-Ruel, Paris, 1898–1906]; A. A. Hébrard, Paris (from 1906); Prince de Wagram, Paris (until 1908); [Durand-Ruel, Paris, 1908–1909]; M. P. Riabouchinski, Moscow (from 1909; collection possibly nationalized along with others in 1918–1919); State Tretyakov Gallery, Moscow (until 1925); Museum of Modern Art, Moscow (1925–1933; Cat., 1928, p. 37, no. 128); [Knoedler, New York, 1933]; Stephen C. Clark, New York (1933–1960).

BEQUEST OF STEPHEN C. CLARK, 1960.

Portrait of a Young Woman
29.100.183

Although the subject of this portrait has not been identified, two other works by Degas may represent the same person, a pastel that Lemoisne dates, as he does our picture, about 1885 (no. 860), and an oil sketch (no. 370) that he places a decade earlier.

Signed (at lower right): *D.*

Oil on canvas. H. 10¾, w. 8¾ in. (27.3 x 22.2 cm.).

REFERENCE: P. A. Lemoisne, *Degas* (1946), III, pp. 498f., no. 861, ill., dates this picture about 1885, considers it a replica of the pastel no. 860.

29.100.183

Dancers in the Rehearsal Room, with a Double Bass 29.100.127

Degas, who once asserted that he had always wished to do murals (Ref., Browse, 1949, p. 71), painted a number of oils similar to this in their frieze-like shape and composition. He reverted frequently, over a period of many years, to representations of a rehearsal room lit by two or three French windows, viewed from a passageway with a dado. Our painting and one in Detroit (Lemoisne no. 900) both use the musical instruments lying on the floor to start the movement of the composition toward the group of dancers in the opposite corner. Lemoisne dates our picture 1887, but Browse would put it four to seven years earlier. There are also a preparatory oil sketch (Lemoisne no. 902) that is very close to our painting and many studies for the individual figures and details. It is interesting that many of Degas's later treatments of the subject show the room in reverse, recalling his fondness for making monotypes and counterproofs (see Nude Drying Her Arm, below), both of which reproduce an original drawing or painting in reverse.

Formerly called The Rehearsal Room.

Signed (at lower left): *Degas*.

Oil on canvas. H. 15⅜, w. 35¼ in. (39 x 89.5 cm.).

REFERENCES: A. Kay, in a letter to the editor of *The Westminster Gazette* (Mar. 29, 1893), published in A. Kay, *Treasure Trove in Art* (1939), pp. 28–30, tells of buying the picture // E. Tietze-Conrat, *Gaz. des B.-A.*, XXVI (1944), pp. 416f., ill. p. 414, fig. 1, discusses the foreshortening of the double bass in this picture and a similar effect obtained by Mantegna // P. A. Lemoisne, *Degas* (1946), III, pp. 528f., no. 905, ill., calls the picture Danseuses au Foyer (la Contrebasse), dates it 1887, lists and illustrates studies for it // L. Browse, *Degas Dancers* [1949], pp. 67, 377f., cat. no. 118, pl. 118, calls it Danseuses avec Contrebasse, dates it about 1880–1883, brings together several examples of similar compositions // R. Pickvance, *Apollo*, LXXVII (1963), p. 396, and in a letter (1966), states that it belonged to the dealer Alexander Reid, who sold it to Arthur Kay, and that it was exhibited by Reid in London in 1891–92 and by Kay in London at the Grafton Galleries in 1893.

EXHIBITED: Mr. Collie's Rooms, 39B Old Bond St., London, 1891–1892, *A Small Collection of Pictures by Degas and Others* (La Société des Beaux-Arts), no. 20 (lent by Alexander Reid); Grafton Galleries, London, 1893, no. 301a, as The Rehearsal (lent by Arthur Kay); Carnegie Art Galleries, Pittsburgh, 1896, *First Annual Exhibition*, no. 86 (as Repetition of the Dance); Metropolitan Museum, 1930, *The H. O. Havemeyer Collection*, no. 54; Newark Museum (New Jersey), 1946, *19th-Century French and American Paintings*, no. 13; Carnegie Institute, Pittsburgh (Pa.), 1958–1959, *Retrospective Exhibition of Paintings from Previous Internationals*, no. 1; Arkansas Arts Center, Little Rock, 1963, *Five Centuries of European Painting*, cat. no. 47.

EX COLL.: [Alexander Reid, Glasgow, in 1891, until 1892]; Arthur Kay, London (in 1892); E. F. Milliken, New York (sale, American Art Association, New York, Feb. 14, 1902, no. 11, as Les Coulisses); [Durand-Ruel, New York, 1902]; H. O. Havemeyer, New York (Cat., 1931, p. 119).

THE H. O. HAVEMEYER COLLECTION. BEQUEST OF MRS. H. O. HAVEMEYER, 1929.

Three Dancers Preparing for Class
29.100.558

Degas appears to be concentrating in this picture on a pattern of converging figures, which he opposes to the diagonals of the floor and the windows. Browse groups it, apparently for their common style, with two other pictures of dancers, dating all three about 1886–1888, whereas Lemoisne had dated this picture 1879 and the other two 1890 and about 1899 (Browse nos. 187, 186; Lemoisne nos. 1012, 1366).

Formerly called Three Dancers at their Toilette.

Signed (at lower left): *degas*.

Pastel on paper. H. 21½, w. 20½ in. (54.6 x 52.1 cm.).

29.100.558

REFERENCES: P. A. Lemoisne, *Degas* (1946), II, pp. 304f., cat. no. 542, ill., dates this pastel about 1879, suggests comparison with two studies, one in the third Degas sale (no. 201–1) and the other, Lemoisne no. 543 // L. Browse, *Degas Dancers* [1949], pp. 59, 397, cat. no. 185, pl. 185, dates it about 1886–1888, calls it Trois Danseuses se preparant à la classe.

EXHIBITED: Metropolitan Museum, 1930, *The H. O. Havemeyer Collection*, no. 151.

EX COLL. H. O. Havemeyer, New York (Cat., 1931, p. 119).

THE H. O. HAVEMEYER COLLECTION. BEQUEST OF MRS. H. O. HAVEMEYER, 1929.

Dancers, Pink and Green   29.100.42

According to Lemoisne, this painting, along with a replica that omits the dancer on the right and is predominantly blue in color, was done about 1890. By that time Degas had been working enthusiastically with pastel for about fifteen years, and though our dancers are painted in oil, the color is handled in a manner that reflects his many original experiments with pastel.

Signed (at lower right): *Degas*.

29.100.42

Oil on canvas. H. 32⅜, w. 29¾ in. (82.2 x 75.6 cm.).

REFERENCES: P. A. Lemoisne, *Degas* (1946), III, pp. 590f., cat. no. 1013, ill., dates this picture 1890, says that the Danseuses bleues is a replica (no. 1014) // L. Browse, *Degas Dancers* [1949], p. 396, cat. no. 180, pl. 180, dates it 1885–1887 // L. W. Havemeyer [Mrs. H. O.], *Sixteen to Sixty, Memoirs of a Collector* (1961), p. 259.

EXHIBITED: Durand-Ruel, New York, 1928, *French Masterpieces of the Late XIX Century*, no. 7 (lent anonymously); Metropolitan Museum, 1930, *The H. O. Havemeyer Collection*, no. 55.

EX COLL. H. O. Havemeyer, New York (by 1917; Cat., 1931, p. 118, ill.).

THE H. O. HAVEMEYER COLLECTION. BEQUEST OF MRS. H. O. HAVEMEYER, 1929.

A Woman Having Her Hair Combed

29.100.35

After concentrating for about a decade on careful studies of dancers, which included some studies of nudes, Degas began early in the eighties to make drawings and pastels of female nudes casually engaged in the various actions of their daily toilet. He showed girls combing their hair, bathing, entering or leaving their tubs, or, with extended arms or legs, drying themselves.

Most of these are acutely observed analytical studies of motion and the play and tension of muscles. This pastel, unlike the Museum's many other pastels of nudes by Degas, is less a study than a finished picture. The mature woman enjoying the combing her maid is giving her heavy hair is fully modeled and seated in luxurious comfort on a tufted chaise longue, a piece of furniture to be seen in many of these pictures. Douglas Cooper has noted a relation between her pose and that of one of Degas's sculptures. Indeed this posture of the upper torso is taken by several of the sculptured dancers (see J. Rewald, *Degas Works in Sculpture*, 1944 and 1956, nos. XXI, XXII, XXIII, and LII). A charcoal study of three dancers also shows it (third Degas sale, no. 381).

In the eighth and last Impressionist Exhibition Degas exhibited ten pastels described in the catalogue as a "series of nudes of women bathing, washing, drying themselves, . . . combing their hair and having it combed." According to Ronald Pickvance (in a letter, 1963), this picture surely must have been one of the ten since it fits the last phrase of the description and is the only one of this subject that can be dated on stylistic grounds about the time of the exhibition. It is not, however, among those described in comments on the exhibition by Félix Fénéon, J. K. Huysmans, or George Moore.[1]

Lemoisne suggested that two other pastels in the Museum's collection might also have been in the series exhibited in 1886: Woman Drying her Foot, and Woman Bathing in a Shallow Tub. The latter might possibly be identified with the one in the exhibition that Fénéon described as a bony woman wetting a wash cloth.

Formerly called The Toilette.

Signed (at lower left): *degas.*

Pastel on paper. H. 29⅛, w. 23⅞ in. (74 x 60.6 cm.).

Note 1. F. Fénéon, *Les Impressionnistes en 1886*, published in *Oeuvres* [1948], p. 72; J. K. Huysmans, *Certains* (1889), p. 24; G. Moore, *Confessions of a Young Man* (1888; 1959 edition), p. 45.

REFERENCES: P. Lafond, *Degas* (1918), I, ill. p. 23 // P. Jamot, *Degas* (1924), pp. 153f., pl. 69, dates this pastel about 1885–1886, states that it was in the Eighth Impressionist Exhibition in 1886 // R. Huyghe, *L'Amour de l'art*, XII (1931), ill. p. 279, fig. 29 // G. Rivière, *M[onsieu]r. Degas* (1935), ill. p. 69, dates it about 1880 // P. A. Lemoisne, *Degas* (1946), I, p. 121, ill. opp. p. 120 (with a typographical error in date); III, pp. 488f., cat. no.

29.100.35

847, ill., dates it about 1885, calls it one of the "Suite de Nuds" *(sic)* shown in the Eighth Impressionist Exhibition // J. Rewald, *The History of Impressionism* (1946), ill. p. 393, dates it 1885–1886; (revised and enlarged edition, 1961), ill. p. 525, dates it about 1885, states that it was exhibited in the Eighth Impressionist Exhibition // D. Cooper, *Pastels by Edgar Degas* [1952], pp. 22f., no. 22, color pl. 22, dates it about 1885, observes that it is exceptional in not representing the hairdressing scene as a struggle, suggests comparison with the sculpture "Dancer resting, hands on her hips" of about 1880–1885 (see J. Rewald, *Degas Works in Sculpture*, 1944, no. xxii) // P. Cabanne, *Edgar Degas* (1957), pp. 55, 99, 119, no. 127, color pl. 127 // L. W. Havemeyer [Mrs. H. O.], *Sixteen to Sixty, Memoirs of a Collector* (1961), p. 261 // P. Poole, *Degas* (1964), p. 44, pl. xliv, states that it was in the Eighth Impressionist Exhibition in 1886, comments on its calmness and monumentality.

EXHIBITED: 1 Rue Laffitte, Paris, 1886, *La 8ᵉ Exposition de peinture* (Eighth Impressionist Exhibition) (probably one of the Suite de Nuds [*sic*], nos. 19–28); Durand-Ruel, Paris, 1909, *Aquarelles et pastels*, no. 48 (La Toilette, by Degas, possibly this picture); Knoedler, New York, 1915, *Loan Exhibition of Masterpieces by Old and Modern Painters*, Degas, no. 28 (La Toilette, pastel, possibly this picture); Metropolitan Museum, 1930, *The H. O. Havemeyer Collection*, no. 147.

EX COLL.: [Possibly Boussod-Valadon, Paris]; [possibly Durand-Ruel, Paris, in 1909]; Roger Marx, Paris (until 1914; sale, Galerie Manzi-Joyant, Paris, May 11–12, 1914, no. 125); H. O. Havemeyer, New York (from 1914; Cat., 1931, pp. 130f., ill.).

THE H. O. HAVEMEYER COLLECTION. BEQUEST OF MRS. H. O. HAVEMEYER, 1929.

Woman Bathing in a Shallow Tub
29.100.41

See comment under Woman Having Her Hair Combed, above.

Signed and dated (at upper left): *Degas 85*.

29.100.41

Pastel on paper. H. 32, w. 22 in. (81.3 x 55.9 cm.).

REFERENCE: P. A. Lemoisne, *Degas* (1946), III, pp. 467f., cat. no. 816, ill., calls this picture *Femme au Tub*; says that it was exhibited at the Eighth Impressionist Exhibition, suggests comparison with other studies of bathers.

EXHIBITED: 1 Rue Laffitte, Paris, 1886, *La 8ᵉ Exposition de peinture* (Eighth Impressionist Exhibition) (possibly one of the Suite de Nuds [*sic*], nos. 19–28); Metropolitan Museum, 1921, *Impressionist and Post-Impressionist Paintings*, no. 32 (The Bather, lent anonymously, probably this picture); Grolier Club, New York, 1922, *Prints, Drawings and Bronzes*, by Degas, no. 14 (le Bain); Metropolitan Museum, 1930, *The H. O. Havemeyer Collection*, no. 146.

EX COLL.: Mary Cassatt, New York and Paris; H. O. Havemeyer, New York (Cat., 1931, p. 132).

THE H. O. HAVEMEYER COLLECTION. BEQUEST OF MRS. H. O. HAVEMEYER, 1929.

Nude Combing Her Hair   56.231

This pastel, which was not published by Lemoisne, appears to be a very close but slightly
less finished version of his no. 849, which he
dates about 1885. The posture of this model
and the gestures of her raised arms must have
interested Degas for some time, as there are
many variations of the pose.

Signed (at lower left): *degas.*

Pastel on paper. H. 24⅛, w. 18⅛ in. (61.3 x
46 cm.).

REFERENCES: T. Bernard, *Renaissance*, XIII
(1930), ill. p. 19 (upper right) // C. Sterling,
Chefs-d'oeuvre de l'art français (exhib. cat.),
Palais National des Arts, Paris (1937), p. 155,
no. 310, catalogues this picture, dating it tentatively about 1890.

EXHIBITED: Galerie de la Renaissance, Paris,
1929, *Oeuvres des XIXe et XXe siècles*, no. 127
(as Femme se coiffant, lent by Jos. Hessel);
Palais National des Arts, Paris, 1937, *Chefs-
d'oeuvre de l'art français*, no. 310 (lent by Jos.
Hessel); Galerie Alfred Daber, Paris, 1947,
Grands Maîtres du XIXe siècle, no. 10; Metropolitan Museum, 1960, *The Nate and Frances
Spingold Collection.*

EX COLL.: Gallimard, Paris; [Jos Hessel, Paris,
1894–after 1937]; private collection, Paris;
[Sam Salz, New York, until 1950]; Mr. and
Mrs. Nate B. Spingold, New York (1950–
1956).

GIFT OF MR. AND MRS. NATE B. SPINGOLD,
1956.

29.100.36

Woman Drying Her Foot   29.100.36

See comment under Woman Having Her Hair
Combed, above.

Formerly called After the Bath.

Signed (at lower left): *degas.*

Pastel on paper. H. 19¾, w. 21¼ in. (50.2 x
54 cm.).

REFERENCE: P. A. Lemoisne, *Degas* (1946),
III, pp. 509f., cat. no. 875, dates this picture
1886, suggests that it might have been shown
at the Eighth Impressionist Exhibition.

EXHIBITED: 1 Rue Laffitte, Paris, 1886, *La
8^e Exposition de peinture* (Eighth Impressionist
Exhibition) (possibly one of the Suite de Nuds
[*sic*], nos. 19–28); Knoedler, New York, 1915,
*Loan Exhibition of Masterpieces by Old and
Modern Painters*, no. 37 (After the Bath, 1887;
probably this picture); Grolier Club, New

56.231

York, 1922, *Prints, Drawings and Bronzes by Degas*, no. 48; Metropolitan Museum, 1930, *The H. O. Havemeyer Collection*, no. 148.

Ex coll.: [Possibly Boussod-Valadon, Paris]; H. O. Havemeyer, New York (by 1915; Cat., 1931, pp. 128f., ill.).

The H. O. Havemeyer Collection. Bequest of Mrs. H. O. Havemeyer, 1929.

Nude Drying Her Arm 29.100.553

Degas often began a composition in one direction, and then in order to work it up in the opposite direction, took a counterproof, which is an imprint with the composition in reverse,

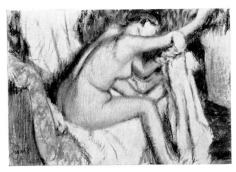

29.100.553

made by pressing a charcoal or pastel study face down on a clean sheet of paper. The large number of studies in both directions that lead up to this pastel provide one of the best revelations of Degas's methods of working. He probably began with the model facing to the left, since all the known counterproofs, like the pastel itself, face to the right (second Degas sale, nos. 363, 385; fourth sale, nos. 319, 329, 355, 364). See also Woman Having Her Hair Combed, above.

Signed (at lower left): *degas*.

Pastel on paper. H. 12, w. 17½ in. (30.5 x 44.5 cm.).

References: J. Meier-Graefe, *Degas* (1923), pl. LXXXVIII, dates this picture about 1890 // P. A. Lemoisne, *Degas* (1946), III, pp.

452f., cat. no. 794, ill., dates it about 1884, cites two studies and related material.

Exhibited: Metropolitan Museum, 1930, *The H. O. Havemeyer Collection*, no. 150.

Ex coll.: [Durand-Ruel, Paris, 1898–1899]; E. F. Milliken, New York; James S. Inglis, New York (1899–1910; sale, American Art Association, New York, Mar. 9–10, 1910, no. 63); [Durand-Ruel, New York, from 1910]; H. O. Havemeyer, New York (Cat., 1931, p. 132).

The H. O. Havemeyer Collection. Bequest of Mrs. H. O. Havemeyer, 1929.

The Bather 29.100.190

See comment under Woman Having Her Hair Combed, above.

Signed (at upper left): *Degas*.

Pastel on paper. H. 22, w. 18¾ in. (55.9 x 47.6 cm.).

References: *Der Cicerone*, V (1913), p. 192, notes that the high prices brought by this picture and others by Degas in the Hayashi sale result from the high price fetched by the Dancers at the Bar (see above) in the

29.100.190

Rouart sale in 1912 // P. A. Lemoisne, *Degas* (1946), III, pp. 602f., cat. no. 1031 *bis*, ill., dates it about 1890, suggests comparison with other pictures // R. Shoolman and C. E. Slatkin, *Six Centuries of French Master Drawings in America* (1950), pp. 188f., pl. 106 // L. W. Havemeyer [Mrs. H. O.], *Sixteen to Sixty, Memoirs of a Collector* (1961), p. 261.

EXHIBITED: Metropolitan Museum, 1930, *The H. O. Havemeyer Collection*, no. 152.

EX COLL.: Tadamasa Hayashi, Tokyo and Paris (by c. 1890–1906; sale, American Art Association, New York, Jan. 8–9, 1913, no. 85); [Durand-Ruel, New York, from 1913]; H. O. Havemeyer, New York (Cat., 1931, p. 133).

THE H. O. HAVEMEYER COLLECTION. BEQUEST OF MRS. H. O. HAVEMEYER, 1929.

29.100.37

Woman with a Towel   29.100.37

Durand-Ruel, who regularly handled Degas's work, bought this picture from the artist in 1901 and sold it in the same year to the Havemeyers. See also comment under Woman Having Her Hair Combed, above.

Signed and dated (at upper right): *Degas 94*.

Pastel on paper. H. 37¾, w. 30 in. (95.9 x 76.2 cm.).

REFERENCE: P. A. Lemoisne, *Degas* (1946), III, pp. 666f., cat. no. 1148, ill., calls this pastel *Après le bain*, suggests comparison with no. 1221.

EXHIBITED: Knoedler, New York, 1915, *Loan Exhibition of Masterpieces by Old and Modern Painters*, no. 39 (After the Tub, 1895; probably this picture in spite of erroneous date); Grolier Club, New York, 1922, *Prints, Drawings and Bronzes by Degas*, no. 34 (La Sortie du Bain; probably this picture); Metropolitan Museum, 1930, *The H. O. Havemeyer Collection*, no. 149.

EX COLL.: [Durand-Ruel, Paris and New York, 1901]; H. O. Havemeyer, New York (from 1901; Cat., 1931, p. 133).

THE H. O. HAVEMEYER COLLECTION. BEQUEST OF MRS. H. O. HAVEMEYER, 1929.

Fantin-Latour

Ignace Henri Jean Théodore Fantin-Latour. Born at Grenoble in 1836; died at Buré (Orne) in 1904. Henri Fantin-Latour was the son of the painter Théodore Fantin-Latour and a Russian mother. He was trained by his father and Horace Lecoq de Boisbaudran, but it was the influence of Courbet that determined his style. He also copied zealously in the Louvre. Fantin first exhibited at the Salon in 1861. Although he never adopted the revolutionary solutions of Manet and the Impressionists he was alert to all the new attitudes in the intellectual movements of his time. He frequented the Café Guerbois, becoming friendly with Manet and his group and later with the most progressive musicians. He was an advocate of realism in painting and did a number of group portraits conceived in the spirit of Courbet. These imaginary gatherings include Homage to Delacroix (1864, Louvre); The Atelier at Batignolles (1870, Louvre), a tribute to Manet; Un Coin de Table (1872, Louvre), which shows several men of letters grouped about Verlaine and Rimbaud; and Around the Piano (1885), a tribute to contemporary musicians, who are shown gathered around Emmanuel Chabrier and Vincent d'Indy.

In spite of the natural look of these groups Fantin-Latour was never a true realist. His sensitive, convincing portraits and his lucid still lifes are characterized by a delicate chiaroscuro that evokes a lyrical and essentially romantic mood. Toward the end of his life he was deeply absorbed in music, especially the works of Wagner. His painting became literary in spirit, somewhat reminiscent of the Pre-Raphaelite school, with which he had become familiar during three visits to England. Fantin-Latour's work, pastel in tone and consistently subdued, retains throughout a quality of great distinction. His intellectualism ranges him with Puvis de Chavannes, Redon, Gauguin, and even Seurat, who all opposed in highly individual ways the sensuous realism of Impressionism.

Portrait of a Lady   10.41

The gentle subject of this quiet, charming portrait has not been identified with certainty.

10.41

A quotation from a notebook kept by the wife of the artist records the circumstances of the sittings and the fact that the artist believed that the name which she used, Mme Leroy, was an assumed one. She was accompanied to one of her sittings by an American gentleman named Becker, who also commissioned a portrait of himself from Fantin-Latour.

In the 1906 exhibition in Paris of Fantin-Latour's works the Museum's portrait was hung as a pendant to that of a man, presumably the portrait of Mr. Becker. The man's portrait, which is the same size as ours but dated one year later, is now in the Smith College Museum of Art, Northampton, Massachusetts. (G. Corcoran of Alex Reid and Lefevre, London, supplied a photograph taken at the exhibition, which shows the two portraits hung as pendants.)

Signed and dated (at upper left): *Fantin. 85.*

Oil on canvas. H. 39½, w. 32 in. (100.3 x 81.3 cm.).

REFERENCES: A. Jullien, *Fantin-Latour, sa vie et ses amitiés* (1909), p. 205, lists a picture called Portrait de Mme Leroy among the works from the year 1885 // B. Burroughs, *Met. Mus. Bull.*, v (1910), pp. 123f., ill. // Mme Fantin-Latour, *Catalogue de l'oeuvre complet de Fantin-Latour* (1911), p. 123, no. 1196, lists a portrait of Mme X from the year 1885, which was no. 59 in the 1906 exhibition of Fantin-Latour // P. Brame, in a letter (Dec. 1965), repeats the anecdote from Mme Fantin-Latour's notebook, supplies information about the two pictures.

EXHIBITED: École des Beaux-Arts, Paris, 1906, *Exposition de l'oeuvre de Fantin-Latour*, no. 59 (as Portrait de Madame X, 1886 [*sic*]); Museum of French Art, 1932, *Fantin-Latour*, no. 15.

EX COLL.: Amédée Pigeon, Paris; [F. and J. Tempelaere, Paris, until 1910]; Bonjean; [E. J. van Wisselingh, Amsterdam, in 1910].

PURCHASE, WOLFE FUND, 1910.

23.280.9

The Palace of Aurora   23.280.9

This painting is an example of Fantin's late style, in which he often used literary themes like those favored by the Pre-Raphaelites. In light and color, however, the allegories of Fantin reflect the techniques of the Impressionists. Here the Goddess of Dawn is seated in her cloud-filled palace, while Night draws aside her veil, her garments illuminated by the first glittering rays of day.

Signed (at lower left): *Fantin.*

Oil on canvas. H. 18⅛, w. 15 in. (46 x 38.1 cm.).

REFERENCES: Mme Fantin-Latour, *Catalogue de l'oeuvre complet de Fantin-Latour* (1911), p. 204, no. 1907, describes this picture, places it in the year 1902 // H. B. Wehle, *Met. Mus. Bull.*, XIX (1924), pp. 64f., ill.

EXHIBITED: Museum of French Art, New York, 1932, *Fantin-Latour*, no. 21.

EX COLL. Anne D. Thomson, New York.

BEQUEST OF ANNE D. THOMSON, 1923.

Cézanne

Paul Cézanne. Born at Aix-en-Provence in 1839; died there in 1906. Cézanne's father, originally a dealer in hats, had become a rich local banker, and his family's financial security relieved Cézanne of any necessity to sell pictures in order to make a living. This had a powerful effect on his attitudes; in spite of his strongly independent spirit and his complete dedication to art, he often betrayed a surprising attachment to middle-class conventions and prejudices. In his youth in Aix he formed a close friendship with the writer Émile Zola, who had received the same solid classical education and who had, like Cézanne, a romantic and passionate southern temperament. Their friendship ended in 1886 when Zola published his novel *L'Oeuvre*, in which Cézanne recognized himself in the unflattering portrayal of an unsuccessful artist.

Cézanne's family wanted him to be a lawyer, but even while he was studying law at the University of Aix he attended the Drawing Academy and dreamed of becoming a painter. His father disapproved, and it was only with great difficulty that he obtained permission to study art in Paris. He passed the summer of 1861 there, but his restless, unhappy nature made him return in the fall to Aix, where he remained for more than a year, part of the time as an employee in his father's bank. Back in Paris in 1862, he failed the examination for admission to the École des Beaux-Arts. From 1863 on, as during his earlier visit, he frequented the Académie Suisse, where he worked from the living model and came into contact with independent painters such as Pissarro. The famous exhibition in 1863 of the Salon des Refusés, to which Cézanne contributed, made a deep impression on him. His way of seeing at this time was much affected by the painting of Daumier, and by Manet and Courbet, who also influenced his choice of subjects, which included both imaginary scenes and realistic landscapes, portraits, and still life. He also drew inspiration from the old masters, responding in a lively way to the movement and drama in the works of Tintoretto, Zurbaran, and Ribera.

In 1872 Cézanne lived in Pontoise and most of the following year in near-by Auvers-sur-Oise, painting frequently in the company of Pissarro, who roused his interest in the aesthetic theories of the Impressionists. He also acquired from Pissarro a life-long preference for subject matter drawn from nature and for light color harmonies. At Auvers-sur-Oise Cézanne saw much of Dr. Gachet, the devoted friend of art and painters who looked after Vincent van Gogh in his last months. Cézanne exhibited with the Impressionists in their first show in 1874 and again in 1877, but he was never really in sympathy with their basic aims. In subjects which they treated with spontaneity and sensuous enthusiasm he sought deliberately to bring out the underlying rhythms and permanent structure, thus giving his work a deeper and more serious effect. Such painting was in sharp opposition to the academic art popular at the time, and both public and critics, already shocked by the Impressionists, reacted with hostility and derision to Cézanne's distortions and simplifications. Ambitious to occupy a respected place at the official Salon and longing for appreciation, Cézanne was deeply hurt by this rejection and withdrew more and more from the company of his contemporaries to work in solitude. Although in his youth he had enjoyed many satisfying friendships, he seems to have grown increasingly uncomfortable in his relations with other human beings. During his later life he divided his time between Paris and Provence, and he retired to the South for good in 1900. A large exhibition of his work at the gallery of Ambroise Vollard in 1895 finally attracted the attention of collectors, and both in 1905 and in 1906, the year of his death, he showed ten paintings at the Salon d'Automne, which at last brought him some public approbation.

The work of Cézanne is characterized by a classical discipline like that of Poussin, but also by a great expressive energy, and these qualities were alternately dominant during the fifty years of his career. His early pictures were simple in construction, with strong contrasts of light and dark, and pure blacks played an important part in them. They were violent and spontaneous in feeling, rendered in a technique marked by passages that were sometimes fluid and sometimes heavily loaded. He often applied the paint with a palette knife, as in the portraits of his uncle Dominic. Cézanne's work grew steadily richer in color, and by about 1870 he achieved impressive effects of harmony and contrast.

From the time of his first contact with Impressionism Cézanne had tried to interpret the style in such a way as to give it the solidity and the order that he felt it lacked. Under Pissarro's influence he abandoned the exaggerated simplification and arbitrary emphasis of his early work, replacing them with subtleties of tone and more objective and sincere presentations of subject. He composed still lifes in an almost musical way and gave them a rich, buttery texture that recalls the painting of Chardin. His landscapes, receding in measured horizontal planes, evoke all the sunny calm and antique grandeur of Provence, which, according to Cézanne, had never before had a true interpreter.

From about the middle of the eighties he was completely obsessed with a search for repeated forms and rhythms in every aspect of nature, and he created geometrical harmonies that opened the way to Cubism and other abstract styles. He always retained, however, the essential character of individual objects and landscapes, their material significance, and the light and air in which they were bathed. In the works of his last decade Cézanne returned to the dramatic intensity of his youth, now, however, depending for expression on all the power of organization he had acquired in long years of experiment rather than on the spontaneous contrasts of his early style.

Cézanne's work shows an extraordinary individuality, which is a result of his way of simplifying what he saw and also of his unique and recognizable touch. After he developed his mature style, he worked very slowly, and kept some pictures in his studio, revising them at intervals, for many years. He gave great importance to color as the medium for conveying mood and meaning. The range of his palette is wide and very subtle, displaying infinite variations of tone even within very small areas. His brush stroke is intensely personal, varying from the heavily loaded application of his youth to the airy, caressing butterfly touch that moves in alternating directions across the surface of the canvas. He laid great emphasis on weight and balance, and through his objective concentration on the essential physical aspects of his subjects, he bestowed on them a quality of permanence and timelessness.

Cézanne was undoubtedly the most influential artist of the last half century. He was unequaled as an innovator, representing at the same time revolution and a return to classicism. In his work the Post-Impressionist artists found the stimulation to explore all the plastic possibilities of painting, and through him they saw the world in a new way.

53.140.1

Uncle Dominic   53.140.1

Cézanne spent a good deal of time in 1865 and 1866 at his family's summer home, the Jas de Bouffan, outside of Aix, and there painted portraits of his family. He worked rapidly at these portraits, often doing an entire picture in a single afternoon, and used the palette knife to obtain simple and forceful form (Ref., Rewald, 1948, pp. 43–45, 81). His mother's brother, Dominique Aubert, a bailiff, posed for him often (Venturi, nos. 72, 74–77, 79, 80, 82). The Museum's portrait is one of the richest in color of the paintings of this period. The pronounced contrasts of light and dark and the exaggerated boldness of presentation are evidences of Courbet's influence, but the use of heavy impasto, sometimes applied with a palette knife, is original.

Formerly called Man in a Blue Cap.

Oil on canvas. H. 31⅜, w. 25¼ in. (79.7 x 64.1 cm.).

REFERENCES: E. Clark, *Art in America*, IX (1921), ill. p. 213, publishes this picture as a self-portrait // G. Rivière, *Le Maître Paul*

Cézanne (1923), p. 204, ill. opp. p. 10, calls this picture L'Homme au bonnet de coton, identifies the sitter as Uncle Dominic, dates it 1877, states erroneously that it belongs to the Berlin Museum // R. Fry, *The New York Times Magazine* (May 1, 1927), ill. p. 6, lists it as a self-portrait // M. Morsell, *Art News*, XXIX (May 23, 1931), ill. p. 3, calls it a self-portrait // J. J. Sweeney, *Creative Art*, VIII (1931), p. 357, discusses the treatment // G. Rivière, *Cézanne, le peintre solitaire* (1933), ill. p. 21, dates the portrait 1868, places it wrongly in the Berlin Museum // J. Klein, *The Lillie P. Bliss Collection* (exhib. cat.), Museum of Modern Art, New York (1934), pp. 9, 21f., no. 1, pl. 1, identifies the sitter as Uncle Dominic, dates the painting about 1865, notes two small areas of restoration in the cap and the tie, comments upon its originality // R. Huyghe, *Paul Cézanne* (1936), p. 32, fig. 11, dates it about 1865, mentions it in a discussion of Géricault's influence on Cézanne // L. Venturi, *Cézanne* (1936), I, pp. 21f., 82, cat. no. 73, II, pl. 19, no. 73, dates it 1865–1867 // R. J. Goldwater, *Art News* (Annual, section 1), XXXVI (Mar. 26, 1938), p. 136, contrasts the objectivity of the portraits of Uncle Dominic with the intensity of the self-portraits painted in the same technique // R. H. Wilenski, *Modern French Painters* [1940], p. 10, pl. 3c // J. Rewald, *The History of Impressionism* (1946), ill. in color opp. p. 40, dates it 1865–1866; (revised and enlarged edition, 1961), ill. in color p. 117; *Paul Cézanne* (1948), fig. 17, dates it c. 1866 // D. C. Rich, *Cézanne* (exhib. cat.), Art Institute of Chicago and Metropolitan Museum (1952), p. 17, no. 5, ill. p. 16 // M. Raynal, *Cézanne* (1954), p. 30, ill. in color p. 23 // K. Badt, *The Art of Cézanne* (1965), p. 300.

EXHIBITED: Metropolitan Museum, 1921, *Impressionist and Post-Impressionist Painting*, no. 4 (as Portrait of the Artist, painted before 1870; lent anonymously [Marius de Zayas]); Brooklyn Academy of Arts and Sciences (New York), 1926, *Summer Exhibition* (as a self-portrait); Museum of Modern Art, New York, 1929, *First Loan Exhibition*, no. 1 (as a self-portrait, lent anonymously), and 1931, *Memorial Exhibition: The Collection of Miss Lizzie P. Bliss*, no. 1 (as a self-portrait); Addison Gallery, Andover (Mass.), 1931, *The Collection of Miss Lizzie P. Bliss*, no. 1 (as a self-portrait); John Herron Art Institute, Indianapolis (Indiana), 1932, *Modern Masters from the Collection of Miss Lizzie P. Bliss*, no. 1 (as a self-portrait); Museum of Modern Art, New York, 1934, *The Lillie P. Bliss Collection*, no. 1 (as Uncle Dominic), and 1934–1935, *Modern Works of Art*, no. 1, and 1939, *Art in Our Time*, no. 56; Art Institute of Chicago and Metropolitan Museum of Art, 1952, *Cézanne*, no. 5 (lent by the Museum of Modern Art).

Ex coll.: [Ambroise Vollard, Paris, until 1898]; Alexander Rosenberg, Paris (1898–1899); Auguste Pellerin, Paris (1899?–1916); [Jos Hessel, Paris, 1916–1920]; Marius de Zayas, New York (1920–1921 or later); Lizzie P. Bliss, New York (c. 1921–1931); Museum of Modern Art, New York (1931–1951; Cat., 1942, no. 83, and 1948, no. 127, ill. p. 24).

Wolfe Fund, 1951; acquired from the Museum of Modern Art, Lizzie P. Bliss Collection.

A Man in a Straw Hat—
Portrait of Boyer   29.100.65

This painting has sometimes been wrongly called a portrait of the artist. Georges Rivière, however, who had a first-hand knowledge of Cézanne and his contemporaries, recognized it as a portrait of Gustave Boyer, who was a lawyer at Eyguières, a town between Aix and Avignon. Boyer had been a friend of Cézanne's during their youth in Aix, and the painter composed some verses about his prowess as a hunter (Ref., Mack, 1935, p. 412). Cézanne painted two other portraits of Boyer, both showing him without a hat (Venturi 130, formerly Pellerin collection, Paris; Venturi 132, Vollard collection, Paris). There is also a drawing by Cézanne of Boyer (collection of Sir Kenneth and Lady Clark; Ref., Andersen, 1964, fig. 35), which, like the Museum's painting, was long considered a portrait of the artist.

This picture was painted about 1870 or 1871. Its expressive drawing and contrasts in tone suggest that it belongs to the period of Cézanne's romantic style. However, he no longer uses the palette-knife technique and has attempted a general harmony of tone, probably under Manet's influence.

Signed (at lower right): *P. Cézanne.*

Oil on canvas. H. 21⅝, w. 15¼ in. (55 x 38.8 cm.).

References: J. Meier-Graefe, *Impressionisten* (1907), ill. p. 181, calls this picture a self-portrait, dates it about 1875; *Paul Cézanne* (1910), ill. p. 48, dates it about 1873 // A. Vollard, *Cézanne* (1914), p. 34, note 1, pl. 11, calls it Man with a Straw Hat (L'Homme au chapeau de paille), dates it 1872 // G. Coquiot, *Cézanne* (1919), pp. 68, 245, dates it 1872 // J. Meier-Graefe, *Cézanne und sein Kreis* (1920), ill. p. 102, calls it a self-portrait, dates it about 1873; (1922), ill. p. 120, dates it 1874 // G. Rivière, *Le Maître Paul Cézanne* (1923), p. 200, identifies the sitter as Boyer, dates the picture 1873 // T. L. Klingsor,

29.100.65

Cézanne [1924], p. 16, considers it a portrait of the artist made about 1872 when he was thirty-three, bases the identification on an etched portrait of Cézanne by Pissarro made two years later (ill. in L. Delteil, *Camille Pissarro*, 1923, no. 13) // F. J. Mather Jr., *The Arts*, XVI (1930), p. 483 // H. B. Wehle, *Met. Mus. Bull.*, XXV (1930), p. 58 // F. Neugass, *Creative Art*, IX (1931), p. 275, ill. p. 274, suggests that the painting may be a self-portrait // L. Venturi, *L'Arte*, XXXVIII (1935), p. 312, lists it as painted about 1870–1872, when Cézanne's romantic period was coming to an end // G. Mack, *Paul Cézanne* (1935), p. 183, lists it as a portrait of Boyer painted in the Auvers period // R. Huyghe, *L'Amour de l'art*, XVII (1936), ill. p. 170, fig. 46 // C. Sterling, *Cézanne* (exhib. cat.), Musée de l'Orangerie, Paris (1936), pp. 61f., no. 15, acknowledges Rivière's identification of the sitter as Boyer, but dates the portrait about 1870–1871 // L. Venturi, *Cézanne* (1936), I, pp. 23, 96, cat. no. 131, II, pl. 33, no. 131, dates it 1870–1871, mentions the portraits of Boyer (nos. 130–132) as examples of Manet's influence // R. J. Goldwater, *Art News* (Annual, section 1), XXXVI (Mar. 26, 1938), p. 136, observes that the lighter tonality and thinner handling of paint in this portrait show Cézanne's movement toward Impressionism // A. C. Barnes and V. de Mazia, *The Art of Cézanne* (1939), pp. 313f., 405, no. 30, ill. p. 168 // B. Dorival, *Cézanne* (1948), pp. 28, 140, no. 23, pl. 23, tentatively dates the three portraits of Boyer about 1870–1871 // D. C. Rich, *Cézanne* (exhib. cat.), Art Institute of Chicago and Metropolitan Museum (1952), p. 19, no. 10, ill. p. 20, observes the influence of Manet in this portrait // M. Schapiro, *Cézanne* (1952), pp. 40f., ill. in color // D. Cooper, *Burl. Mag.*, XCVI (1954), p. 346, dates it about 1871, at the conclusion of Cézanne's first, romantic period // L. Gowing, *Cézanne* (exhib. cat.), Royal Scottish Academy, Edinburgh, and Tate Gallery, London (1954), no. 7, dates it about 1871, suggests that the portrait of Boyer (Venturi no. 132) may be a study for ours // M. Raynal, *Cézanne* (1954), ill. in color p. 31 // P. Feist, *Paul Cézanne*

(1963), p. 23, pl. 10, dates it 1870–1871, finding it in comparison with earlier pictures more controlled, more like Courbet, and more seriously observed // W. V. Andersen, *Burl. Mag.*, CVI (1964), pp. 284–287, fig. 34, calls it the most important of the three oil portraits of Boyer, dates it on stylistic grounds not later than 1872, finds a likeness to Cézanne's own appearance in the Clark drawing (fig. 35) and in other male portraits, and ascribes it to the artist's imposing of his own image on that of his subjects.

EXHIBITED: Metropolitan Museum, 1930, *The H. O. Havemeyer Collection*, no. 4; Musée de l'Orangerie, Paris, 1936, *Cézanne*, no. 15; Toledo Museum of Art, 1936, *Cézanne-Gauguin*, no. 23; Minneapolis Institute of Arts, 1950, *The Art of Cézanne*; Art Institute of Chicago and Metropolitan Museum, 1952, *Cézanne*, no. 10; Aix-en-Provence and Nice, 1953, *P. Cézanne*, no. 4; Grenoble, 1953; Royal Scottish Academy, Edinburgh, and Tate Gallery, London, 1954, *Cézanne*, no. 7; Gemeentemuseum, The Hague, 1956, *Paul Cézanne*, no. 5; Kunsthaus, Zurich, 1956, *Paul Cézanne*, no. 10; Haus der Kunst, Munich, 1956, *Paul Cézanne*, no. 6; Kunsthaus Lempertz (Wallraf-Richartz Museum collection), Cologne, 1956–1957, *Cézanne*, no. 2; Österreichische Galerie, Oberes Belvedere, Vienna, 1961, *Paul Cézanne*, no. 6.

Ex COLL. H. O. Havemeyer, New York.

THE H. O. HAVEMEYER COLLECTION. BEQUEST OF MRS. H. O. HAVEMEYER, 1929.

Still Life   29.100.66

This is one of twelve paintings, still lifes and portraits, in which Cézanne used wallpaper with a geometrical pattern and flowers as a background. Venturi convincingly placed this one (no. 213) and six of the others (nos. 209, 210, 212, 214, 291, 292), which resemble it in style, in a group that he dated about 1877. The other five (nos. 356, 358, 363, 364, 365) he believed were painted a few years later. The same cup appears as a central motif in three other still lifes (Venturi nos. 186, 187, 188) that Venturi dated 1873–1877. Objects used by Cézanne in arranging his still lifes cannot, however, be regarded as reliable bases for dating, since they were studio properties over a period of many years and some of them may be seen today in the studio of Cézanne, preserved at Aix.

Oil on canvas. H. 23⅞, w. 29 in. (60.6 x 73.7 cm.).

REFERENCES: F. J. Mather Jr., *The Arts*, XVI (1930), p. 483 // H. B. Wehle, *Met. Mus. Bull.*, XXV (1930), p. 58 // L. Venturi, *Cézanne* (1936), I, pp. 35, 112, cat. no. 213, II, pl. 58, no. 213, dates this painting about 1877 // T. Rousseau Jr., *Paintings by Paul Cézanne* (*Met. Mus. Miniatures*, 1952), no. 6, ill. in color // D. Cooper (verbally, 1964), dates it 1876–1877 because of the impasto and heavy modeling and evidences of the lingering influence of Pissarro.

EXHIBITED: Metropolitan Museum, 1930, *The H. O. Havemeyer Collection*, no. 7; Pennsylvania Museum of Art, Philadelphia, 1934, *Cézanne*, no. 43; Arnold Seligmann-Helft Galleries, New York, 1947, *Chardin to Cézanne*, no. 5; Columbus Gallery of Fine Arts (Ohio), 1948, *The Springtime of Impressionism*, no. 3; Fort Worth Art Association (Texas), 1949, hundredth anniversary celebration of Fort Worth; Art Gallery of Toronto, 1949, The Canadian National Exhibition; French Embassy, New York, 1951–1952, *Gastronomy in the Fine Arts*, no. 15; Art Institute of Chicago and Metropolitan Museum, 1952, *Cézanne*, no. 20; Milwaukee Art Institute (Wisconsin) and Cincinnati Art Museum, 1956, *Still Life Painting since 1470*, no. 11.

Ex COLL. H. O. Havemeyer, New York.

THE H. O. HAVEMEYER COLLECTION. BEQUEST OF MRS. H. O. HAVEMEYER, 1929.

Apples   61.103

Cézanne has painted on this canvas two separate studies of red and yellow apples. They are in a style that is characterized by heavy paint,

29.100.66

widely varying brush strokes, and flat patches of color laid on top of each other. Douglas Cooper dates it 1878–1879.

A brownish tone that now covers areas at the lower left and along the right edge could have been added by the painter Vuillard, to whom the picture once belonged or, perhaps, by the dealer Vollard, who owned at various times a number of pictures with passages treated in the same way.

Oil on canvas. H. 9, w. 13 in. (22.9 x 33 cm.).

REFERENCES: L. Venturi, *Cézanne* (1936), I, p. 174, no. 508, II, pl. 156, no. 508, calls it *Quelques Pommes*, dates it 1883–1887 // D. Cooper (verbally, 1964), dates it 1878–1879, considers it a study or possibly two separate studies.

61.103

EXHIBITED: Bernheim-Jeune, Paris, 1926, *Cézanne*, no. 23 (lent by Édouard Vuillard).

EX COLL.: [A. Vollard, until c. 1895]; Édouard Vuillard (c. 1895–1940); Jacques Roussel, Paris (from 1940); [Sam Salz, New York, until 1961].

PURCHASE, MR. AND MRS. HENRY ITTLESON JR. FUND, 1961.

Madame Cézanne in the Conservatory   61.101.2

Hortense Fiquet, born in the Jura in 1850, was a former model whom Cézanne met about 1869. He married her in 1886 when their son Paul was fourteen years old. There seems to have been little sympathy between them, and Cézanne preferred living with his mother and sister in Aix while his wife spent much time in Paris. Nevertheless, when she visited the Midi she was one of his most frequent models, having, apparently, more of the requisite patience than most of his acquaintances.

The attractive mood of this portrait and the appearance of the sitter, who would seem to be a woman of about thirty, as well as the handling, which produces a bright and cheerful effect, combine to place it about 1880, although Douglas Cooper, judging from the style, puts it in 1883 or 1884, between the Museum's Jas de Bouffan (below) and the View of Gardanne (below), which was painted in 1885 or 1886. The painting, which seems to have been left unfinished, reveals the artist's deep preoccupation with the purely aesthetic problems of volume and composition but at the same time suggests the essential qualities of the model and is a superb example of the indissoluble relationship between form and content in a great work of art. See also Madame Cézanne in a Red Dress, below.

Oil on canvas. H. 36¼, w. 28¾ in. (92.1 x 73 cm.).

REFERENCES: *Apollon*, III (1912), part 1, nos. 3, 4, p. 23, ill. after p. 28 // J. Meier-Graefe, *Paul Cézanne* (1910), ill. p. 46, dates this picture about 1885 // F. Burger, *Cézanne und Hodler* (1913), pp. 86f., discusses Cézanne's attitude toward portrait painting // A. Vollard, *Paul Cézanne* (1914), p. 58, pl. 24, dates the picture 1891 // R. Fry, *Burl. Mag.*, XXXI (1917), pp. 6of., ill. // G. Coquiot, *Paul Cézanne* (1919), p. 247, dates it 1891 // G. Rivière, *Le Maître Paul Cézanne* (1923), p. 218, dates it 1891, states that it was painted at the Jas de Bouffan // Ternovietz, *L'Amour de l'art*, VI (1925), p. 470, ill. p. 473, gives an account of its ownership // P. Ettinger, *Cicerone*, XVIII (1926), p. 111, ill. p. 114, calls it unfinished // J. Meier-Graefe, *Cézanne* (1927), p. 63, pl. XCIII, dates it 1891 // G. Rivière, *Cézanne* (1933), p. 145 // *Art News*, XXXII (May 12, 1934), ill. p. 3 // L. Venturi, *L'Arte*, XXXVIII (1935), pp. 393f., 397, fig. 19, dates it shortly after 1890; *Cézanne* (1936), I, p. 188, no. 569, II, pl. 181, no. 569, dates it about 1890, considers it unfinished // A. M. Frankfurter, *Art News*, XXXIV (Feb. 1, 1936), p. 6, ill. in color on cover // R. J. Goldwater, *Art News* (Annual, section 1), XXXVI (Mar. 26, 1938), p. 156, ill. in color on cover // A. M. Frankfurter, *Art News* (Annual, section 2), XXXVI (Mar. 26, 1938), p. 17, ill. p. 15 // J. W. Lane, *Art News* (Annual), XXXVII (Feb. 25, 1939), p. 133, ill. p. 138 // L. Venturi, *Cézanne* (exhib. cat.), Paul Rosenberg Gallery, New York (1942), pp. 17, 30, no. 15, ill. // J. Rewald, *The History of Impressionism* (1946), ill. p. 413, dates it about 1890; (revised and enlarged edition, 1961), ill. p. 561 // B. Dorival, *Cézanne* (1948), pp. 57–59, 151, no. 108, pl. 108, analyzes the picture's composition and the importance of the color // L. Venturi, *Impressionists and Symbolists* (1950), pp. 134f., fig. 134 // J. M. Carpenter, *Art Bull.*, XXXIII (1951), p. 182, discusses Cézanne's use of color in this picture // T. Rousseau Jr., *Paintings by Paul Cézanne* (*Met. Mus. Miniatures*, 1952), no. 14, ill. in color // M. Schapiro, *Cézanne* (1952), pp. 82f., ill. in color, considers it unfinished // M. Raynal, *Cézanne* (1954), ill. in color p. 87 // L. Venturi, *Four Steps Toward Modern Art* (1956), p. 72, fig. 29 // P. Feist, *Paul Cézanne* (1963), pp. 32, 76, no. 47, pl. 47, dates it about 1890, calls it incomplete, and comments on the friendly mood combined with dignity // D.

Cooper (verbally, 1964), dates it 1883 or 1884 // K. Badt, *The Art of Cézanne* (1965), p. 187.

EXHIBITED: Galerie Vollard, Paris, 1895, *Cézanne*; Salon d'Automne, Paris, 1907, *Rétrospective d'oeuvres de Cézanne*, no. 18 (lent by Pellerin); Vienna, 1907; Museum of Modern Western Art, Moscow, 1926, *Paul Cézanne and Vincent van Gogh*, no. 15; Art Institute of Chicago, 1934, *A Century of Progress*, no. 296 (lent anonymously); Museum of Modern Art, New York, 1934–1935, *Modern Works of Art*, no. 5 (lent anonymously); The Century Association, New York, 1936, *French Masterpieces of the Nineteenth Century*, no. 17 (lent by Stephen C. Clark); Cleveland Museum of Art, 1936, *Twentieth Anniversary Exhibition*, no. 254 (lent by Stephen C. Clark); San Francisco Museum of Art (California), 1937, *Cézanne*, no. 27 (lent by Stephen C. Clark); Durand-Ruel, New York, 1938, *Cézanne*, no. 16 (lent by Stephen C. Clark); Museum of Modern Art, New York, 1939, *Art In Our Time*, no. 60 (lent by Stephen C. Clark); World's Fair, New York, 1940, *Masterpieces of Art*, no. 341 (lent by Stephen C. Clark); Paul Rosenberg, New York, 1942, *Cézanne*, no. 15 (lent by Stephen C. Clark); The Century Association, New York, 1946, *Paintings from the Stephen C. Clark Collection;* Wildenstein, New York, 1947, *Cézanne*, no. 48 (lent by Mr. and Mrs. Stephen C. Clark); Knoedler, New York, 1949, *To Honor Henry McBride*, no. 2 (lent by Stephen C. Clark); Art Institute of Chicago and Metropolitan Museum, 1952, *Cézanne*, no. 68 (lent by Stephen C. Clark); Knoedler, New York, 1954, *A Collector's Taste: Selections from the Collection of Mr. and Mrs. Stephen C. Clark*, no. 12; Museum of Modern Art, New York, 1955, *Paintings from Private Collections* (lent by Stephen C. Clark); Metropolitan Museum, *Paintings from Private Collections*, 1958, no. 16, 1959, no. 9, 1960, no. 9 (lent by Stephen C. Clark); Yale University Art Gallery, New Haven (Conn.), 1960, *Paintings, Drawings and Sculpture Collected by Yale Alumni*, no. 76 (lent by Stephen C. Clark).

Ex COLL.: Pellerin, Paris (in 1907); [Ambroise Vollard, Paris, in 1911]; I. A. Morosoff, Moscow (1911–1919); Museum of Modern Art, Moscow (1919–1933; cat., 1928, no. 560, pl. 25); [Knoedler, New York, 1933]; Stephen C. Clark, New York (1933–1960).

BEQUEST OF STEPHEN C. CLARK, 1960.

Still Life—Apples and a Pot of Primroses   51.112.1

This still life has a quiet, almost static quality that is increased by the emphasis on the simple, round, hard form of the fruit. The clear pattern of the leaves against the light background is unusual in Cézanne's work, as is the finished, almost polished handling.

Our painting once belonged to Claude Monet, who lent it in 1925 to a major exhibition in Paris, where it was dated 1886 in the catalogue (see Exhibitions, below). The date 1880, however, has been given to a very similar still life, also with a primrose (Venturi no. 623; see D. Cooper, *Burl. Mag.*, XCVI, 1954, p. 379).

Oil on canvas. H. 28⅜, w. 35½ in. (72 x 90.2 cm.).

REFERENCES: *Cézanne-Mappe* (1912), pl. 10 // S. Bourgeois, *Formes*, XXVIII–XXIX (1932), p. 301, ill. after p. 304, notes that this picture once belonged to Claude Monet // R. Huyghe, *Cézanne* (1936), p. 66, no. 36, ill. p. 48, dates it about 1885 // J. de Laprade, *Beaux-Arts* (May 22, 1936), p. 2, ill. p. 10 // C. Sterling, *Cézanne* (exhib. cat.), Musée de l'Orangerie, Paris (1936), p. 96, no. 70, dates it about 1886–1888 // L. Venturi, *Cézanne* (1936), I, pp. 57, 194, cat. no. 599, II, pl. 194, no. 599, dates it 1890–1894 // F. Novotny, *Cézanne* (1937), fig. 74, dates it 1886–1890 // R. J. Goldwater, *Art News* (Annual, section 1), XXXVI (Mar. 26, 1938), p. 160, ill. p. 143, dates it 1890–1894, mentions it as one of the untypical still lifes of the 1890's // A. C. Barnes and V. de Mazia, *The Art of Cézanne* (1939), p. 72, note 313, pp. 363, 414, no. 121

51.112.1

// S. A. Lewisohn, *Art News* (Annual), xxxvii (Feb. 25, 1939), ill. p. 69, hanging in the Lewisohn house // B. Dorival, *Cézanne* (1948), pp. 55, 150, no. 95, pl. 95, comments that this is one of the few pictures in which Cézanne painted plants // L. Guerry, *Cézanne et l'expression de l'espace* (1950), pp. 70, 99 // D. C. Rich, *Cézanne* (exhib. cat.), Art Institute of Chicago and Metropolitan Museum (1952), p. 75, no. 83, ill. // T. Rousseau Jr., *Paintings by Paul Cézanne* (*Met. Mus. Miniatures*, 1952), no. 16, ill. in color // M. Raynal, *Cézanne* (1954), ill. in color p. 85.

Exhibited: Musée des Arts Décoratifs, Paris, 1925, *Cinquante Ans de peinture française*, no. 12 (lent by Claude Monet); Museum of Modern Art, New York, 1929, *First Loan Exhibition*, no. 29 (lent by Adolph Lewisohn); Toledo Museum of Art, 1935, *Cézanne—Gauguin* (lent by Mr. and Mrs. Sam A. Lewisohn); Musée de l'Orangerie, Paris, 1936, *Cézanne*, no. 70 (lent by Adolph Lewisohn); Anglo-French Art and Travel Society, New Burlington Galleries, London, 1936, *Masters of French 19th-Century Painting*, no. 89 (lent by Adolph Lewisohn); Palais National des Arts, Paris, 1937, *Chefs-d'oeuvre de l'art français*, no. 253 (lent by Adolph Lewisohn); Durand-Ruel, New York, 1938, *Paintings by Cézanne*, no. 18 (lent by Adolph Lewisohn); World's Fair, New York, 1940, *Masterpieces of Art*, no. 346 (lent from the Lewisohn Collection); Museum of Modern Art, New York, 1944, *Art in Progress*, p. 24 (lent by Mr. and Mrs. Sam A. Lewisohn); Wildenstein, New York, 1947, *Cézanne*, no. 51 (lent by Sam A. Lewisohn); Metropolitan Museum, 1951, *The Lewisohn Collection*, no. 13; Art Institute of Chicago and Metropolitan Museum, 1952, *Cézanne*, no. 83; Museum Boymans-van Beuningen,

Rotterdam, 1954, *Vier Eeuwen Stilleven in Frankrijk*, no. 109.

Ex coll.: Claude Monet, Giverny (until 1926); [Paul Rosenberg, Paris]; Adolph Lewisohn, New York (by 1929–until 1938); Samuel A. Lewisohn, New York (1938–1951).

Bequest of Samuel A. Lewisohn, 1951.

61.101.5

Near the Pool at the Jas de Bouffan
61.101.5

In 1859, when Cézanne was twenty, his father bought a property near Aix to use as a summer place. It was called in Provençal the Jas de Bouffan, or Abode of the Winds. It included a handsome eighteenth-century house with a formal garden or park and seven acres of land with farm and vineyards. Cézanne always regarded the Jas as his home and returned to paint there at frequent intervals for forty years, until he regretfully sold it in 1899, after the death of his mother.

This picture of the grounds shows the pool or reservoir and a stone trough for washing. Because of its tawny warm tones and the way it is painted Douglas Cooper dates it about 1883.

Oil on canvas. H. 25½, w. 31⅞ in. (64.8 x 80.9 cm.).

References: [J. and G.] Bernheim-Jeune (eds.), *Cézanne* (1914), p. 74, pl. 55, call this picture

Les Marronniers du Jas de Bouffan // G. Rivière, *Le Maître Paul Cézanne* (1923), p. 214, describes it, dates it 1887, wrongly places it in the Pellerin collection // R. R. Tatlock, *Burl. Mag.*, LIX (1931), ill. opp. p. 194 // L. Venturi, *Cézanne* (1936), I, p. 204, cat. no. 648, II, pl. 207, no. 648, dates it 1888–1890 // F. Novotny, *Cézanne und das Ende der wissenschaftlichen Perspektive* (1938), pp. 38, 41, 199, no. 45, dates it 1888–1890 // L. Guerry, *Cézanne et l'expression de l'espace* (1950), p. 76, mentions it as an example of a late picture in a style resembling that of the first years of the Auvers period // J. de Beucken, *Cézanne* (1960), p. 136, ill. pp. 76, 77 (photograph of the pool at the Jas), dates it c. 1885–1886 // D. Cooper (verbally, 1964), dates it about 1883, placing it a little before the portrait of Mme Cézanne in the Conservatory, above.

Exhibited: Musée des Arts Décoratifs, Paris, 1925, *Cinquante Ans de peinture française*, no. 13 (as Les Marronniers du Jas de Bouffan, lent by Josse and Gaston Bernheim-Jeune); Knoedler, New York, 1931, *The Landscape in French Painting*, no. 23 (placed in 1884–1885); Art Institute of Chicago, 1933, *A Century of Progress*, no. 311; Gazette des Beaux-Arts, Paris, 1934, *Gauguin et ses amis*, no. 27 (lent by MM. Bernheim-Jeune); Bernheim-Jeune, Paris, 1935, *Quelques Tableaux d'Ingres à Gauguin*, no. 2; The Century Association, New York, 1946, *Paintings from the Stephen C. Clark Collection;* Knoedler, New York, 1954, *A Collector's Taste: Selections from the Collection of Mr. and Mrs. Stephen C. Clark*, no. 10; Pavillon de Vendôme, Aix-en-Provence, 1956, *Exposition pour commémorer le cinquantenaire de la mort de Cézanne*, no. 36 (placed in 1885–1886; lent by Stephen C. Clark); Metropolitan Museum, *Paintings from Private Collections*, 1958, no. 17, 1959, no. 10, 1960, no. 10 (as Graveyard, lent by Stephen C. Clark); Yale University Art Gallery, New Haven (Conn.), 1960, *Paintings, Drawings and Sculpture Collected by Yale Alumni*, no. 75 (lent by Stephen C. Clark).

Ex coll.: Baron Denis Cochin, Paris; Bernheim-Jeune, Paris (by 1913–after 1935; coll.

cat., *L'Art moderne* . . ., 1919, I, pl. 36); Mrs. Louis Schaffer (until 1939); Dr. Philip Sandbloom, Lund, Sweden (1939–1946); [Durand-Ruel, Paris, 1946]; Stephen C. Clark, New York (from 1946).

BEQUEST OF STEPHEN C. CLARK, 1960.

The Gulf of Marseilles
Seen from L'Estaque   29.100.67

Cézanne was already interested in painting the blue Mediterranean from the little village of L'Estaque as early as 1876, when he wrote to Pissarro that he had begun two studies of the motif. The subject occupied him at intervals for many years. The Museum's picture was probably painted about 1883–1885. In composition it bears a superficial resemblance to versions in the Art Institute of Chicago and the Louvre, but these are much less detailed than ours (Venturi nos. 493, 428). In spite of the detail, however, and the rich and subtle harmonies of many colors, strong blue is the dominant tone, and the source of the picture's unified effect of great depth and space.

Oil on canvas. H. 28¾, w. 39½ in. (73 x 100.4 cm.).

REFERENCES: F. J. Mather Jr., *The Arts*, XVI (1930), p. 483 // H. B. Wehle, *Met. Mus. Bull.*, XXV (1930), p. 58 // L. Venturi, *L'Arte*, XXXVIII (1935), pp. 302, 386, 389 (fig. 15), 391, observes that the same subject had been painted by Émile Loubon in a picture in the Museum of Marseilles (p. 299, fig. 1) // D. Lord, *Burl. Mag.*, LXIX (1936), p. 35, dates this picture 1878 // L. Venturi, *Cézanne* (1936), I, pp. 16, 53f., 157, cat. no. 429, II, pl. 122, no. 429, dates it 1883–1885, analyzes the composition, color, and technique, considers it the best-balanced version of the three (nos. 428, 429, 493) // R. J. Goldwater, *Art News* (Annual, section 1), XXXVI (Mar. 26, 1938), pp. 153f., discusses the treatment of space in this picture and other versions of the

29.100.67

subject // R. H. Wilenski, *Modern French Painters* [1940], p. 76, pl. 20 B, dates it about 1884 // B. Dorival, *Cézanne* (1948), pp. 51f., 69, 147, no. 74, pl. 74, considers it the best of the views of L'Estaque showing the bay, dates it 1883–1885 // L. Guerry, *Cézanne et l'expression de l'espace* (1950), pp. 88–92, 95, fig. 17 // L. Venturi, *Impressionists and Symbolists* (1950), p. 132, fig. 130 // D. C. Rich, *Cézanne* (exhib. cat.), Art Institute of Chicago and Metropolitan Museum (1952), p. 49, ill. p. 48, no. 49 // T. Rousseau Jr., *Paintings by Paul Cézanne* (*Met. Mus. Miniatures*, 1952), no. 9, ill. in color // M. Raynal, *Cézanne* (1954), p. 65, ill. in color // L. Venturi, *Four Steps Toward Modern Art* (1956), p. 71 // L. Dittmann, "Zur Kunst Cézannes," in *Festschrift Kurt Badt* (1961), p. 207, ill. after p. 208, fig. 6.

EXHIBITED: Metropolitan Museum, 1930, *The H. O. Havemeyer Collection*, no. 5; Musée de l'Orangerie, Paris, 1936, *Cézanne*, no. 43; Art Institute of Chicago and Metropolitan Museum, 1952, *Cézanne*, no. 49; Hofstra College, Hempstead (New York), 1952; Portland Art Museum (Oregon) and University of Oregon, Eugene, 1953.

EX COLL. H. O. Havemeyer, New York.

THE H. O. HAVEMEYER COLLECTION. BEQUEST OF MRS. H. O. HAVEMEYER, 1929.

Gardanne   57.181

In the autumn of 1885 and most of the following year Cézanne painted in Gardanne, a hill town in the center of the coal district near Aix. Besides this picture he also painted a horizontal one from almost the same angle, now in the Barnes Foundation in Merion, Pennsylvania (Venturi 430), and another, a vertical, observed from the opposite side of the town, now in the Brooklyn Museum (Venturi 431).

Cézanne's vision and his search for the essential elements in nature and inanimate objects directed him toward principles only fully explored much later by the Cubists. In the three paintings of Gardanne the square

shapes of the architecture are combined with the landscape in an abstract manner that is prophetically cubist. Ten years earlier Cézanne had apparently been groping for a similar solution in his treatment of the buildings of the Hermitage clustered on the steep hillside at Pontoise (Venturi 176).

1886 was a year of great significance in Cézanne's personal life, for in it occurred his marriage, the death of his father and his inheritance of a fortune, and the painful break with Zola as a result of the publication of Zola's novel *L'Oeuvre.*

Oil on canvas. H. 31½, w. 25¼ in. (80 x 64.2 cm.).

REFERENCES: A. Dreyfuss, *Zeitschrift für bildende Kunst*, XXIV (1913), pp. 202f., ill. // A. Vollard, *Paul Cézanne* (1914), p. 59, pl. 37, dates this picture 1886, lists it among those exhibited in 1895 at Vollard's gallery // J. Gasquet, *Cézanne* (1921), p. 49, discusses Cézanne's pictures of this subject // F. Knapp, *Die Künstlerische Kultur des Abendlandes* (1923), III, p. 281, fig. 201 // G. Rivière, *Paul Cézanne* (1923), p. 213, dates this picture 1886 and the horizontal version (Barnes Foundation) 1885 // A. H. B[arr] Jr., *First Loan Exhibition* (cat.), Museum of Modern Art, New York (1929), pp. 22, 36, cat. no. 20, pl. 20 // E. d'Ors, *Paul Cézanne* (1930), pl. 14, dates the painting 1880 // Ozenfant, *Foundations of Modern Art* (1931), pp. 68f., contrasts a detail of this picture with a Picasso of the cubist period // A. H. Barr Jr., *Cubism and Abstract Art* (1936), pp. 42, 206, cat. no. 33, fig. 29, compares this picture with two works by Picasso (figs. 27, 30) // C. Sterling, *La Renaissance*, XIX (1936), pp. 11, 14, fig. 10 // L. Venturi, *Cézanne* (1936), I, pp. 55, 158, cat. no. 432, II, pl. 124, no. 432, dates it about 1885–1886 // R. J. Goldwater, *Art News* (Annual, section 1), XXXVI (Mar. 26, 1938), pp. 152f., ill., discusses the composition and treatment of the three pictures of Gardanne, considers the version in the Barnes Foundation the earliest // F. Novotny, *Cézanne und das Ende der wissenschaftlichen Perspektive* (1938), pp. 34 (note 32), 46, 205, no. 103 //

E. Loran, *Cézanne's Composition* (1943), pp. 122f., ill. (the painting and a photograph taken from the same vantage point), analyzes the composition; see also note and illustrations on the last page of the catalogue of the Cézanne exhibition at the San Francisco Museum of Art, 1937 // D. Cooper, *Burl. Mag.*, xcvi (1954), p. 379, considers that this picture and the Brooklyn picture were done probably in 1886, after the version in the Barnes Foundation // M. Raynal, *Cézanne* (1954), p. 68, ill. in color // J. Richardson, *Burl. Mag.*, xcviii (1956), pp. 412f., fig. 27, dates this picture 1885–1886, states that it is "surely the direct inspiration of early cubist (1908–09) landscapes by Braque and Picasso and even by Derain."

EXHIBITED: Galerie Vollard, Paris, 1895, *L'Oeuvre de Cézanne*; Museum of French Art, New York, 1928, *Paintings by Paul Cézanne*, no. 18 (lent by Dr. and Mrs. F. H. Hirschland); Wildenstein, New York, 1928, *Paul Cézanne*, no. 18 (lent by Dr. and Mrs. F. H. Hirschland); Museum of Modern Art, New York, 1929, *First Loan Exhibition*, no. 20 (lent by Dr. and Mrs. F. H. Hirschland); Wildenstein, New York, 1947, *Cézanne*, no. 32 (lent by Dr. and Mrs. F. H. Hirschland); Museum of Modern Art, New York, 1955, *Paintings from Private Collections*, cat. p. 7 (lent by Dr. and Mrs. F. H. Hirschland); Pavillon de Vendôme, Aix-en-Provence, 1956, *Exposition pour commémorer le cinquantenaire de la mort de Cézanne*, no. 30 (lent from a private collection, New York).

Ex COLL.: [Ambroise Vollard, Paris, until 1924]; [Justin K. Thannhauser, Lucerne, in 1924]; Dr. and Mrs. Franz H. Hirschland, Harrison, New York (from 1924).

GIFT OF DR. AND MRS. FRANZ H. HIRSCHLAND, SUBJECT TO A LIFE ESTATE IN THE DONORS, 1957.

Mont Sainte-Victoire   29.100.64

This mountain was a favorite motif with Cézanne, who used it as a dominant theme in

57.181

many paintings, both in water color and in oil. Between 1885 and 1887 he painted several pictures in which it formed a background for the vast panorama of the valley of the Arc river, crossed by the railroad viaduct. This picture, which is unusually complete and finished, is one of four painted from the little hill at Bellevue, the estate of Cézanne's brother-in-law, Maxime Conil (Venturi 453–455). In these the calm silhouette of the mountain is an integral part of the vista, whereas in the late paintings of Mont Sainte-Victoire, done at the end of his life, the mountain dominates the entire scene.

Formerly called Landscape with a Viaduct.

Oil on canvas. H. 25¾, w. 32⅛ in. (65.5 x 81.7 cm.).

REFERENCES: F. J. Mather Jr., *The Arts*, xvi (1930), p. 483 // H. B. Wehle, *Met. Mus. Bull.*, xxv (1930), p. 58 // L. Venturi, *Cézanne* (1936), I, p. 162, cat. no. 452, II, pl.

132, no. 452, dates this picture 1885–1887 //
A. Vollard, *Recollections of a Picture Dealer*
(1936), p. 142 // R. J. Goldwater, *Art News*
(Annual, section 1), xxxvi (Mar. 26, 1938),
p. 154 // F. Novotny, *Cézanne und das Ende
der wissenschaftlichen Perspektive* (1938), pp.
21, 49, 94 (note 89), 203, no. 85 // A. C.
Barnes and V. de Mazia, *The Art of Cézanne*
(1939), pp. 357, 412, no. 95 // B. Dorival,
Cézanne (1948), pp. 52, 148, no. 85, pl. 85,
analyzes the composition of this picture //
L. Guerry, *Cézanne et l'expression de l'espace*
(1950), pp. 193f., note 47 (from p. 82) //
Metropolitan Museum, *Art Treasures* (1952),
p. 233, cat. no. 149, pl. 149 // D. C. Rich,
Cézanne (exhib. cat.), Art Institute of Chicago
and Metropolitan Museum (1952), p. 53, no.
53, ill. p. 51 // T. Rousseau Jr., *Paintings by
Paul Cézanne* (Met. Mus. Miniatures, 1952),
no. 11, ill. in color, analyzes the composition
// M. Schapiro, *Cézanne* (1952), pp. 66f., ill.
in color // T. Rousseau Jr., *Cézanne* (1953),
pl. 12, in color // C. Biederman, *The New
Cézanne* (1958), pp. 36f., 39, figs. 11, 12, dia-
grams it.

EXHIBITED: Metropolitan Museum, 1930, *The
H. O. Havemeyer Collection*, no. 6, and 1934,
Landscape Paintings, no. 54; World's Fair, New
York, 1940, *Masterpieces of Art*, no. 342; Art
Institute of Chicago and Metropolitan Mu-
seum, 1952, *Cézanne*, no. 53; Aix-en-Provence
and Nice, 1953, *P. Cézanne*, no. 14.

EX COLL.: [Ambroise Vollard, Paris]; H. O.
Havemeyer, New York (Cat., 1931, pp. 56f.,
ill.; 1958, p. 13, no. 62, ill. after p. 125).

THE H. O. HAVEMEYER COLLECTION. BE-
QUEST OF MRS. H. O. HAVEMEYER, 1929.

Still Life—Apples and Pears
(Les Grosses Pommes) 61.101.3

Venturi dates this picture 1885–1887, grouping it with other still lifes of fruit composed with horizontal emphasis. The banded wall that changes direction in the background not only intensifies the deepness of the space, but with the lines of the table produces a satisfying effect of strength and balance.

Oil on canvas. H. 17⅝, w. 23⅛ in. (44.8 x 58.7 cm.).

REFERENCES: L. Venturi, *Cézanne* (1936), I, p. 173, cat. no. 502, II, pl. 155, no. 502, dates this picture 1885–1887 // J. W. Lane, *Art News* (Annual), XXXVII (Feb. 25, 1939), p. 133 // L. Guerry, *Cézanne et l'expression de l'espace* (1950), p. 95 // D. Cooper, verbally (1964), dates it 1886–1887.

EXHIBITED: Bernheim-Jeune, Paris, 1920, *Cézanne*, no. 17 (belonging to MM. Bernheim-Jeune), and 1925, *Oeuvres du XIXᵉ et XXᵉ siècles, Exposition au bénéfice de l'Hôpital Saint-Michel*, no. 14, and 1926, *Rétrospective Paul Cézanne*; Grand Palais, Paris, 1926, *Trente Ans d'art indépendant*, no. 2875 (lent from a private collection); Lucerne, 1929, *Peintures de l'école impressionniste et néo-impressionniste*, no. 1; Lefevre Gallery, Glasgow, 1929, *Masterpieces by XIXth-Century French Painters*, no. 1; Lefevre Gallery, London, 1929, *Ten Masterpieces by XIXth-Century French Painters*, no. 1; Museum of Modern Art, New York, 1930, *Summer Exhibition: Retrospective*, no. 22 (lent by Stephen C. Clark); Marie Harriman Gallery, New York, 1936, *Chardin and the Modern Still Life*, no. 13, and 1939, *Cézanne Centennial Exhibition*, no. 11 (lent by Stephen C. Clark); Co-ordinating Council of French Relief Societies, New York, 1944, *Jardin d'Été* (lent by Stephen C. Clark); The Century Association, New York, 1946, *Paintings from the Stephen C. Clark Collection*; Knoedler, New York, 1954, *A Collector's Taste: Selections from the Collection of Mr. and Mrs. Stephen C. Clark*, no. 9; Yale University Art Gallery, New Haven (Conn.), 1956, *Pictures Collected by Yale Alumni*, no. 109 (lent by Stephen C. Clark);

61.101.3

Metropolitan Museum, *Paintings from Private Collections*, 1958, no. 15, 1959, no. 12, 1960, no. 12 (lent by Stephen C. Clark).

EX COLL.: Mme Ceccaldi, Berlin (in 1912); Bernheim-Jeune, Paris (by 1919, until after 1925; coll. cat., *L'Art moderne . . .*, 1919, I, pl. 29); [Alex Reid and Lefevre, London, in 1929]; [M. Knoedler, New York, 1929]; Stephen C. Clark, New York (1929–1960).

BEQUEST OF STEPHEN C. CLARK, 1960.

Madame Cézanne in a Red Dress
62.45

This severe portrait of Madame Cézanne was probably painted about ten years later than the one in the conservatory (see above). The mood is entirely different. She looks ten years older here, and further support for a date around 1890 is supplied by comparison with other works by Cézanne. The portrait is not yet so thickly painted nor so heavily handled as the portrait of Gustave Geffroy, which we know was done in 1895, and which shows the beginnings of the rough, forceful, free style that characterizes late works like the portrait of Vallier and the Mont Sainte-Victoire landscapes. Certain motifs in the portrait of Madame Cézanne in a Red Dress, however, appear in pictures usually dated in the middle of the decade of the nineties. The same molding and broad dark band are to be found in three of the paintings of a boy with a red vest. The figured drapery at the right of the Mu-

seum's picture also appears in the series of the boy with a red vest, as well as in a number of pictures that are generally dated from the mid to late nineties, including a portrait of a young man (Venturi 679), of a seated older man (Venturi 697), and many still lifes.

Three smaller portraits of Madame Cézanne (Venturi 571, 572, 573), which seem to be preliminary phases of the same pictorial theme, show her seated in the same chair and wearing the same dress as in the Museum's picture.

Oil on canvas. H. 45⅝, w. 35 in. (105.9 x 88 cm.).

REFERENCES: G. Coquiot, *Paul Cézanne* [1919], p. 238, ill. opp. p. 248, calls this painting Portrait de Mme Cézanne à la pincette // J. Meier-Graefe, *Cézanne und sein Kreis* (1922), ill. p. 201, dates it about 1888; and *Cézanne* (English edition, 1927), pl. LXVIII // R. Fry, *L'Amour de l'art*, VII (1926), p. 408, ill.; and *Cézanne* (1927), pp. 68f., pl. XXIII, fig. 34, dates it at the end of the 1880's, observing that it is, however, "definitely in the new manner," analyzes the composition, finds the color reminiscent of Vermeer; and *Sammleren*, VI (1929), p. 136, ill. p. 131, dates it 1890 // G. Rivière, *Cézanne le peintre solitaire* (1933), p. 139, ill. p. 111, dates it 1887 on plate and in list of plates but in text says that in 1888 Cézanne painted in Paris, Quai d'Anjou, two portraits of his wife, in one of which she wears a dress of red wool // G. Mack, *Paul Cézanne* (1935), pl. 17, dates it about 1888 // M. Raynal, *Cézanne* (1936), p. 146, pl. LXX, on p. 102, calls it Mme Cézanne aux pincettes, dates it about 1880 // R. Huyghe, *Cézanne* [c. 1936], p. 44, fig. 28, dates it about 1888 // C. Sterling, *Cézanne* (exhib. cat.), Musée de l'Orangerie, Paris (1936), pp. 101f., no. 76, calls it Grand Portrait de Mme Cézanne en rouge, dates it 1888–1890, states that it belongs to a group of portraits of 1888–1892, in all of which the curtain appears // L. Venturi, *Cézanne* (1936), I, p. 188, no. 570, II, pl. 182, calls it Mme Cézanne au fauteuil jaune, dates it 1890–1894 // A. C. Barnes and V. de Mazia, *The Art of Cézanne* (1939), pp. 373f., ill. p. 217, describes her as holding a handkerchief

(actually a rose), dates it in the early 1890's // J. de Beucken, *Cézanne* (1960), p. 137, ill. p. 93, dates it 1890–1893, asserts that it was painted in the Quai d'Anjou [Paris], observing that it opens a new epoch in Cézanne's work // D. Cooper (verbally, Feb. 1964), dates it 1889/90 // K. Badt, *The Art of Cézanne* (1965), p. 153.

EXHIBITED: Paris, 1907, *Salon d'Automne, Rétrospective . . . Cézanne*, no. 18 (lent by M. Pellerin); Musée de l'Orangerie, Paris, 1936, *Cézanne*, no. 76 (lent by M. et Mme Pellerin, Paris).

EX COLL.: Auguste Pellerin, Paris (until 1936); Jean Victor Pellerin, Paris (1936–1962).

PURCHASE, MR. AND MRS. HENRY ITTLESON JR. FUND, 1962.

Still Life with a Ginger Jar and Eggplants   61.101.4

Douglas Cooper dates this picture 1890, observing that it is painted in a green tonality that Cézanne discarded after that year. Most of the objects in it appear together in a similar arrangement in a still life in the National Gallery, Washington (Venturi 598), and separately in a number of other pictures.

Oil on canvas. H. 28½, w. 36 in. (72.4 x 91.4 cm.).

REFERENCES: *Art News*, XXVI (Mar. 24, 1928), p. 8, ill. // L. Venturi, *Cézanne* (1936), I, p. 194, cat. no. 597, II, pl. 193, no. 597, dates this picture 1890–1894 // R. J. Goldwater, *Art News* (Annual, section I), XXXVI (Mar. 26, 1938), p. 160, ill. p. 140 // *Art News*, XLVII (Feb. 1949), ill. p. 44 // D. Cooper, verbally (1964), dates it 1890.

EXHIBITED: Durand-Ruel, New York, 1928, *French Masterpieces of the Late XIX Century*, no. 4 (lent anonymously); The Century Association, New York, 1949, *Trends in European Painting* (lent by Stephen C. Clark); Knoedler, New York, 1954, *A Collector's Taste: Selections from the Collection of Mr. and Mrs. Stephen C. Clark*, no. 13; Art Institute of Chicago, 1955, *Great French Paintings*, no. 4 (lent by

61.101.4

Stephen C. Clark); Museum of Modern Art, New York, 1955, *Paintings from Private Collections* (lent by Stephen C. Clark); Metropolitan Museum, *Paintings from Private Collections*, 1958, no. 18, 1959, no. 11, 1960, no. 11 (lent by Stephen C. Clark); Yale University Art Gallery, New Haven (Conn.), 1960, *Paintings, Drawings and Sculpture Collected by Yale Alumni*, no. 78 (lent by Stephen C. Clark).

EX COLL.: [Durand-Ruel, Paris and New York]; H. O. Havemeyer, New York (Cat., 1931, p. 329); Horace Havemeyer, New York (until 1948); [Knoedler, New York, 1948]; Stephen C. Clark, New York (from 1948).

BEQUEST OF STEPHEN C. CLARK, 1960.

The Cardplayers   61.101.1

A group of cardplayers seated about a table

was a favorite subject with many seventeenth-century painters, and Cézanne probably was inspired to take it up by an example which he must have known in the museum at Aix, a work now ascribed to Mathieu Le Nain (*The Splendid Century*, exhib. cat., Metropolitan Museum, 1960, no. 31, fig. 31). Sometime around 1892, no doubt using as models peasants from the country around his farm, the Jas de Bouffan, he painted five different pictures of cardplayers. In three of them there are only two figures seated at a table (Louvre, Pellerin, and Courtauld collections; Venturi 558, 556, 557). A second group with more figures and more complicated compositions is made up of the Museum's picture and a very large one in the Barnes Foundation at Merion, Pennsylvania (Venturi 560). In the Museum's there is a third player seated at the table and a fourth man, standing looking on from behind. The same figure standing in the same position appears in the Barnes example, and the youthful head of another observer is inserted between the central and right-hand players. The monumental Barnes picture is Cézanne's most important fully carried-out picture and one of his largest.

It is impossible to determine the order in which Cézanne painted these five different pictures of cardplayers; in view of the strong probability that he was inspired by the Le Nain in Aix, which has four figures, it seems likely that he began with the larger and more complex composition in contrast to the procedure of most artists, and then, by eliminating figures and decreasing the size of the canvas, worked toward the simplified, more classic pictures with two figures and more complex and subtle color harmonies. The Museum's Cardplayers would thus have been painted immediately after the Barnes picture and before the three versions with only two figures, which are, furthermore, in a completely different setting.

There are a number of studies of the peasant models, some of them made directly in preparation for our painting. An oil study of the standing man with the pipe (Lecomte collection, Paris; Venturi 563) was exhibited at the Salon d'Automne of 1907. There it was given the date 1892, which is probably a reliable indication that the entire group of pictures was painted about that time. There are four other studies for the Museum's painting: an oil sketch of the center figure, in the Museum at Worcester, Massachusetts (Venturi 568); a water color for the seated man at the left, in the collection of Chauncey McCormick in Chicago (Venturi 1085); and two drawings for the man at the right, one in the Rhode Island School of Design in Providence (Venturi 1086) and another of unknown whereabouts (ill. in A. Vollard, *Cézanne*, 1914, p. 47).

Oil on canvas. H. 25½, w. 32 in. (64.7 x 81.2 cm.).

REFERENCES: M. Leblond, *Apollon*, I (1910), part 1, no. 6, p. 99, ill. opp. p. 89 // F. Burger, *Cézanne und Hodler* (1913), pp. 90f., pl. 72, implies that this picture was painted after the version now in the Barnes Foundation // [J. and G.] Bernheim-Jeune (eds.), *Cézanne* (1914), p. 71, pl. XLIII // J. Gasquet, *Cézanne* (1921), ill. in color opp. p.14 // T. L. Klingsor, *Cézanne* [1924], p. 42, pl. 32, considers it the final version of the series of Cardplayers // G. Rivière, *Le Maître Paul Cézanne* (1923), p. 218, ill. p.168, dates it 1890 // E. Faure, *P. Cézanne* (1926), p. 53 // L. Venturi, *Il Gusto dei Primitivi* (1926), p. 324, pl. 90 // R. Fry, *Cézanne* (1927), pp. 26, 72, pl. XXVI // M. Osborn, *Deutsche Kunst und Dekoration*, LIX (1927), p. 336, ill. p. 339 // G. Rivière, *Cézanne, le peintre solitaire* (1933), pp. 140, 145, ill. p. 137, asserts that the Museum's picture is the oldest version of the subject and that it was done in 1890 // L. Venturi, *L'Arte*, XXXVIII (1935), pp. 394, 403, fig. 21 // R. Huyghe, *Cézanne* (1936), pp. 44, 54, no. 41, ill., dates it about 1892 // C. Sterling, *Cézanne* (exhib. cat.), Musée de l'Orangerie, Paris (1936), pp. 106f., no. 83, pl. XV, considers it a reduction of the large composition in the Barnes collection // L. Venturi, *Cézanne* (1936), I, pp. 185f., cat. no. 559, II, pl. 177, no. 559, dates it 1890–1892 // R. J. Goldwater, *Art News* (Annual, section 1), XXXVI (Mar. 26, 1938), p. 156, ill. p. 145, considers it and the Barnes version earlier than those with two figures // A. M. Frankfurter, *Art News* (Annual, section 2), XXXVI (Mar. 26, 1938), p. 30, ill. p. 16 // A. C. Barnes and V. de Mazia, *The Art of Cézanne* (1939), pp. 364, 415, no. 125, ill. p. 271 // J. W. Lane, *Art News* (Annual), XXXVII (Feb. 25, 1939), p. 133, ill. p. 143 // L. Venturi, *Cézanne* (exhib. cat.), Paul Rosenberg Gallery, New York (1942), pp. 16, 29f., no. 14, ill. // J. Rewald, *The History of Impressionism* (1946), ill. p. 410, dates it 1890–1892; (revised and enlarged edition, 1961), ill. p. 556 // B. Dorival, *Cézanne* (1948), pp. 60–63, 153, no. 121, pl. 121, considers the Museum's painting the second of the five versions of The Cardplayers, made after the Barnes collection picture and superior to it in composition and color, observes that Cézanne probably was inspired by The Cardplayers in the Museum at Aix, which Dorival attributes to a pupil of Louis Le Nain // J. Rewald, *Paul Cézanne* (1948), ill. in color opp. p. 174 // L. Guerry, *Cézanne et l'expression de l'espace* (1950), p. 196, note 61, tentatively places this and the Barnes picture earlier than the versions with two figures // J. M. Carpenter, *Art Bull.*, XXXIII (1951), pp. 179, 185, fig. 6, discusses the composition and method // D. C. Rich, *Cézanne* (exhib. cat.), Art Institute of Chicago and Metropolitan Museum (1952), p. 71, no. 79, ill., mentions the probable influence on Cézanne of the Le Nain brothers // D. Panofsky, *Gaz. des B.-A.*, XXXIX (1952), pp. 338f., ill. fig. 13, suggests (with Walter Friedlaender, note 46) that Cézanne patterned this composition after Caravaggio's Christ and the Disciples at Emmaus (fig. 14) // T. Rousseau Jr., *Art News*, LI (Apr. 1952), p. 33, ill. p. 29, discusses its similarity to the work of the Le Nain brothers; *Paintings by Paul Cézanne* (Met. Mus. Miniatures, 1952), no. 15, ill. in color // A. Châtelet,

Hommage à Cézanne (exhib. cat.), Musée de l'Orangerie, Paris (1954), pp. 21f., considers the versions with four and five figures the latest // D. Cooper, *Burl. Mag.*, XCVI (1954), p. 380, agrees with Châtelet (above), places the two-figure versions in 1892, before this picture and the Barnes example // M. Raynal, *Cézanne* (1954), pp. 99f., ill. in color p. 91 (the Museum's painting) and p. 89 (the watercolor study for the figure on the left, in the collection of Chauncey McCormick, Chicago) // H. Perruchot, *La Vie de Cézanne* (1958), pp. 317–319, states that the version with five figures was painted first, then this picture, and then the two-figure versions // A. Frankfurter, *Art News Annual*, XXVIII (1959), p. 39, ill. // P. Feist, *Paul Cézanne* (1963), pp. 33, 76, no. 55, pl. 55, states his belief that the composition was planned originally in its larger form, and agrees with other scholars who hold

that the four- and five-figured compositions preceded the ones with only two // K. Badt, *The Art of Cézanne* (1965), pp. 89, 92, pl. 9, in a full study of the paintings of Cardplayers places the Museum's example before the two-figured examples; finds a connection between its composition and a drawing Cézanne made in 1859 // M. T. de Forges (verbally, Oct. 1965), dates our painting and the Barnes one 1880–1885, places the Louvre example c. 1895.

EXHIBITED: Galerie Bernheim-Jeune, Paris, 1910, *Cézanne*, no. 47 (lent by "MM. X"); Grosvenor Galleries, London, 1914, *Modern French Art*, no. 7 (lent from a private collection); Galerie Bernheim-Jeune, Paris, 1917, *Peinture moderne*, no. 4; Kunsthaus, Zurich, 1917, *Französische Kunst des XIX und XX Jahrhunderts*, no. 34 (lent from "Coll. B. J."); Galerie Bernheim-Jeune, Paris, 1920, *Cézanne*, no. 14 (belonging to MM. Bernheim-Jeune), and 1926, *Rétrospective Paul Cézanne*, no. 39; Künstlerhaus, Berlin, 1927, *Erste Sonderausstellung* (organized by Thannhauser, Munich), no. 29 (lent from a private collection); Galerie Georges Petit, Paris, 1930, *Cent Ans de peinture française*, no. 28; Art Institute of Chicago, 1933, *A Century of Progress*, no. 307 (lent by Stephen C. Clark); California Palace of the Legion of Honor, San Francisco, 1934, *French Painting*, no. 68 (lent by Stephen C. Clark); Museum of Modern Art, New York, 1934–1935, *Modern Works of Art*, no. 6 (lent anonymously); Musée de l'Orangerie, Paris, 1936, *Cézanne*, no. 83 (lent by Stephen C. Clark); Durand-Ruel, New York, 1938, *Cézanne*, no. 17 (lent by Stephen C. Clark); Museum of Modern Art, New York, 1939, *Art in Our Time*, no. 62 (lent by Stephen C. Clark), and 1940, *Modern Masters*, no. 9 (lent by Stephen C. Clark); World's Fair, New York, 1940, *Masterpieces of Art*, no. 340 (lent by Stephen C. Clark); Paul Rosenberg Gallery, New York, 1942, *Cézanne*, no. 14 (lent by Stephen C. Clark); Museum of Modern Art, New York, 1944, *Art in Progress*, cat. p. 25 (lent by Stephen C. Clark); The Century Association, New York, 1946, *Paintings from the Stephen C. Clark Collection*; Wildenstein,

New York, 1947, *Cézanne*, no. 45 (lent by Mr. and Mrs. Stephen C. Clark); Art Institute of Chicago and Metropolitan Museum, 1952, *Cézanne*, no. 79 (lent by Stephen C. Clark); Knoedler, New York, 1954, *A Collector's Taste: Selections from the Collection of Mr. and Mrs. Stephen C. Clark*, no. 11; Museum of Modern Art, New York, 1955, *Paintings from Private Collections* (lent by Stephen C. Clark); Yale University Art Gallery, New Haven (Conn.), 1956, *Pictures Collected by Yale Alumni*, no. 111 (lent by Stephen C. Clark); Metropolitan Museum, *Paintings from Private Collections*, 1958, no. 14, 1959, no. 8, 1960, no. 13 (lent by Stephen C. Clark).

Ex COLL.: [Ambroise Vollard, Paris, until 1898]; Bernheim-Jeune, Paris (from 1898; coll. cat., *L'Art moderne . . .*, 1919, I, pl. 23); [Étienne Bignou, Paris, 1931]; [Knoedler, New York, 1931]; Stephen C. Clark, New York (from 1931).

BEQUEST OF STEPHEN C. CLARK, 1960.

View of the Domaine Saint-Joseph (La Colline des Pauvres) 13.66

This landscape is one of the very few that satisfied Cézanne sufficiently to lead him to sign his name. The fact that he considered as finished, and affixed his signature to, a painting which shows many areas of bare canvas proves his regard for the contrast he achieved by deliberately leaving these places unpainted. The feathery touch of the brush and these bare areas relate the picture in style to works of his late maturity and probably place it about 1895.

At this time the *domaine*, or estate, called Saint-Joseph was occupied by the Jesuits, who were obliged to leave it in 1901 under the laws of separation of church and state. The property passed into the hands of private owners, who transformed all of the buildings except the chapel and the pigeon tower. It is situated on a hill known locally as the Colline des Pauvres, on the road between Aix and the

13.66

village of Le Tholonet. This region to the east of Aix was dear to Cézanne throughout his life: in his youth he made frequent excursions there with Émile Zola, and, decades later, after his family home was sold in 1899, he tried to buy the Château Noir, which lies near the Domaine Saint-Joseph on the same road.

This painting was purchased at the Armory Show for a price higher than that of any other picture in the Armory Show and was the first Cézanne to enter a public collection in America.

Formerly called The Poorhouse on the Hill (La Colline des Pauvres).

Signed (at lower right): *P. Cézanne*.

Oil on canvas. H. 25⅝, w. 32 in. (65.1 x 81.3 cm.).

REFERENCES: B. B[urroughs], *Met. Mus. Bull.*, VIII (1913), pp. 108f., ill., states that this picture was painted about 1887 near Cézanne's home in Aix, discusses the difference between the technique here and that of the Impressionists // A. Vollard, *Paul Cézanne* (1914), pl. 1 // [J. and G.] Bernheim-Jeune (eds.), *Cézanne* (1914), p. 73, pl. LI, identify the painting as La Colline des Fauves *(sic)* // B. B[urroughs], *Met. Mus. Bull.*, XIII (1918), pp. 180f., ill. // G. Rivière, *Paul Cézanne* (1923), p. 219, calls

this picture Paysage de Provence, Le Petit Roquefavour, painted about 1892 // L. Venturi, *Cézanne* (1936), I, p. 207, cat. no. 660, II, pl. 211, no. 660, dates it 1888–1894 // F. Novotny, *Cézanne und das Ende der wissenschaftlichen Perspektive* (1938), p. 197, no. 33, calls it Domaine Saint Joseph (La Colline des Pauvres), dates it about 1890 // A. C. Barnes and V. de Mazia, *The Art of Cézanne* (1939), pp. 356, 413, no. 110, analyze the treatment // H. McBride, *Art News* (Annual), XXXVII (1939), p. 66, gives an account of how the picture was acquired by the Metropolitan Museum // J. Mellquist, *Mag. of Art*, XXXVI (1943), ill. p. 301, publishes it as the first work by Cézanne to enter an American public collection // *Cézanne* (exhib. cat.), Pavillon de Vendôme, Aix-en-Provence (1956), no. 52, dates it 1895–1897 // J. Richardson, *Burl. Mag.*, XCVIII (1956), p. 412, considers 1890 a more likely date for this picture than 1895–1897 (the date assigned it in the catalogue of the exhibition at Aix), finds it "somewhat indifferent" // *Paul Cézanne* (exhib. cat.), Österreichische Galerie, Oberes Belvedere, Vienna (1961), p. 28, no. 35, dates it about 1895 // L. Marchutz (in a letter, 1962), supplies information about the subject // M. Brown, *Armory Show, 50th Anniversary Exhibition* (cat.), Utica and New York (1963), p. 37, ill. p. 51, quotes the price of $6,700 that the Museum paid for this painting as the highest paid at the Armory Show.

EXHIBITED: New York, 1913, *International Exhibition of Modern Art* ("The Armory Show"), no. 217 (lent by A. Vollard); Metropolitan Museum, 1934, *Landscape Paintings*, no. 53; Pennsylvania Museum of Art, Philadelphia, 1934, *Cézanne*, no. 41; Cincinnati Art Museum, 1944, *Pictures for Peace*, no. 4; Pavillon de Vendôme, Aix-en-Provence, 1956, *Exposition pour commémorer le cinquantenaire de la mort de Cézanne*, no. 52; Kunsthaus, Zurich, 1956, *Paul Cézanne*, no. 64; Haus der Kunst, Munich, 1956, *Paul Cézanne*, no. 46; Kunsthaus Lempertz (Wallraf-Richartz Museum collection), Cologne, 1956–1957, *Cézanne*, no. 25; Mead Arts Building, Amherst College,

Amherst (Mass.), 1958, *The 1913 Armory Show in Retrospect*, no. 6; Musée d'Art Moderne, Paris, 1960–1961, *Les Sources du XXe siècle*, no. 84; Österreichische Galerie, Oberes Belvedere, Vienna, 1961, *Paul Cézanne*, no. 35; Munson-Williams-Proctor Institute, Utica (N.Y.), and Armory of the Sixty-Ninth Street Regiment, New York, 1963, *Armory Show, 50th Anniversary Exhibition*, no. 217; Wildenstein Gallery, New York, 1965, *Olympia's Progeny*, no. 66.

Ex coll. [Ambroise Vollard, Paris, until 1913].

Purchase, Wolfe Fund, 1913.

29.100.194

Rocks in the Forest   29.100.194

It is difficult to identify the exact location of Cézanne's later landscapes because he no longer concentrated on the particular aspects of a scene but tried to express its vital force and essential rhythm. Venturi and Charles Sterling tend to think that the forest of Fontainebleau is the probable subject of this picture, but Douglas Cooper believes it was painted in the south of France, near the Château Noir. He dates it about 1898, commenting on its purplish gray tonality, which is a common feature of landscapes by Cézanne painted between 1896 and 1900.

Formerly called Rocks—Forest of Fontainebleau.

Oil on canvas. H. 28⅞, w. 36⅜ in. (73.4 x 92.4 cm.).

References: F. J. Mather Jr., *The Arts*, XVI (1930), p. 483 // H. B. Wehle, *Met. Mus. Bull.*, XXV (1930), p. 58 // L. Venturi, *Cézanne* (1936), I, p. 209, cat. no. 673, II, pl. 216, no. 673, dates this picture 1894–1898, suggests that the site may be Fontainebleau // R. J. Goldwater, *Art News* (Annual, section 1), XXXVI (Mar. 26, 1938), p. 158, ill. p. 156 // A. C. Barnes and V. de Mazia, *The Art of Cézanne* (1939), pp. 43 (footnote), 419, no. 171, group this picture among paintings made in the late 1890's, comment on its unusual color scheme // D. Cooper (in a letter, 1964), dates it about 1898 and identifies the site as the area around the Château Noir.

Exhibited: Metropolitan Museum, 1930, *The H. O. Havemeyer Collection*, no. 8; Pennsylvania Museum of Art, Philadelphia, 1934, *Cézanne*, no. 42; San Francisco Museum of Art, 1937, *Paul Cézanne*, no. 31; Wildenstein, New York, 1948, *Six Masters of Post-Impressionism*, no. 9; Detroit Institute of Arts and Art Gallery of Toronto, 1951, City Art Museum, St. Louis, and Seattle Art Museum, 1952, traveling exhibition from the Metropolitan Museum; Wadsworth Atheneum, Hartford (Conn.), 1955, *Twentieth Century Painting from Three Cities*, no. 9; Schloss Charlottenburg, Berlin, 1963, *Die Ile de France und ihre Maler* (exhibition organized by the Nationalgalerie), no. 5.

Ex coll.: [Ambroise Vollard, Paris]; [Durand-Ruel, Paris]; H. O. Havemeyer, New York.

The H. O. Havemeyer Collection. Bequest of Mrs. H. O. Havemeyer, 1929.

Sisley

Alfred Sisley. Born in Paris in 1839; died in Moret in 1899. Sisley was the son of a well-to-do English family living in Paris, where his father carried on a successful business. At the age of eighteen he was sent to London to prepare himself for a career in business, but his four years there were spent for the most part in visiting museums and acquiring familiarity with the works of the English landscapists, especially Turner and Constable. Returning to France in 1862, he easily obtained his father's permission to study art and entered the studio of Charles Gleyre, where Monet, Renoir, and Bazille were his fellow students. All four deserted Gleyre the following year. They became friends and Sisley was often joined by Monet or Renoir on painting excursions to one of the villages of the forest of Fontainebleau. In 1866 he made his debut at the Salon with two landscapes and he exhibited there again in 1868 and 1870. His style in this early time shows the influence of Corot and Daubigny. During these years Sisley was given complete financial security by his father, and he painted only as an amateur. He often took part in the famous discussions held by the young Impressionists at the Café Guerbois. This phase of his life came to a rude halt, however, during the years of the Franco-Prussian war, when the elder Sisley, having suffered heavy losses and ruin, died, leaving Alfred utterly dependent on painting for his livelihood. From this time until his death unremitting poverty and anxiety pursued him. In spite of frequent appearances in important exhibitions and some favorable critical notices, his pictures always sold at low prices if at all.

Sisley's work was noticed early by Paul Durand-Ruel, who included pictures by him in exhibitions in London and, when he was able, bought from him regularly. A member of the original group of Impressionists, Sisley contributed five paintings to their historic first exhibition in 1874. That same year, at the invitation of the singer and collector Jean Baptiste Faure, he spent four months in England, where he painted views of the Thames and the regattas at Hampton Court. In 1881 he made a brief trip to the Isle of Wight, and in 1897, through the generosity of his friend the Norman industrialist François Depeaux, he made a third and last visit to England. He twice considered becoming a French citizen, but on both occasions the formalities and the expense involved in the process of naturalization deterred him. Although Faure, Doctor de Bellio, Doctor Viau, the restaurateur Eugène Murer, the editor Georges Charpentier, and the critic Théodore Duret were all sympathetic to Sisley, acquiring pictures by him and giving him financial help and encouragement, he was repeatedly in debt and in 1886 in desperation considered learning to make fans. In the spring of 1889 Durand-Ruel, who had opened a gallery in New York two years before, held a one-man showing there of works by Sisley.

During the earlier part of his career Sisley stayed in the general area of Paris, choosing his sites for landscapes in the little towns near the Seine. In the late eighteen seventies he lived for a few years at Sèvres. In 1880 he moved south to the edge of the forest of Fontainebleau, and spent the last ten years of his life at Moret-sur-Loing.

Sisley painted little else but landscape, often making many versions of the same theme. He specialized in scenes of river banks and bridges and was also, like Monet and Pissarro, attracted to views of countryside and town muffled under heavy snow. Architecture also interested him. The short separate brush strokes with which he depicted flickering light on water resemble those of Monet, but in his work they create an effect of limpid brightness which is altogether original. The pure and strong blue of his skies, moreover, dappled with white floating clouds, recalls English painting and perhaps reflects his English heritage.

The Bridge at Villeneuve-la-Garenne
64.287

This picture dates from the beginning of Sisley's serious pursuit of painting as a career. He produced at this time a very large number of works of high quality, which employ to advantage the discoveries made by the young Impressionists about light and colored shadow and the scintillant effect procured by broken color. Sisley's friend the singer Faure acquired the picture soon after it was painted.

Signed and dated (at lower left): *Sisley 1872.*

Oil on canvas. H. 19½, w. 25¾ in. (49.5 x 65.4 cm.).

REFERENCES: G. Poulain, *La Renaissance,* 13 (1930), pp. 343–346, ill. p. 345 (as Pont d'Argenteuil), describes it, calling it a masterpiece // J. Rewald, *The History of Impressionism* (1946), ill. p. 274, dates it erroneously 1873 and locates it in the Louvre; (revised and enlarged edition, 1961), ill. frontispiece in color // F. Daulte, *Alfred Sisley* (1959), no. 37, pp. 17 (pl. in color), 24, catalogues it fully, comments on the harmony of colors.

EXHIBITED: Galerie Georges Petit, Paris, 1917, *Alfred Sisley,* no. 54; Metropolitan Museum, *Paintings from Private Collections,* 1958, no. 130, 1960, no. 115, 1961, no. 87, 1962, no. 87, 1963, no. 74 (lent by Mr. and Mrs. Henry Ittleson Jr.); Rosenberg, New York, 1961, *Sisley,* no. 3 (lent by Mr. and Mrs. Henry Ittleson Jr.).

EX COLL.: [Durand-Ruel, Paris, bought from the artist in 1872, until 1873]; Jean Baptiste Faure, Paris (from 1873); A. Bergaud, Paris (sale, Georges Petit, Paris, Mar. 1–2, 1920, no. 56); [Gérard frères, Paris, from 1920]; Fernand Bouisson, Paris (by 1930); [Sam Salz, New York]; Mr. and Mrs. Henry Ittleson Jr., New York (by 1961).

GIFT OF MR. AND MRS. HENRY ITTLESON JR., 1964.

A Road near Louveciennes 64.154.2

Although it was in the years 1872 and 1873 that Sisley chose most of his landscape motifs from the region around Louveciennes, this picture appears to have been painted some six years later, after he was established at Sèvres. On the basis of style Daulte also places it in 1879.

Signed (at lower left): *Sisley.*

Oil on canvas. H. 18½, w. 22¼ in. (47 x 56.5 cm.).

REFERENCES: F. Daulte, *Alfred Sisley* (1959), no. 318, ill., catalogues it fully under the year

64.154.2

1879; and in a letter (1965), finds it similar in technique to pictures painted in 1879.

EXHIBITED: Durand-Ruel, New York, 1927, *Sisley,* no. 7; and 1939, *Alfred Sisley Centennial,* no. 16; Knoedler Galleries, New York, 1941, *Early Impressionism, 1868–1883,* no. 25; Wadsworth Atheneum, Hartford (Conn.), 1959, *The Music Makers,* no. 16 (lent by Mr. and Mrs. Richard Rodgers).

EX COLL.: [Probably Durand-Ruel, Paris]; Erwin Davis, New York (until 1899); [Durand-Ruel, New York, by 1899, in 1947]; [Sam Salz, New York]; Mr. and Mrs. Richard Rodgers, New York (until 1964).

GIFT OF RICHARD RODGERS, SUBJECT TO A LIFE ESTATE IN THE DONOR, 1964.

Washerwomen near the Bridge at Moret 64.149.2

This picture was probably painted about 1888, at the beginning of the last period of Sisley, when his little town of Moret and the banks of the river Loing, on which it is situated, provided him with all his subject matter. He repeated the same motif many times, with slight and subtle variations. At this time the style of Monet seems to have exerted a strong influence on that of Sisley.

Signed (at lower right): *Sisley.*

Oil on canvas. H. 14, w. 17 in. (35.6 x 43.2 cm.).

REFERENCE: F. Daulte, *Alfred Sisley* (1959), no. 673, ill., catalogues it.

Ex coll.: Foinard, Paris (sale, Hôtel Drouot, Paris, Dec. 7, 1918, no. 122); [Bernheim-Jeune, Paris]; Hermann, Paris (sale, "Vente Anonyme," Hôtel Drouot, Paris, June 7, 1923, no. 109); René Keller, Paris; Madame Juan de Seré, Buenos Aires; [Wildenstein, New York]; Mary V. T. Eberstadt, New York.

GIFT OF MARY V. T. EBERSTADT, SUBJECT TO A LIFE ESTATE IN THE DONOR, 1964.

64.149.2

Monet

Claude Oscar Monet. Born in Paris in 1840; died at Giverny in 1926. Monet passed his childhood and youth at Le Havre, where his father was a grocer. His career began in his teens with a series of witty and skillful caricatures that he sold for small sums. In Le Havre he took drawing lessons from François Jacques Ochard. The decisive influence upon him, however, came from the teaching of Eugène Boudin, who worked with him and, with some difficulty, persuaded him to paint landscapes and seascapes out of doors. In 1859 Monet went to Paris for what was intended to be a brief visit, but, encouraged by Troyon, he determined to settle there, against his family's wishes. In Paris he worked with the academic painter Charles Jacque and at the Académie Suisse, where he met Pissarro.

From 1860 until 1862 Monet was in Algeria for his term of military service, which he could not complete because of ill health. After returning home to Le Havre he worked out of doors again with Boudin and then with the Dutch landscape painter Jongkind. In the fall of 1862 he went back to Paris and enrolled in the studio of Charles Gleyre. He disliked the instruction there, but he met Renoir, Sisley, and Bazille, who became his companions in out-of-door painting and were to be his intimate friends.

The Salon of 1865 accepted two of Monet's seascapes, which were well received, and the next year he showed a landscape and a full-length portrait, about which the critics were enthusiastic. In spite of these successes, during the next three years he found himself in desperate financial straits, going hungry and lacking paints with which to work. Once he even attempted suicide. He had met Manet, whose paintings he admired, and also Courbet, who was friendly to him but discouraged him about his large picture Déjeuner sur l'Herbe, which Monet abandoned in an unfinished state. After Courbet's adverse criticism and the Salon's refusal of another large picture,

Women in a Garden, he began to concentrate on landscape and still life. His scenes painted along the Norman coast at Le Havre, Étretat, and Fécamp and his views of Paris show that he was constantly exploring and developing. He became increasingly sensitive to effects of light and to reflections in water, which he rendered with broad, flexible brush strokes. His tonality, which in the emphatic paintings of the middle sixties had shown, perhaps under Manet's influence, strong contrasts of blacks, grays, and whites, became much lighter at the end of the decade, as in the paintings of La Grenouillère that he did in 1869.

In September 1870, after the outbreak of the Franco-Prussian War, Monet went to England, where he remained for many months. Pissarro was in London at the same time, as was Daubigny, who introduced Monet to Durand-Ruel. This dealer bought pictures from him, exhibited them, and played an important role in his life. Monet's stay in London was also important because of his discovery there of the works of Turner and other English painters of landscape.

After a visit to the Low Countries Monet returned to France in the winter of 1871 and established himself at Argenteuil on the Seine, where he worked for the greater part of the next five years. He set up a studio on a little floating barge, similar to the *Botin* that Daubigny had used. Manet visited him in Argenteuil and was converted there to painting out of doors. The most important event of this period was the organization of an exhibiting society of independent painters, in which Monet was the prime mover. They held their first exhibition in 1874 in Paris in the former studio of the photographer Nadar. Monet contributed seven pastels and five paintings, including the one called Impression—Sunrise, which earned for the whole group the name Impressionists. He sent large numbers of his works to four of the subsequent group exhibitions but abstained from three of them.

In 1878 Monet moved still farther away from Paris to Vétheuil on the Seine, where he worked for several years, painting views of the town at all seasons. At this time he also made many pictures of flowers and still life.

He settled in 1883 in Giverny in the department of the Eure. He went often to the Channel coast to paint the sea and after his first visit to the French Riviera, which he made in the company of Renoir, returned to the South frequently. The Mediterranean light caused him to use more lively and iridescent colors, which from now on were to characterize even the pictures that he painted in the north.

Monet's paintings, which by the eighties were widely exhibited in France and abroad, began at last to appeal to collectors. Genuine success and freedom from financial care finally came to him in 1889 when the Galerie Georges Petit held a joint exhibition of works by Monet and Rodin.

In 1877 Monet had made his first experiments with painting several versions of the same theme, beginning with a number of closely similar views of the Saint Lazare railroad station in Paris. From about 1890 on he worked on his famous series of haystacks, poplar trees, and views of the façade of the cathedral of Rouen. He now worked more systematically than he had with the Saint Lazare set, examining each subject under various conditions of atmosphere and light, according to the different seasons and hours of the day. A number of exhibitions of these series, most of them organized by Durand-Ruel, made a great impression on the public and on other painters. Monet never ceased to look for new motifs. He traveled to Norway and made several trips to London and Venice. In France he continued to paint the banks of the Seine and the beaches of Normandy.

After seven years in Giverny, Monet bought in 1890 a house and property there. He had always been interested in cultivating flowers, and by diverting a small stream he now began the creation of a water garden with an arching Japanese footbridge. From 1899 until the end of his life this garden provided his favorite subject matter. He produced more than sixty finished paintings and several hundred studies. In 1914, encouraged by his friend the statesman Clemenceau, he embarked on a project of painting a group of large scenes with water lilies as murals destined to be presented to the state. The donation was formally accepted by the French Government in 1921 and installed two years later in specially rebuilt rooms in the Orangerie in Paris. In spite of severe eye trouble, which required an operation for cataract and eventually made him almost totally blind, Monet worked whenever he could during his last years, retouching the Orangerie murals even after their installation and doing landscapes at Giverny.

As the founder of Impressionism Monet is one of the chief figures in modern art. The arbitrary compositions of his pictures of water lilies and his rendering of space and light by varying tones and textures prepared the way for the style of Bonnard. Indeed, few artists in the entire history of painting have exerted such widespread influence. Although his work was very unequal, his visual sensitiveness and strength place him among the greatest of the Western landscape painters.

Dr. Leclenché 51.32

The subject of this portrait, according to the artist's son, was Monet's doctor.[1] The penetrating, incisive way that his personality is summarized and presented recalls the fact that Monet began his career making and selling caricatures. The rapid execution and impressionistic accents reflect the influence of Manet.

Signed and dated (at lower right): *Claude Monet – 64.*

Oil on canvas. H. 18, w. 12¾ in. (45.7 x 32.4 cm.).

Note 1. His name has been variously spelled Leclenché, Leclanché, Lanclanché.

REFERENCES: *French Impressionists* (*Met. Mus. Miniatures*, 1951), no. 9, ill. in color // M. Salinger, *Monet* (1957), pl. 13, ill. in color // C. M. Mount, *The Art Quarterly*, XXI (1958), pp. 386f., fig. 3, identifies the sitter for this portrait as Dr. Lanclanché // W. C. Seitz, *Monet* (1960), p. 11, fig. 3.

EXHIBITED: Wildenstein Galleries, New York, 1945, *Claude Monet*, no. 1 (as Portrait d'homme, lent by M. Knoedler).

Ex COLL.: [Ambroise Vollard, Paris]; private collection, Paris (until 1943); [M. Knoedler, New York, 1943–1947]; Mr. and Mrs. Edwin C. Vogel, New York (1947–1951).

51.32

<small>Gift of Mr. and Mrs. Edwin C. Vogel, 1951.</small>

The Green Wave   29.100.111

This picture was probably painted in the fall of 1865 when Monet was working at Trouville with Boudin, Daubigny, and Courbet. Although Monet was deeply impressed in these

29.100.111

early years by Courbet, in this painting the influence of Manet is dominant. Manet's two paintings of the encounter of the American warships the *Kearsarge* and the *Alabama* had recently been exhibited in Paris, and it is highly probable that Monet had seen and admired them. Even before painting The Green Wave he had made two seascapes so dependent on the style of Manet that the older artist complained of plagiarism.

Signed and dated (at lower right): *Cl. Monet 65.*

Oil on canvas. H. 19⅛, w. 25½ in. (48.6 x 64.8 cm.).

References: H. B. Wehle, *Met. Mus. Bull.*, XXV (1930), p. 56 // *French Impressionists* (*Met. Mus. Miniatures*, 1951), no. 2, ill. in color.

Exhibited: Metropolitan Museum, 1930, *The H. O. Havemeyer Collection*, no. 81, and 1934, *Landscape Paintings*, no. 49; Currier Gallery of Art, Manchester (New Hampshire), 1949, *Monet and the Beginnings of Impressionism*, no. 32.

Ex coll. H. O. Havemeyer, New York (Cat., 1931, p. 151, ill.).

The H. O. Havemeyer Collection. Bequest of Mrs. H. O. Havemeyer, 1929.

The Chailly Road   64.210

Chailly, a village on the edge of the Forest of Fontainebleau, not far from Barbizon, was frequented by Monet and his friends Bazille, Renoir, and Sisley from 1863 until 1866. It was there that they all came in contact with the painters of the Barbizon school and Monet again met Courbet, who became a particular friend. giving him financial aid as well as artistic advice. In 1865 and 1866 in Chailly Monet worked on his large picture Le Déjeuner sur l'herbe, as well as on numerous landscapes, some of which served as preliminary sketches for the big picture. The Museum's picture of a road in the forest has strong similarities to the Déjeuner and was probably

64.210

painted at about the same time, around 1866. Passages of rich, relatively dark color and heavy opaque areas betray the influence of Courbet and of the painters of Barbizon.

There are at least two other paintings by Monet with this same title and approximately the same measurements. One, dated about 1865, is in the Ordrupgaard collection in Copenhagen; the other belonged in 1959 to the Durand-Ruel galleries.

Signed (at lower right): *Claude Monet.*

Oil on canvas. H. 37⅞, w. 50⅞ in. (96.2 x 129.2 cm.).

REFERENCES: J. Rewald, *The History of Impressionism* (1946), ill. p. 85, with the date c. 1867; (revised and enlarged edition, 1961), ill. p. 95, with the date c. 1866 // R. L. Herbert, *Barbizon Revisited* (exhib. cat.), California Palace of the Legion of Honor, Toledo Museum of Art, Cleveland Museum of Art, and Boston Museum of Fine Arts (1962–1963), p. 203, no. 109, ill., with the date c. 1867.

EXHIBITED: Durand-Ruel, Paris, 1959, *Claude Monet*, no. 4 (dated 1866); California Palace of the Legion of Honor, San Francisco, Toledo Museum of Art, Cleveland Museum of Art, and Boston Museum of Fine Arts, 1962–1963, *Barbizon Revisited*, no. 109 (lent by Sam Salz).

EX COLL.: Claude Monet, Paris (until 1891); [Durand-Ruel, Paris and New York, from 1891, until 1900]; possibly C. J. Blair, Chicago

(in 1900); [Durand-Ruel, New York, 1900–c. 1962]; [Sam Salz, New York, by 1962].

BEQUEST OF JULIA W. EMMONS AND GIFT OF SAM SALZ, 1964.

The Beach at Sainte-Adresse 51.30.4

Monet's poverty forced him to spend the summer of 1867 with an aunt at Sainte-Adresse, the first little town north of Le Havre on the Channel coast. On June 25 of that year, in a letter to Bazille, he described a marine that he was doing, which seems to be our picture "with many people on the beach and the ship lane full of little sails" (J. Rewald, *The History of Impressionism*, 1961, p. 180). Our painting is closely related in composition and treatment to a painting of the same site dated 1867 now in the Art Institute of Chicago (W. Seitz, *Monet*, 1960, ill. in color p. 75). Soon after painting The Green Wave (see above) Monet abandoned the broad, sweeping brush strokes used in that picture and developed the short, staccato touch to be seen in the foreground of this seashore scene. As in the Chicago painting he employs a variety of kinds of strokes in different areas of the picture.

Signed (at lower left): *Claude Monet.*

Oil on canvas. H. 29⅝, w. 40 in. (75.3 x 101.6 cm.).

REFERENCES: C. Mauclair, *Claude Monet* [c. 1926], p. 42, pl. 8 // F. Fosca, *Claude Monet* (1927), ill. opp. p. 60 // *Art News*, XXXI (Mar. 18, 1933), p. 5, ill. p. 3 // M. Malingue, *Claude Monet* (1943), p. 145, no. 44, pl. 44, states that Monet's father was the model for the man with a stick // O. Reuterswärd, *Monet* (1948), p. 281, dates this picture 1867 // *French Impressionists (Met. Mus. Miniatures*, 1951), no. 3, ill. in color.

EXHIBITED: Durand-Ruel, London, 1874, *Eighth Exhibition of the Society of French Artists*, no. 142 (Ste Adresse near Havre, possibly this picture); Metropolitan Museum, 1921, *Impressionist and Post-Impressionist Paintings*, no. 76 (lent by William Church Osborn); Durand-Ruel, New York, 1928, *French Mas-*

51.30.4

terpieces of the Late XIX Century, no. 12 (lent anonymously), and 1933, *Claude Monet,* no. 12 (lent from a private collection); Palace of Fine Arts, San Francisco, 1940, *Golden Gate International Exhibition,* no. 284 (lent by William Church Osborn); Wildenstein Galleries, New York, 1945, *Claude Monet,* no. 4 (placed in 1865; lent by William Church Osborn).

EX COLL.: [Durand-Ruel, Paris, c. 1888]; P. A. B. Widener, Ashbourne, near Philadelphia (1891–1907; Cat., 1900, no. 84, probably this painting, with which it coincides in subject and measurements although the description is given in reverse); [Durand-Ruel, New York, 1907]; William Church Osborn, New York (from 1907).

BEQUEST OF WILLIAM CHURCH OSBORN, 1951.

La Grenouillère   29.100.112

Maupassant described La Grenouillère in his story *La Femme de Paul.* It was a popular resort, a boating and bathing establishment with a café on a covered raft floating in the Seine. It was connected with the island of Croissy by two footbridges. In the summer of 1869 Monet was living near by at Saint-Michel, not far from Bougival, and it was at this time that he painted this view of La Grenouillère, as well as two others, one in the collection of Mrs. W. S. Walzer in Oxford,

the other formerly in a Berlin collection. The Oxford picture, taken from a point farther to the left, shows many bathers near the little bathhouse and a number of rowboats moored in the foreground. The Berlin picture is more like the Museum's but is wider, with more boats and water at the left (Ref., Reuterswärd, 1948, ill. pp. 43, 45).

Renoir, who was living in the same neighborhood in the summer of 1869, also painted views of La Grenouillère with Monet. His pictures of the place are now in Stockholm, Moscow, and the Reinhart collection, Winterthur. For both artists this was a period of dire poverty.

Signed (at lower right): *Claude Monet.*

Inscribed (at right): LOCATI[ON DE] CANOTS.

Oil on canvas. H. 29⅜, w. 39¼ in. (74.6 x 99.7 cm.).

REFERENCES: R. A. Meyer, *Die Kunst unserer Zeit,* XIX (1908), ill. p. 63 (this picture and, opposite it, the version in the Walzer collection) // G. Geffroy, *Claude Monet* (1922), p. 262, ill. opp. p. 52 // C. Mauclair, *Claude Monet* [c. 1926], p. 47, pl. 17 // M. Malingue, *Claude Monet* (1943), p. 146, no. 51, pl. 51 // J. Rewald, *The History of Impressionism* (1946), pp. 191, 196, ill. p. 192, quotes a letter to Bazille (Sept. 25, 1869) in which Monet mentions some "bad sketches" that he had made for a picture of La Grenouillère, which both he and Renoir wanted to paint; (revised and enlarged edition, 1961), pp. 228, 232, ill. p. 229 // O. Reuterswärd, *Monet* (1948), pp. 45–47, 280, ill. p. 47, fig. 12 // C. Schweicher, *Monet* (1949), pp. 12f., pl. 11 (version in the Walzer collection), describes the Museum's picture // L. Venturi, *Impressionists and Symbolists* (1950), p. 57, fig. 51 // *French Impressionists* (*Met. Mus. Miniatures,* 1951), no. 4, ill. in color // J. Leymarie, *Impressionism* (1955), I, pp. 81–83, ill. in color, asserts that Monet made "countless sketches" for this picture, compares it with Renoir's version of the same scene (ill. in color) // L. Venturi, *Four Steps Toward Modern Art* (1956), p. 56, pl. 21 // D. Cooper and J. Richardson, *Claude Monet* (exhib. cat.), Edinburgh and London

(1957), pp. 21, 43, no. 16, pl. 17b, discuss Monet's three versions of La Grenouillère, hesitate to identify them with the "bad sketches" mentioned by Monet in his letter to Bazille (see above, Rewald, 1946) // M. Salinger, *Monet* (1957), pl. 17, ill. in color, compares Monet's treatment of the subject with Renoir's // L. Degand and D. Rouart, *Claude Monet* (1958), pp. 8, 46f., ill. in color, find Monet's paintings of this subject bolder than Renoir's // W. C. Seitz, *Monet* (1960), pp. 84f., ill. in color.

EXHIBITED: Galeries Durand-Ruel, 11 Rue Le Peletier, Paris, 1876, *La 2ᵉ Exposition de peinture* (Second Impressionist Exhibition) (as Les Bains de la Grenouillère, possibly this version); Galerie Georges Petit, Paris, 1889, *Claude Monet, A. Rodin*, no. 9 (La Grenouillère, Bougival, 1869, lent by Charles Ephrussi; possibly this version); Metropolitan Museum, 1930, *The H. O. Havemeyer Collection*, no. 82; Wildenstein Gallery, New York, 1943, *From Paris to the Sea*, no. 36; Currier Gallery of Art, Manchester (New Hampshire), 1949, *Monet and the Beginnings of Impressionism*, no. 38; Paul Rosenberg Gallery, New York, 1950, *Nineteenth-Century Heritage*, no. 16; Detroit Institute of Arts and Art Gallery of Toronto, 1951, City Art Museum, St. Louis, and Seattle Art Museum, 1952, traveling exhibition from the Metropolitan Museum; Gemeentemuseum, The Hague, 1952, *Claude Monet*, no. 14; Royal Scottish Academy, Edinburgh, and Tate Gallery, London, 1957, *Claude Monet*, no. 16.

EX COLL.: Possibly Charles Ephrussi, Paris (in 1889); [Durand-Ruel, Paris, until 1897]; H. O. Havemeyer, New York (from 1897; Cat., 1931, pp. 152f., ill.).

THE H. O. HAVEMEYER COLLECTION. BEQUEST OF MRS. H. O. HAVEMEYER, 1929.

26.186.1

Apple Trees in Bloom   26.186.1

In the spring of 1873, the date of this picture, Monet had been living for more than a year at Argenteuil on the Seine. During the four years that had elapsed since painting La Grenouillère he had again altered the character of his brush strokes, making them shorter, and laying less stress on the forms of objects than on their shimmering impressionistic surface.

Formerly called Apple Blossoms.

Signed and dated (at lower left): *73 Claude Monet.*

Oil on canvas. H. 24½, w. 39⅝ (62.2 x 100.7 cm.).

REFERENCE: O. Reuterswärd, *Monet* (1948), p. 282, lists this picture among those that Monet painted at Argenteuil.

EXHIBITED: Union League Club, New York, 1891, *Paintings by Old Masters and Modern . . . together with an Exhibition of the Work of Claude Monet the Impressionist,* no. 55 (as Plum Blossoms, lent by W. H. Fuller); Lotos Club, New York, 1899, *Pictures by Claude Monet,* no. 19 (as Plum Blossoms, lent by W. H. Fuller); Art Gallery Association, Civic Auditorium, Winnipeg (Canada), 1951, *European and American Paintings;* Arkansas Arts Center, Little Rock, 1963, *Five Centuries of European Painting,* cat. p. 45.

EX COLL.: William H. Fuller, New York (by 1891–1903; sale, American Art Association,

New York, Mar. 12–13, 1903, no. 151, to Knoedler); Mary Livingston Willard, New York (by 1907–1926).

BEQUEST OF MARY LIVINGSTON WILLARD, 1926.

The Parc Monceau, Paris   59.206

In the late seventies Monet painted several views of this pretty little park situated on the Boulevard de Courcelles. The park, which is surrounded by fine old town houses, was laid out in the form of an English garden, after designs made by Carmontelle for Philippe d'Orléans in the late eighteenth century.

Georges de Bellio owned this painting and probably also the Museum's other view of the Parc Monceau (see below). He was a Rumanian physician whom Monet called in consultation when his wife, Camille, became very ill in 1876. He owned a number of paintings by Monet, who wrote to him several times appealing for financial help (C. M. Mount, *Art Quarterly,* xxv, no. 4, 1962, pp. 324–326).

Signed and dated (at lower right): *Claude Monet 76.*

Oil on canvas. H. 23½, w. 32½ in. (59.7 x 82.5 cm.).

EXHIBITED: 6 Rue Le Peletier, Paris, 1877, *La 3ᵉ Exposition de peinture* (Third Impressionist Exhibition), no. 96 (lent by M. de Bellio; very probably this picture); Waldorf-

59.206

Astoria Hotel, New York, 1957, *Festival of Art*, no. 124 (lent by Miss Loula D. Lasker).

Ex coll.: Georges de Bellio, Paris (in 1877?); Mme Dufour, Paris (until 1953); [Wildenstein, New York, 1953–1954]; Loula D. Lasker, New York (from 1954).

Bequest of Loula D. Lasker, New York, 1961.

Parisians Enjoying the Parc Monceau 59.142

The broad brush strokes in the foreground contrast with the feathery touch Monet employed in painting the foliage and the figures. The cheerful contentment with which he has infused the little scene contrasts vividly with the distressing poverty from which he was still suffering in 1878. See also comment above under The Parc Monceau.

Signed and dated (at lower right): *Claude Monet 78.*

Oil on canvas. H. 28⅝, w. 21⅜ in. (72.7 x 54.3 cm.).

Formerly called Le Parc Monceau.

References: M. Malingue, *Claude Monet* (1943), p. 147, no. 89, pl. 89 // O. Reutersward, *Monet* (1948), p. 281, ill. p. 115, connects this picture with the one of the Parc Monceau that Dr. de Bellio purchased at the Impressionist Exhibition of 1879.

Exhibited: 28 Avenue de l'Opéra, Paris, 1879, *La 4ᵉ Exposition de peinture* (Fourth Impressionist Exhibition), no. 152 (possibly this picture, lent by M. de Bellio); Galerie Georges Petit, Paris, 1889, *Claude Monet, A. Rodin*, no. 36 (dated 1878, possibly this picture; lent by M. de Bellio); Musée de l'Orangerie, Paris, 1931, *Claude Monet*, no. 47 (lent by M. Lindon); Galerie Durand-Ruel, Paris, 1935, *Claude Monet*, no. 26 (lent by Alfred Lindon); Galerie Charpentier, Paris, 1951, *Plaisir de France*, no. 134 (lent by Mme Alfred Lindon); Galerie Durand-Ruel, Paris, 1959, *Claude Monet*, no. 21 (lent by Mme Alfred Lindon).

59.142

Ex coll.: Probably Georges de Bellio, Paris (1879–after 1889); [Durand-Ruel, Paris]; [Georges Bernheim, Paris, until c.1930]; Alfred Lindon, Paris (c. 1930–1948); Mme Alfred Lindon, Paris (1948–1959); [Jacques Lindon, New York, 1959].

Purchase, Mr. and Mrs. Henry Ittleson Jr. Fund, 1959.

Apples and Grapes 57.183

Early in his career under Manet's influence, Monet had been interested in painting still life. He returned to it in the years around 1880, when he became preoccupied with the creation of color harmonies for their own sake. He began to forsake the visual realism of true impressionism and directed his efforts toward the more plastic expression of form that was to become a characteristic of Post-Impressionist painting. Two other still lifes composed of apples and grapes, and similar to this picture in treatment and in the handling of the light,

57.183

are dated 1880, and ours may safely be placed about the same year (Art Institute of Chicago and Kunsthalle, Hamburg).

Signed (at upper right): *Claude Monet.*

Oil on canvas. H. 26⅜, w. 35½ in. (67 x 90.2 cm.).

REFERENCE: G. Geffroy, *Claude Monet* (1922), p. 219, describes this picture.

EXHIBITED: Royal Academy, Burlington House, London, 1932, *French Art, 1200–1900,* no. 548, commemorative catalogue, no. 458 (lent by Mme Barret-Decap, Biarritz); Museo Nacional de Bellas Artes, Buenos Aires, 1939, *La Pintura Francesa . . . de David a Nuestros Días,* no. 99 (lent from the Barret-Decap collection, Paris); Montevideo, 1940; Rio de Janeiro, 1940; M. H. de Young Museum, San Francisco, 1940–1941, *Painting of France since the French Revolution,* no. 78 (lent from the Barret-Decap collection); Metropolitan Museum, 1941, *French Painting from David to Toulouse-Lautrec,* no. 93 (lent from the Barret-Decap collection).

EX COLL.: Victor Chocquet, Paris (until 1899; posthumous sale, Georges Petit, Paris, July 1, 3, 4, 1899, no. 79, ill.); Mme Barret-Decap, Biarritz (by 1932); the Barret-Decap collection, Paris (until after 1941); Marcel Kapferer, Paris (until 1950); [Wildenstein, New York, in 1950]; Henry R. Luce, New York (from 1950).

GIFT OF HENRY R. LUCE, SUBJECT TO A LIFE ESTATE IN THE DONOR, 1957.

Vétheuil in Summer 51.30.3

Monet settled in 1878 at Vétheuil, a village on the Seine halfway between Paris and Rouen. This view was taken from across the river. The church, which towers above the clustered buildings of the little town, is Romanesque of the twelfth century but was remodeled during the Renaissance.

This painting is extraordinarily refined in texture. It displays many different kinds of brush strokes, separate and lively and often repeated in echoing patterns, as in the reflections on the surface of the water.

Signed and dated (at lower right): *Claude Monet 1880.*

Oil on canvas. H. 23⅝, w. 39¼ in. (60 x 99.7 cm.).

REFERENCES: A. Alexandre, *Claude Monet* (1921), ill. opp. p. 74 // C. Mauclair, *Claude Monet* [c. 1926], pl. 26 // J. Rewald, *The History of Impressionism* (1946), ill. p. 339; (revised and enlarged edition, 1961), ill. p. 431 // O. Reuterswärd, *Monet* (1948), p. 283, lists this picture // *French Impressionists (Met. Mus. Miniatures,* 1951), no. 5, ill. in color // J. Leymarie, *Impressionism* (1955), II, ill. in color p. 79 // W. I. Homer, *Seurat and the Science of Painting* (1964), pp. 60, 89, ill. p. 63, fig. 24, comments on the similarity in handling to Seurat's technique.

EXHIBITED: Metropolitan Museum, 1920, *Fiftieth Anniversary Exhibition,* cat. p. 10, and 1921, *Impressionist and Post-Impressionist Paintings,* no. 75 (lent by William Church Osborn); Durand-Ruel Galleries, New York, 1928, *French Masterpieces of the Late XIX Century,*

51.30.3

no. 14 (lent anonymously); Wildenstein Gallery, New York, 1943, *From Paris to the Sea*, no. 48, and 1945, *Claude Monet*, no. 33 (lent by William Church Osborn).

Ex coll.: Mme Berend (until 1912); [Durand-Ruel, Paris, 1912]; William Church Osborn, New York (by 1912).

BEQUEST OF WILLIAM CHURCH OSBORN, 1951.

Île aux Fleurs 56.135.5

The Île aux Fleurs is one of the islands of the Seine at Vétheuil. This lush scene, which, like *Vétheuil in Summer* (see above), was painted in the summer of 1880, takes its accents from

56.135.5

the stiffly vertical poplars on the farther shore. There is a closely similar version of this picture in the Chester Dale collection. In composition these paintings of the Île aux Fleurs resemble the *Floating Ice* of the J. Watson Webb collection, painted in the same year. In that picture, however, there is no near foreground of vegetation but only the water and the line of trees against the horizon (L. Degand and D. Rouart, *Monet*, 1958, ill. in color, p. 74).

Signed (at lower left): *Claude Monet.*

Oil on canvas. H. 26, w. 32 in. (66.1 x 81.4 cm.).

EXHIBITED: Durand-Ruel Galleries, Paris,

1902, *Claude Monet*, no. 5 (Île aux fleurs, possibly this picture); Wildenstein Gallery, New York, 1943, *From Paris to the Sea*, no. 47 (lent by Mrs. A. B. Emmons).

Ex coll.: [Durand-Ruel, Paris, 1891–1897, and New York, 1897–1906]; Arthur B. Emmons, New York and Newport (1906–1922); Mrs. Arthur B. Emmons (Julia W.), New York and Newport (1922–1956).

BEQUEST OF JULIA W. EMMONS, 1956.

The Seine at Vétheuil 30.95.271

This painting is a view of the Seine near Vétheuil and the chalky cliffs that rise along its bank. See also comments above under *Vétheuil in Summer* and *Île aux Fleurs*.

Signed and dated (at lower right): *Claude Monet 1880.*

Oil on canvas. H. 23¾, w. 39½ in. (60 x 100.3 cm.).

EXHIBITED: Copley Society, Boston (Mass.), 1905, *Claude Monet*, no. 33 (as Coteaux de Vétheuil, lent by Theodore M. Davis); Pensacola Art Center (Florida), 1955, *Opening Exhibition*; Jacksonville Art Museum (Florida), 1956; Art Gallery of Toronto, 1957, *Comparisons*, no. 9.

Ex coll.: [Durand-Ruel, New York, until 1895]; Theodore M. Davis, New York (1895–1915).

THE THEODORE M. DAVIS COLLECTION. BEQUEST OF THEODORE M. DAVIS, 1915.

30.95.271

56.135.1

A Path in the Île Saint-Martin, Vétheuil   56.135.1

Monet painted several versions of this view of a sunny field traversed by a footpath leading toward Vétheuil. They all have as focal point in the distance the tower of the Romanesque church that is the chief landmark of the little town.

Signed and dated (at lower left): *1880 Claude Monet.*

Oil on canvas. H. 31½, w. 23¾ in. (80 x 60.3 cm.).

REFERENCE: W. I. Homer, *Seurat and the Science of Painting* (1964), p. 64, notes that Monet intensified his effects in this painting by using complementary colors.

EXHIBITED: Salons du Panorama de Reichshoffen, 251 Rue Saint Honoré, Paris, 1882, *La 7ᵉ Exposition des artistes indépendants* (Seventh Impressionist Exhibition), no. 89 (Sentier dans l'Île Saint-Martin, possibly this picture); Chase's Gallery, Boston, 1891, *Paintings by the Impressionists of Paris . . . from the Galleries of Durand-Ruel*, no. 12 (Sentier de l'Île

Saint Martin, possibly this picture); Durand-Ruel Galleries, New York, 1902, *Claude Monet*, no. 10 (Sentier dans l'Île St. Martin, possibly this picture).

EX COLL.: Docteur X . . . (sale, Hôtel Drouot, Paris, Nov. 21, 1901, no. 52, ill., as Dans les coquelicots, "to Leclanché"); Leclanché (from 1901); G. Liaore [Leclanché?] (from 1911); [Durand-Ruel, Paris and New York, 1911–1912]; Arthur B. Emmons, New York and Newport (1912–1920; sale, American Art Association, New York, Jan. 14, 1920, no. 27, ill., to Durand-Ruel, possibly bought in for A. B. Emmons); Mrs. Arthur B. Emmons (Julia W.), New York and Newport (until 1956).

BEQUEST OF JULIA W. EMMONS, 1956.

Sunflowers   29.100.107

Monet's lively, rhythmical treatment of the petals and leaves of these flowers presents a vivid contrast to the famous, less naturalistic pictures of bouquets of sunflowers in a vase that Vincent van Gogh painted in Arles in 1888.

29.100.107

Signed and dated (at upper right): *Claude Monet 81*.

Oil on canvas. H. 39¾, w. 32 in. (101 x 81.3 cm.).

REFERENCES: O. Reuterswärd, *Monet* (1948), p. 280, lists this picture // Metropolitan Museum, *Art Treasures* (1952), p. 233, cat. no. 146, pl. 146 // W. C. Seitz, *Monet* (1960), pp. 114f., ill. in color.

EXHIBITED: Metropolitan Museum, 1930, *The H. O. Havemeyer Collection*, no. 83; Newark Museum (New Jersey), 1950, *Flower Painting*, no. 9; Virginia Museum of Fine Arts, Richmond, 1950, *Impressionists and Post-Impressionists*; City Art Museum, St. Louis, and Minneapolis Institute of Arts, 1957, *Claude Monet*, no. 47.

Ex COLL. H. O. Havemeyer, New York (Cat., 1931, p. 154).

THE H. O. HAVEMEYER COLLECTION. BEQUEST OF MRS. H. O. HAVEMEYER, 1929.

29.100.106

Chrysanthemums   29.100.106

This bouquet is distinguished by its blending of light and color and by the rhythm of the composition.

Signed and dated (at lower left): *Claude Monet 82*.

Oil on canvas. H. 39½, w. 32¼ in. (100.3 x 81.9 cm.).

REFERENCES: O. Reuterswärd, *Monet* (1948), p. 280, lists this picture // *French Impressionists* (Met. Mus. Miniatures, 1951), no. 6, ill. in color.

EXHIBITED: Metropolitan Museum, 1930, *The H. O. Havemeyer Collection*, no. 84; Toledo Museum of Art, 1949, *Flower Paintings*, no. 20; Hofstra College, Hempstead (New York), 1952.

Ex COLL.: Lambert (until 1899); [Durand-Ruel, New York, 1899]; H. O. Havemeyer, New York (from 1899; Cat., 1931, pp. 154f., ill.).

THE H. O. HAVEMEYER COLLECTION. BEQUEST OF MRS. H. O. HAVEMEYER, 1929.

The Cabin of the Customs Watch (La Cabane de Douaniers)   59.188.2

From 1880 to 1886 Monet's favorite subject matter was the sea, particularly along the Channel coast. In 1882 he spent some time in the neighboring villages of Pourville, Varengeville, and Dieppe. A group of scenes at Varengeville were shown the following year at the galleries of Durand-Ruel.

This painting shows a hut or cabin, perched high over the water, which was used as a lookout post by the customs officers. It is one of at least four of the same subject, all dated 1882, and though there are several other later ones that combine with these to form a large

59.188.2

group, Monet apparently never regarded them as a series like the Water Lilies or the Haystacks.

Signed and dated (at lower right): *Claude Monet 82.*

Oil on canvas. H. 23, w. 27½ in. (58.4 x 69.8 cm.).

REFERENCES: C. Roger-Marx, *Monet* (1949), pl. 39 (incorrectly dated 1883) // C. Schweicher, *Monet* (1949), pl. 39 (incorrectly dated 1883).

EXHIBITED: Chase's Gallery, Boston, 1891, *Paintings by the Impressionists of Paris*, no. 11 (Cabane de douanier—Pourville, possibly this painting; lent by Durand-Ruel); St. Botolph Club, Boston, 1899, *A Loan Exhibition of Paintings by Claude Monet*, no. 11 (Fisherman's Hut, lent by Henry Sayles); Durand-Ruel, New York, 1927, *Paintings by Claude Monet*, no. 13 (La Cabane de douanier, 1882, possibly this painting).

EX COLL.: [Durand-Ruel, Paris, until 1891]; Henry Sayles, Boston (1891–1907); [Durand-Ruel, New York, 1907–1928]; Mr. and Mrs. Charles S. McVeigh (1928–1959).

GIFT OF MR. AND MRS. CHARLES S. MC-VEIGH, SUBJECT TO A LIFE ESTATE IN THE DONORS, 1959.

The Sea at Pourville   56.135.2

This view of the ocean from high ground is one of Monet's various studies of the cliffs above the Normandy coast. Much later in his life, in 1896 and 1897, he returned to the same region and again took up the themes that he had worked on there fourteen years before. Two of these later views are also in the Museum's collection (see two paintings of The Cliffs at Pourville below).

Signed and dated (at lower right): *Claude Monet 82.*

Oil on canvas. H. 23¾, w. 32 in. (60.3 x 81.3 cm.).

EXHIBITED: Union League Club, New York, 1891, *Paintings by Old Masters and Modern, . . . together with an Exhibition of the Work of Claude Monet the Impressionist*, no. 54 (as Cliffs, lent by W. H. Fuller; possibly this picture); Lotos Club, New York, 1899, *Pictures by Claude Monet*, no. 20 (On the Cliff, lent by William H. Fuller; possibly this picture); Durand-Ruel Galleries, New York, 1907, *Claude Monet*, no. 10 (Bords de la Falaise, Pourville, 1882, possibly this picture).

EX COLL.: William H. Fuller, New York (by 1891?–1903; sale, American Art Association, New York, Mar. 12–13, 1903, no. 152, to Durand-Ruel); [Durand-Ruel, New York, 1903–1907]; Arthur B. Emmons, New York and Newport (1907–1922); Mrs. Arthur B. Emmons (Julia W.), New York and Newport (1922–1956).

BEQUEST OF JULIA W. EMMONS, 1956.

56.135.2

51.30.5

The Manneporte, Étretat, I   51.30.5

In 1883, the year this picture was painted, Monet visited Étretat, a village on the Norman coast between Le Havre and Fécamp. The Manneporte, the strange, dramatically arched rock that forms the subject of this picture and a number of others that he painted at the same time, lies southwest of Étretat and of the two other curious rock formations at either side of the town, the Porte d'Aval and the Porte d'Amont. This is one of Monet's finest seascapes. The sun's rays illuminate one surface of the rock and seem to penetrate the water, and the whole painting is suffused with a harmony of golden light and bluish shadow. See also comment below under The Manneporte, Étretat, II.

Formerly called The Cliff at Étretat.

Signed and dated (at lower left): *Claude Monet 83.*

Oil on canvas. H. 25¾, w. 32 in. (65.4 x 81.3 cm.).

REFERENCES: *French Impressionists (Met. Mus. Miniatures,* 1951), no. 7, ill. in color // M. Salinger, *Monet* (1957), pl. 27, ill. in color // W. C. Seitz, *Monet* (1960), pp. 118f., ill. in color; *Claude Monet* (exhib. cat.), Museum of Modern Art, New York, and Los Angeles County Museum (1960), pp. 19f., ill.

EXHIBITED: American Art Association and National Academy of Design, New York, 1886, *Works in Oil and Pastel by the Impres-*sionists of Paris, no. 123 (as La Manne Porte à Étretat, possibly this picture); Lotos Club, New York, 1899, *Pictures by Claude Monet,* no. 21 (as The Great Arch at Étretat, lent by William H. Fuller); Copley Society, Boston, 1905, *Claude Monet,* no. 20 (as L'Aiguille d'Étretat, incorrectly dated 1889, lent by William Church Osborn); Museum of Modern Art, New York, and Los Angeles County Museum, 1960, *Claude Monet,* no. 36.

EX COLL.: William H. Fuller, New York (sale, American Art Association, New York, Mar. 12–13, 1903, no. 153, as L'Aiguille d'Étretat); [Durand-Ruel, New York, from 1903]; William Church Osborn, New York (from 1903).

BEQUEST OF WILLIAM CHURCH OSBORN, 1951.

The Valley of the Nervia   30.95.251

The Nervia is a river that empties into the Mediterranean near the French-Italian border between the towns of Ventimiglia and Bordighera. The Maritime Alps rising in shining peaks contrast with the shadowed foothills and the river valley below. This painting has a new broad treatment of form, and, like the painting of The Manneporte, Étretat, II (see below), shows the lighter, brighter color that resulted from Monet's stay on the Riviera, which he saw for the first time at the end of 1883.

Signed and dated (at lower left): *Claude Monet 84.*

Oil on canvas. H. 26, w. 32 in. (66 x 81.3 cm.).

30.95.251

EXHIBITED: Georges Petit, Paris, 1885, *4ᵉ Exposition internationale de peinture* (as Vue prise près de Ventimiglia, possibly this picture); Copley Society, Boston, 1905, *Claude Monet*, no. 38 (as Vallée de la Mervia [*sic*], 1884; lent by Theodore M. Davis).

EX COLL.: [Durand-Ruel, Paris and New York, until 1895]; Theodore M. Davis, New York (1895–1915).

THE THEODORE M. DAVIS COLLECTION. BEQUEST OF THEODORE M. DAVIS, 1915.

The Manneporte, Étretat, II   31.67.11

Compared with the Museum's other painting of the Manneporte, made three years earlier (see above), this picture shows the new lightening of color that followed Monet's discovery of the Riviera at the end of 1883.

Signed and dated (at lower left): *Claude Monet 86.*

31.67.11

Oil on canvas. H. 32, w. 25¾ in. (81.3 x 65.4 cm.).

REFERENCES: B. Burroughs, *Met. Mus. Bull.*, XXVI (1931), p. 264, ill. p. 262 // J. Rewald, *The History of Impressionism* (1946), ill. p. 397 // O. Reuterswärd, *Monet* (1948), p. 284, lists this picture, incorrectly identifies the subject as the Porte d'Aval at Étretat // J. Leymarie, *Impressionism* (1955), II, ill. in color, p. 83.

EXHIBITED: Metropolitan Museum, 1921, *Impressionist and Post-Impressionist Paintings*, no. 77 (lent anonymously); Museum of Modern Art, New York, 1931, *Memorial Exhibition of the Collection of Miss Lizzie P. Bliss*, no. 99; Metropolitan Museum, 1934, *Landscape Paintings*, no. 51; Kunsthaus, Zurich, 1952, *Claude Monet*, no. 67 (incorrectly called Le Pic à Étretat); Gemeentemuseum, The Hague, 1952, *Claude Monet*, no. 52 (wrongly called Le Pic te Étretat).

EX COLL.: [Durand-Ruel, Paris, 1887–1892]; Potter Palmer, Chicago (1892–1893); [Durand-Ruel, New York, 1893–1909]; Cornelius N. Bliss, New York (from 1909); Lizzie P. Bliss, New York.

BEQUEST OF LIZZIE P. BLISS, 1931.

Poplars (Les Quatre Arbres)
29.100.110

In 1891 and 1892 Monet painted more than twenty pictures of the poplar trees that bordered the Epte River near his house at Giverny. This picture differs from the others in showing only four trees and including only the trunks and their reflections. With the broad horizontal line of the vegetation on the river's edge, the trees form a geometrical pattern, so simplified that it gives an almost abstract effect.

Signed and dated (at lower left): *Claude Monet 91.*

Oil on canvas. H. 32¼, w. 32⅛ in. (81.9 x 81.6 cm.).

REFERENCES: O. Reuterswärd, *Monet* (1948), p. 286, lists this picture // L. Degand and D.

29.100.110

Rouart, *Claude Monet* (1958), p. 85, ill. in color // W. C. Seitz, *Monet* (1960), pp. 140f., ill. in color; and *Claude Monet* (exhib. cat.), Museum of Modern Art, New York, and Los Angeles County Museum (1960), p. 26, ill. p. 29 // F. Seiberling, *Impressionism and Its Roots* (exhib. cat.), The University of Iowa, Iowa City (1964), pp. 7, 40, no. 34, ill., observes in it a deliberately abstract effect.

EXHIBITED: Metropolitan Museum, 1930, *The H. O. Havemeyer Collection*, no. 85; Newark Museum (New Jersey), 1946, *19th-Century French and American Paintings*, no. 23; City Art Museum, St. Louis, and Minneapolis Art Institute, 1957, *Claude Monet*, no. 75; Museum of Modern Art, New York, and Los Angeles County Museum, 1960, *Claude Monet*, no. 57; Arkansas Arts Center, Little Rock, 1963, *Five Centuries of European Painting*, cat. pp. 40f.; The University of Iowa, Iowa City, 1964, *Impressionism and Its Roots*, no. 34.

Ex COLL. H. O. Havemeyer, New York (Cat., 1931, p. 160, ill.).

THE H. O. HAVEMEYER COLLECTION. BEQUEST OF MRS. H. O. HAVEMEYER, 1929.

Haystacks in the Snow 29.100.109

The Museum is fortunate in owning examples of each of the important series of paintings exploring a single motif which occupied Monet for more than three decades, from about 1890 on. At Giverny, where he had been established for a number of years, he began with methodical studies of the haystacks and poplars. In May, 1891, he showed at the gallery of Durand-Ruel in Paris fifteen pictures of haystacks, including this one, in an exhibition that was so successful that all the paintings were sold.

The Museum's picture displays great boldness of vision and an attitude of detachment from the subject for the sake of the visual impression. The color is almost arbitrary, with violet tones and greenish ochers side by side in frankly blue shadow, in a combination that foretells Bonnard.

Signed and dated (at lower left): *Claude Monet 91*.

Oil on canvas. H. 25¾, w. 36¼ in. (65.4 x 92.1 cm.).

REFERENCE: O. Reuterswärd, *Monet* (1948), p. 286, lists this picture.

EXHIBITED: Galerie Durand-Ruel, Paris, 1891, *Oeuvres récentes de Claude Monet*, no. 7; Metropolitan Museum, 1930, *The H. O. Havemeyer Collection*, no. 86; Newark Museum (New Jersey), 1946, *19th-Century French and American Paintings*, no. 22; University Gallery, University of Minnesota, Minneapolis, 1952, *Space in Painting*; Phoenix Fine Arts Association (Arizona), 1955; Milwaukee Art Center,

29.100.109

1958–1959, *Man's Concept of Outer Space*; Museum of Modern Art, New York, and Los Angeles County Museum, 1960, *Claude Monet*, no. 46.

Ex coll.: Potter Palmer, Chicago (1891?, until 1893); [Durand-Ruel, New York, 1893–1894]; H. O. Havemeyer, New York (from 1894; Cat., 1931, pp. 158f., ill.).

THE H. O. HAVEMEYER COLLECTION. BEQUEST OF MRS. H. O. HAVEMEYER, 1929.

The Ice Floe (La Débâcle)

29.100.108

In the winters of 1879 and 1880 after the death of his first wife, Camille, Monet painted landscapes of the frozen or flooded Seine at Vétheuil. Early in the nineties at Giverny he took this subject up again. In the Museum's example Monet rendered with extraordinary subtlety and exactness of tones and values the ghostly quality of the pale winter light.

Signed and dated (at lower right): *Claude Monet 93*.

Oil on canvas. H. 26, w. 39½ in. (66 x 100.3 cm.).

REFERENCE: O. Reuterswärd, *Monet* (1948), p. 282, lists this picture.

EXHIBITED: Metropolitan Museum, 1930, *The H. O. Havemeyer Collection*, no. 87.

Ex coll.: Montagnac (possibly I. Montaignac; until 1897); [Durand-Ruel, Paris, 1897]; H. O.

29.100.108

Havemeyer, New York (from 1897; Cat., 1931, pp. 158f., ill.).

THE H. O. HAVEMEYER COLLECTION. BEQUEST OF MRS. H. O. HAVEMEYER, 1929.

Rouen Cathedral

30.95.250

In February 1892 Monet went to Rouen, where he began the most intensively studied and probably the most famous of his series of paintings, his studies of the cathedral. He worked from the window of a room on the second floor of a shop on the Rue du Grand-Pont, which borders one side of the square in front of the cathedral. From this vantage point he painted successively on several canvases a day, each one destined to record accurately the appearance of the façade at a certain moment in a particular kind of light.

Monet remained in Rouen until April of 1892, and the following year at the same season he went back to make additional direct observations of the cathedral. He then spent more than a year reworking the paintings from memory at Giverny. Douglas Cooper ascribes the heavy impasto characteristic of the Rouen Cathedral series to this practice of repainting and also to Monet's deliberate attempt to suggest the tactile quality of the stone. The Museum's picture reproduces the intense glow illuminating the façade around noon. In 1895 it was shown with seventeen other paintings of the façade in an exhibition of fifty works by Monet held at the galleries of Durand-Ruel, who sold it after the exhibition to Theodore M. Davis.

Signed and dated (at lower left): *Claude Monet 94*.

Oil on canvas. H. 39¼, w. 25⅞ in. (99.7 x 65.8 cm.).

REFERENCES: O. Reuterswärd, *Monet* (1948), p. 287, lists this picture // G. H. Hamilton, *Claude Monet's Paintings of Rouen Cathedral* (Charlton Lecture on Art, Kings College, University of Durham, Newcastle upon Tyne, 1960), fig. 2 // W. C. Seitz, *Monet* (1960), p. 38, fig. 49.

EXHIBITED: Galerie Durand-Ruel, Paris, 1895, *Claude Monet*; Worcester Art Museum, 1898–1899, *Winter Exhibition*, no. 45 (lent by T. M. Davis); Metropolitan Museum, 1934, *Landscape Paintings*, no. 50; Museum of Modern Art, New York, 1960, *Claude Monet*, no. 65.

EX COLL.: [Durand-Ruel, Paris, 1895]; Theodore M. Davis, New York (1895–1915).

THE THEODORE M. DAVIS COLLECTION. BEQUEST OF THEODORE M. DAVIS, 1915.

The Cliffs at Pourville, I   61.250

See comment above under The Sea at Pourville.

61.250

64.149.1

Signed and dated (at lower left): *Claude Monet 96.*

Oil on canvas. H. 25¾, w. 39¾ in. (65.4 x 101 cm.).

EXHIBITED: Copley Hall, Boston, 1905, *Claude Monet*, no. 65 (lent by Elizabeth W. Perkins); Boston Museum of Fine Arts, 1925–1928 (lent by Elizabeth W. Perkins).

EX COLL.: [Boussod-Valadon, Paris, until 1902; sale, American Art Association, New York, Feb. 26–28, 1902, no. 161, as *La Falaise*]; [Durand-Ruel, New York, 1902–1904]; Elizabeth W. Perkins, Boston (1904–1928); [Durand-Ruel, New York, 1928–1931]; Mr. and Mrs. Charles S. McVeigh, New York (1931–1961).

GIFT OF MR. AND MRS. CHARLES S. McVEIGH, SUBJECT TO A LIFE ESTATE IN THE DONORS, 1961.

The Cliffs at Pourville, II   64.149.1

See comment above under The Sea at Pourville.

Signed and dated (at lower left): *Claude Monet 96.*

Oil on canvas. H. 25¾, w. 36⅜ in. (64.4 x 92.5 cm.).

EX COLL.: [Durand-Ruel, Paris]; Adolphe Tavernier, Paris, until 1907 (sale, Galerie Georges Petit, Paris, Mar. 6, 1900, no. 5, bought in; sale, Hôtel Drouot, Paris, Apr. 15, 1907, no. 33); [Durand-Ruel, Paris]; [Wildenstein, New York]; Mary V. T. Eberstadt, New York.

GIFT OF MARY V. T. EBERSTADT, SUBJECT TO A LIFE ESTATE IN THE DONOR, 1964.

Île aux Orties, near Vernon   60.154

It was probably after his return home from Pourville, where he had spent the early months of 1897, that Monet painted this scene. Vernon is a town very close to Giverny, situated where the Epte joins the Seine.

Signed and dated (at lower left): *Claude Monet 97.*

Oil on canvas. H. 28⅞, w. 36½ in. (73.3 x 92.7 cm.).

EX COLL.: Frederic Bonner (until 1912; sale, American Art Association, New York, Jan. 24, 1912, no. 37, ill.); [Durand-Ruel, New York, 1912–1916]; Mrs. Charles H. Senff, New York (1916–1927); Mr. and Mrs. Charles S. Mc-Veigh, New York (1927–1960).

GIFT OF MR. AND MRS. CHARLES S. Mc-VEIGH, SUBJECT TO A LIFE ESTATE IN THE DONORS, 1960.

60.154

Morning on the Seine near Giverny
56.135.4

In the summers of 1896 and 1897 Monet worked on a series of views very similar to this one, and he exhibited eighteen of them in 1898. These paintings are more abstract than any that have preceded them, in composition and design and in their prevailing unified harmony of color.

Signed and dated (at lower left): *Claude Monet 97.*

Oil on canvas. H. 32⅛, w. 36⅝ in. (81.6 x 93.1 cm.).

REFERENCE: C. Greenberg, *Art News Annual* (1957), ill. p. 142.

EXHIBITED: Galerie Georges Petit, Paris, 1898, *Claude Monet*; Wildenstein Gallery, New York, *From Paris to the Sea*, no. 46 (lent by Mrs. A. B. Emmons); Museum of Modern Art, New York, and Los Angeles County Museum, 1960, *Claude Monet*, no. 73.

EX COLL.: [Possibly Bernheim-Jeune, Paris, 1906]; [Durand-Ruel, Paris and New York, 1906–1907]; Arthur B. Emmons, New York and Newport (1907–1922); Mrs. Arthur B. Emmons (Julia W.), New York and Newport (1922–1956).

BEQUEST OF JULIA W. EMMONS, 1956.

56.135.4

A Bridge over a Pool of Water Lilies
29.100.113

Although Monet painted at least one picture of the little Japanese bridge in his garden as early as 1892, soon after he had had it built, the series of water-garden landscapes was not actually begun until 1899. He continued it at intervals throughout the rest of his life. These paintings can be roughly divided into three main groups. The first, to which this picture belongs, dates from 1899 and 1900 and was shown at the gallery of Durand-Ruel in the late autumn of 1900. The second group, painted between 1903 and 1908, was exhibited in 1909. The decorations of the two oval rooms in the Orangerie in Paris, which form the third, were painted in the years during and after the first World War.

The Museum's picture resembles one in the Tate Gallery, London, and another in the Louvre, both painted, like ours, in 1899. It still reveals Monet's effort to give an illusion of depth and in this respect contrasts markedly with the later, more abstract paintings of the water garden, which are characterized by his preoccupation with the painted surface and the juxtaposition of high-keyed colors. This late style of Monet's comes close to the modern movement known as abstract expressionism.

Signed and dated (at lower right): *Claude Monet 99.*

29.100.113

Oil on canvas. H. 36½, w. 29 in. (92.7 x 73.7 cm.).

REFERENCES: R. A. Meyer, *Die Kunst unserer Zeit*, XIX (1908), ill. p. 75 // G. Geffroy, *Claude Monet* (1922), ill. opp. p. 264 // G. Clemenceau, *Claude Monet* [c. 1928, German edition], ill. opp. p. 144 // W. Uhde, *The Impressionists* (1937), pl. 68 // O. Reuterswärd, *Monet* (1948), p. 288, lists this picture.

EXHIBITED: Galerie Durand-Ruel, Paris, 1900, *Claude Monet*; Metropolitan Museum, 1930, *The H. O. Havemeyer Collection*, no. 88.

EX COLL.: [Durand-Ruel, Paris, from 1900–1901]; H. O. Havemeyer, New York (from 1901; Cat., 1931, pp. 156f., ill.).

THE H. O. HAVEMEYER COLLECTION. BEQUEST OF MRS. H. O. HAVEMEYER, 1929.

The Houses of Parliament   56.135.6

Monet painted his first views of London when he was there during the Franco-Prussian War in 1870. After a brief visit in 1891 he resolved to spend some time in London painting, and in 1899 and the two following years he worked there on a series of Thames scenes, which he completed from memory in Paris. He produced in all nearly one hundred pictures, thirty-seven of which were exhibited at Durand-Ruel's gallery in 1904.

The Thames pictures may be divided into three separate sets according to their subjects. The first is a series of studies of Waterloo Bridge, and the second is of Charing Cross Bridge with the Houses of Parliament in the distance. Both of these series were views from the balcony of Monet's fifth-floor room at the Hotel Savoy, which is situated between the two bridges. The paintings of the third set, to which the Museum's example belongs, are views of the Houses of Parliament alone, seen from Saint Thomas's Hospital on the opposite bank of the river. In these late pictures varying degrees of fog and mist shroud the architecture or soften the outlines of the bridge.

Signed and dated (at lower left): *Claude Monet 1903*.

Oil on canvas. H. 32, w. 36⅜ in. (81.3 x 92.4 cm.).

REFERENCE: A. Alexandre, *Claude Monet* (1921), ill. opp. p. 104.

EXHIBITED: Galerie Durand-Ruel, Paris, 1904, *Claude Monet*, no. 31 (Le Parlement, effet de brouillard, 1903, probably this picture).

EX COLL.: [Bernheim-Jeune, Paris, 1909–1911]; [Durand-Ruel, Paris and New York, 1911]; Arthur B. Emmons, New York and Newport (1911–1922); Mrs. Arthur B. Emmons (Julia W.), New York and Newport (1922–1956).

BEQUEST OF JULIA W. EMMONS, 1956.

56.135.6

The Doge's Palace, Venice, Seen from San Giorgio Maggiore

59.188.1

Monet was nearly sixty-eight when he visited Venice for the first time, in the autumn of 1908, and he was captivated by its peculiar light and atmosphere.

Some years later he worked from memory at Giverny on his Venetian scenes, exhibiting twenty-nine of them in 1912 at the gallery of Bernheim-Jeune. The Museum's painting must be one of the five of the Doge's Palace shown in this exhibition.

The changing color and light that give Venice its characteristically romantic effects, and the importance of decoration rather than mass in the typical architecture of its palaces and churches, made this city an especially sympathetic subject for Monet, and he heartily wished that he had gone there when he was younger (W. C. Seitz, *Claude Monet*, n.d., p. 152).

Signed and dated (at lower right): *Claude Monet 1908*.

Oil on canvas. H. 25¾, w. 36½ in. (65.1 x 92.1 cm.).

EXHIBITED: Galerie Bernheim-Jeune, Paris, 1912, *Claude Monet*, no. 17 or 18 (possibly this picture); Galerie Durand-Ruel, Paris, 1923, *Paintings by Claude Monet*, no. 18 (possibly this picture); Musée de l'Orangerie, Paris, 1931, *Claude Monet*, no. 117 (possibly this picture; lent by Durand-Ruel).

EX COLL.: [Durand-Ruel, Paris, 1912–1931]; Mr. and Mrs. Charles S. McVeigh, New York (1931–1959).

GIFT OF MR. AND MRS. CHARLES S. McVEIGH, 1959.

59.188.1

Renoir

Pierre Auguste Renoir. Born in Limoges in 1841; died in Paris in 1919. Renoir was the son of a tailor, who moved his family to Paris when the child was four. At an early age he showed an inclination toward drawing and was apprenticed to a porcelain manufacturer, for whom he decorated ceramics in the eighteenth-century style. In 1862 and 1863 he attended classes at the École des Beaux-Arts in Paris. He also frequented Gleyre's studio, where he met Sisley, Pissarro, and Monet. In the company of Monet, Bazille, and Sisley he began to paint landscapes around Paris, and he also did portraits and nudes. Until about 1867 his work reflected the influence of Courbet in the solid rendering of the volumes of bodies and in his use of a darkish palette. But Renoir's innate feeling for nuances of color and modeling led him beyond Courbet's opaque, static vision. He was drawn more toward Delacroix, and ultimately toward impressionism, which he adopted under the tutelage of Monet. In 1864, 1865, and 1868 he had some pictures accepted by the Salon, and in 1874 he took an active part in the first exhibition of the Impressionists, sharing all their difficulties. Only courageous collectors like Caillebotte and Chocquet gave him genuine encouragement. By 1883, however, he had produced a whole series of masterpieces that showed his very personal style fully crystallized. These included The Loge of 1874 (Courtauld coll., London), The Ball at the Moulin de la Galette, 1876 (Louvre), Madame Charpentier and her Children, 1878 (see below), and The Boatmen's Lunch, painted in 1881 (Phillips Memorial Gallery, Washington). About 1881 his financial difficulties began gradually to lessen, and he had works admitted regularly to the Salon. Journeys in 1881 and 1882 to countries of intense sunlight—Algeria, Italy, and the south of France—resulted in his using lighter, more rainbow-hued color. In Italy he fell under the influence of the Renaissance painters, especially Raphael. It was about this time that he experienced a reaction against absolute impressionism. Believing that he had explored all its possibilities, he began to stress instead precision in drawing and careful arrangements, but with no sacrifice of richness in color. The chief work of this new style of Renoir's, which he later called his "sour" or "dry" manner, is the large Bathers in the Carroll Tyson collection in Philadelphia, painted in 1887, in which the nudes are solid in form, drawn with emphatic contours, and disposed in a traditional, classic composition. This kind of painting, however, had a rigidity foreign to Renoir's temperament, and he soon returned to his supple and caressing manner, using the pearly tones he had observed in the south of France, where he ultimately settled. In 1892 there was an exhibition of his work at the Durand-Ruel Gallery; from that time on he was regarded as a modern master. The Autumn Salon of 1904 was a triumph for him, and his pictures were exhibited widely and bought by collectors all over the world.

During the last years of his life Renoir was afflicted with illness. He was badly crippled with arthritis, but his vitality was so great that he managed still another transformation in style. As he had noticed that his early pictures were already beginning to fade, he heightened his color, aiming at the same time for stronger form and clearer composition. This late manner shows him as an original colorist and a magnificent painter of form. The best paintings of the last period, like The Judgment of Paris of 1914 (Tyson coll., Philadelphia), with its large female nudes, are comparable to the last works of Titian and Rubens. His preoccupation in them with the problems of form belongs to the twentieth century, but the confident serenity of Mediterranean paganism which emanates from these pictures is still in the spirit of the nineteenth.

Madame Darras 51.200

This portrait is a pendant to the portrait of Captain Darras in the Dresden Museum (Ref., Meier-Graefe, 1929, ill. p. 43). It has been said that Darras was the captain of Renoir's regiment of cavalrymen in the south of France during the war of 1870, but Douglas Cooper states that Darras was stationed in Germany and in Metz in Lorraine and suggests instead that Renoir met Captain Darras and his wife through his good friends the Le Coeurs (Ref., Cooper, 1959, p. 327, note 35). Renoir also painted an equestrian portrait of Madame Darras riding with the son of Charles Le Coeur in the Bois de Boulogne and a bust portrait of her that strongly resembles this equestrian portrait (Kunsthalle, Hamburg, and coll. of the late Baron Napoléon Gourgaud, Paris; both ill. in J. Rewald, *The History of Impressionism*, 1961, pp. 305, 304).

Signed and dated (at right): *A. Renoir '71.*

Oil on canvas. H. 30¾, w. 24½ in. (78.9 x 62.2 cm.).

REFERENCES: J. Meier-Graefe, *Renoir* (1929), p. 52, note 1, ill. p. 42 // W. George, *Formes* (1932), nos. XXVIII–XXIX, p. 305, ill. after p. 302 // H. B. Wehle, *Renoir* (exhib. cat.), Metropolitan Museum (1937), p. 4, notes the influence of Delacroix in the rich color of this picture // S. A. Lewisohn, *Art News* (Annual), XXXVII (Feb. 25, 1939), p. 154 // R. H. Wilenski, *Modern French Painters* [c. 1940], pp. 61, 339, says that this portrait and that of Captain

Darras were painted in Renoir's studio in the Rue Notre Dame des Champs // C. Terrasse, *Cinquante Portraits de Renoir* (1941), text and pl. 4, comments on Renoir's objectivity in painting this portrait, and on its studied quality, calls it an "image of bourgeois opulence" // B. F. Schneider, *Renoir* [c. 1957], p. 22, dates the portraits of Madame and Captain Darras early in 1871, when Renoir was a cuirassier in a regiment in Marseilles; finds them brilliantly painted but lacking in spirit // D. Cooper, *Burl. Mag.*, CI (1959), pp. 163, 168 (note 44), states that the two portraits were painted later in 1871 than the portrait of Mme Maître, which was done in April // F. Fosca, *Renoir* (1962), p. 24, ill. p. 32 // F. Daulte (in a letter, April 4, 1963), gives information about the provenance of this portrait.

EXHIBITED: Metropolitan Museum, 1921, *Impressionist and Post-Impressionist Paintings*, no. 101 (as Lady in Black, lent by Joseph Stransky), and 1932, *Taste of Today* (lent by Adolph Lewisohn), and 1937, *Renoir*, no. 1 (lent from the Adolph Lewisohn Collection); Wildenstein Gallery, New York, 1938, *Great Portraits from Impressionism to Modernism*, no. 36 (lent from the Adolph Lewisohn Collection); Metropolitan Museum, 1951, *The Adolph Lewisohn Collection*, no. 67 (lent by Mrs. Arthur Lehman [Adele Lewisohn Lehman]), and 1957, *Impressionist and Modern Paintings from Private Collections* (lent by Mrs. Arthur Lehman); and *Paintings from Private Collections*, 1958, no. 117, 1959, no. 92, 1960, no. 102, 1961, no. 80, 1962, no. 76, 1963, no. 64 (lent by Mrs. Arthur Lehman).

Ex coll.: J. Bernier, Paris (until 1919); [Durand-Ruel, Paris and New York, 1919–1920]; Josef Stransky, New York (in 1921); Adolph Lewisohn, New York (1925–1938; Cat., 1928, pp. 128f., ill.); Samuel A. Lewisohn, New York (1938–1951); Adele Lewisohn Lehman, New York (1951).

Gift of Margaret Seligman Lewisohn, in memory of her husband, Samuel A. Lewisohn, and of her sister-in-law, Adele Lewisohn Lehman, 1951.

Head of a Young Girl 58.45

This rapid sketch is said to have been painted in 1875, at the time of Renoir's complete participation in the Impressionist movement. The loose, free brush stroke is characteristic of several pictures dated in that year or convincingly placed about that time. An early patron of the Impressionists, the Paris banker Charles Ephrussi, whose portrait appears in Renoir's famous Boatmen's Lunch, once owned this picture.

Signed (at upper right): *Renoir*.

Oil on canvas. H. 16½, w. 12½ in. (41.9 x 31.8 cm.).

EXHIBITED: Metropolitan Museum, 1957, *Impressionist and Modern Paintings from Private Collections* (lent by Mr. and Mrs. R. J. Bernhard).

EX COLL.: Charles Ephrussi, Paris; [Julien Reinach, Paris]; Mr. and Mrs. R. J. Bernhard, New York (1957); [Wildenstein, New York, 1957–1958].

PURCHASE, MR. AND MRS. RICHARD J. BERNHARD FUND, 1958.

A Waitress at Duval's Restaurant 61.101.14

Duval established a chain of low-priced restaurants in Paris, in which Renoir may have eaten many times during his early, difficult years. It was in one of them that he noticed this waitress and asked her to come to his studio to pose for him. With her quiet attitude, her wide-set eyes, and gentle smile she is clearly one of those placid women Renoir always loved to paint. This portrait, which is especially interesting for its pattern of light and dark, was probably painted about 1875.

Signed (at lower left): *Renoir*.

Oil on canvas. H. 39½, w. 28⅛ in. (100.3 x 71.4 cm.).

REFERENCES: R. Jean, *L'Art français à Saint-Pétersbourg* (1912), p. 90, note 2, describes this picture // F. Monod, *Gaz. des B.-A.*, VII

58.45

(1912), p. 318 // *Les Arts* (Sept. 1912), ill. p. 30 // F. Fosca, *Renoir* [c. 1923], pl. 7 // Ternovietz, *L'Amour de l'art*, VI (1925), p. 462, note 1, ill. p. 459 // A. M. Frankfurter, *Art News*, XXXIV (Feb. 1, 1936), pp. 5f., ill. // J. L. Allen, *Met. Mus. Bull.*, XXXII (1937), p. 112, ill. p. 109 // H. B. Wehle, *Renoir* (exhib. cat.), Metropolitan Museum (1937), p. 5, no. 13 // J. W. Lane, *Art News* (Annual), XXXVII (Feb. 25, 1939), p. 132, ill. p. 138, finds it reminiscent of Japanese prints and of Whistler's portraits of the early 1880's // H. Huth, *Gaz. des B.-A.*, XXIX (1946), p. 239, note 22, connects it with the picture entitled "A Servant" exhibited by Durand-Ruel in New York in 1886 at the American Art Association and the National Academy of Design (no. 213) // D. Rouart, *Renoir* (1954), p. 32, observes that it recalls the work of Manet // F. Daulte (in a letter, 1963), gives information about the provenance.

EXHIBITED: American Art Association and National Academy of Design, New York, 1886, *Works in Oil and Pastel by the Impressionists of Paris*, no. 213 (A Servant, possibly this picture); St. Petersburg, 1912, *Centennale*

61.101.14

no. 11 (lent by Stephen C. Clark); Metropolitan Museum, *Paintings from Private Collections*, 1958, no. 113, 1959, no. 89, 1960, no. 94 (lent by Stephen C. Clark); National Gallery of Art, Washington (D.C.), 1959, *Masterpieces of Impressionist and Post-Impressionist Painting*, no. 41 (lent by Stephen C. Clark).

Ex COLL.: [Durand-Ruel, Paris, 1887–1906]; A. A. Hébrard, Paris (from 1906); [Paul Guillaume, Paris]; [Barbazanges, Paris, until 1912]; S. A. Scherbatow, Russia (1912–1918/19); Museum of Modern Art, Moscow (1918/19–1933; Cat., 1928, no. 508, pl. 21); [Knoedler, New York, 1933]; Stephen C. Clark, New York (1933–1960).

BEQUEST OF STEPHEN C. CLARK, 1960.

Young Girl in a Pink and Black Hat
64.150

In painting very young and innocent models like the baby Margot Bérard (see below) and the girl in this picture Renoir often used a vague, loose brushstroke to create a soft, appealing effect. The Young Girl in a Pink and Black Hat was probably made a little later than the Head of a Young Girl (above), but

de l'art français, no. 529 (lent by Barbazanges); Century Association, New York, 1936, *French Masterpieces of the Nineteenth Century*, no. 15 (lent by Stephen C. Clark); Metropolitan Museum, 1937, *Renoir*, no. 13 (lent by Stephen C. Clark); World's Fair, New York, 1940, *Masterpieces of Art*, no. 336 (lent by Stephen C. Clark); Duveen Gallery, New York, 1941, *Renoir*, no. 15 (lent by Stephen C. Clark); Century Association, New York, 1946, *Paintings from the Stephen C. Clark Collection*; Paul Rosenberg, New York, 1953, *Collectors' Choice*, no. 5 (lent by Stephen C. Clark); Knoedler Gallery, New York, 1954, *A Collector's Taste: Selections from the Collection of Mr. and Mrs. Stephen C. Clark*, no. 14; Yale University Art Gallery, New Haven (Conn.), 1956, *Pictures Collected by Yale Alumni*, no. 110 (lent by Stephen C. Clark); Wildenstein Gallery, New York, 1958, *Renoir*,

64.150

before Margot Bérard (below), that is, between 1875 and 1879.

Signed (at lower left): *Renoir*.

Oil on canvas. H. 16, w. 12¾ in. (40.6 x 32.4 cm.).

REFERENCE: M. Florisoone, *Renoir* (1938), p. 53, ill.

GIFT OF KATHRYN B. MILLER, SUBJECT TO A LIFE ESTATE IN THE DONOR, 1964.

Madame Charpentier and Her Children   07.122

Marcel Proust, who had seen this picture when he visited the Charpentiers, declared in *Le Temps retrouvé* (1928) that it would evoke for posterity the poetry of an elegant home of its time and the beauty of contemporary dress more effectively than fashionable portraits of noblewomen by Cot and Chaplin (Ref., Robida, 1958, p. 56). Renoir was presented to the publisher Georges Charpentier in 1875, after Charpentier had bought his first picture by Renoir, Le Pêcheur à la Ligne (Ref., Robida, 1958, pl. VIII). The commission for the family portrait, painted in 1878, was a great opportunity for Renoir to make himself known, and he worked enthusiastically during many sittings. He has shown his patroness in the midst of her bourgeois opulence, in the small, or Japanese, drawing room of her mansion on the Rue de Grenelle, without, according to his brother Edmond Renoir, rearranging anything for effect (exhib. cat., Wildenstein, New York, 1958, p. 9). Madame Charpentier, born Marguerite Lemonnier, was the sister of Isabelle Lemonnier, who often sat for Manet (see p. 47). Married to Georges Charpentier in 1872, she enjoyed considerable importance in the world of letters in Paris and received at her parties, among other distinguished guests, Daudet, Edmond de Goncourt, Zola, Flaubert, and Maupassant. The portrait was accepted for the Salon of 1879, and at Madame Charpentier's urging, it was hung in a good place, where it was admired by almost all of the foremost critics.

Renoir also painted individual portraits of the two children who appear in our picture, and of another daughter, Jeanne Charpentier, as well as a bust-length of Madame Georges Charpentier, of which there are two other versions (Refs., Drucker, 1944, and Robida, 1948). For the stairway of the town house, one of the few places in the mansion not filled with paintings and Japanese art, he made a pair of decorative panels that show a man and a woman leaning on a balustrade.

Our painting is one of Renoir's most important works. In Madame Charpentier's dress, which was designed by Worth, and in the coat of the big Newfoundland dog, Porto, he has made generous use of passages in black, which he regarded as "the queen of colors." With his usual richness of color and surface, he captured the sophisticated elegance of the setting, and its abundance of detail. He has demonstrated here how well Impressionism could solve the problems of painting interiors, anticipating the interiors of Bonnard and Vuillard.

Although it has usually been assumed from their costumes and appearance that both children in the group portrait were girls, it is now established that the child sitting on the sofa beside his mother is three-year-old Paul, whose godfather was Émile Zola. Paul died at the age of twenty, while doing his military service. The little girl sitting on the dog's back is Georgette, aged six. The second daughter, Jeanne, was born in 1880, two years after the picture was painted.

When the painting was auctioned in Paris with the Charpentier collection in 1907, it fetched a very high price and was acquired for the Museum on the recommendation of Roger Fry, who was at that time Curator of Paintings. Several critics have commented on color changes in the picture, but a cleaning has restored all its original brilliance.

Signed and dated (at lower right): *Renoir 78*.

Oil on canvas. H. 60½, w. 74⅞ in. (153.7 x 190.2 cm.).

REFERENCES: A. Baignières, *Gaz. des B.-A.*, xx (1879), p. 54, hails this picture as an evidence of Renoir's return to an acceptable style of painting, praises the color // Bertall, *L'Artiste* (1879), II, pp. 86f., complains that it shows a "complete ignorance of drawing" and that it lacks perspective, commending only the color // P. Burty, *La République française* (May 27, 1879), praises the palette and the general effect, which he compares to that of pastel // J. Castagnary, *Salon de 1879*, reprinted in *Salons, 1857–1879* (1892), II, p. 384, criticizes the proportions but praises the execution for its freedom and spontaneity // F. C. de Syène, *L'Artiste* (1879), II, p. 11, praises the color // C. Pissarro, in a letter to Eugène Murer (May 27, 1879), quoted in J. Rewald, *The History of Impressionism* (1946), p. 339, considers the 1879 Salon the beginning of Renoir's success // P. A. Renoir, in letters to Octave Maus (Jan. 3, 4, and c. 5–10, 1886), printed in L. Venturi, *Les Archives de l'impressionnisme* (1939), II, pp. 227–229, lists this picture as one of the entries he intends to send to the 1886 exhibition in Brussels // A. Alexandre, *Renoir* (exhib. cat.), Durand-Ruel, Paris (1892), p. 34, praises the spirit of the picture, cat. no. 110 (Portrait) // L. Bénédite, *Burl. Mag.*, XII (1907), pp. 130–135, ill. opp. p. 129, comments on the price the painting fetched at the Charpentier auction, the highest yet paid for an Impressionist picture; states that the child on the sofa is Paul // R. F[ry], *Met. Mus. Bull.*, II (1907), pp. 102–104, ill. // T. Duret, *Manet and the French Impressionists* (1910), p. 165, ill. opp. p. 164, speaks of both children as girls, praises the picture and observes that Mme Charpentier's influence obtained its admission to the Salon // J. Huneker, *Promenades of an Impressionist* (1910), pp. 242–244, 249 // R. Descharmes, *Revue d'histoire littéraire de la France*, XVIII (1911), pp. 632 (note 4), 635 (note 3), 639 (note 2), 640 (note 1), 659, quotes letters of Flaubert that establish the identity of the Charpentier children // J. Meier-Graefe, *Auguste Renoir* (1911), pp. 58, 66–70, ill., considers this one of Renoir's major works, praising the use of blacks, finds it prophetic of Bonnard's treatment of interiors and of various later developments in painting // C. L. Borgmeyer, *The Master Impressionists* (1913), pp. 124–126, 148, 229, ill. p. 99 // B. B[urroughs], *Met. Mus. Bull.*, XIII (1918), pp.

179f., ill., describes it as a masterpiece of Renoir's earlier style, before he became completely impressionistic // *Bull. de la vie artistique*, I (Dec. 15, 1919), p. 36, ill. p. 33 // G. Rivière, *Renoir et ses amis* (1921), pp. 77, 177, ill. opp. p. 180 // P. Jamot, *Gaz. des B.-A.*, VIII (1923), pp. 274f., 336, ill. p. 277, analyzes the composition // T. Duret, *Renoir* (1924), pp. 54–58, 65f., ill. opp. p. 44 // A. Vollard, *Renoir, An Intimate Record* (1925), pp. 96f., notes that the painter received at least 1000 francs for the picture // J. Meier-Graefe, *Renoir* (1929), pp. 104–108, 217, ill., analyzes the composition and the still life on the right, observes that the color has deteriorated // R. Fry, *Characteristics of French Art* (1932), pp. 142f., pl. XXXVII // A. C. Barnes and V. de Mazia, *The Art of Renoir* (1935), pp. 398f., 412, 449, no. 79, criticizes the picture adversely // J. L. Allen, *Met. Mus. Bull.*, XXXII (1937), p. 110 // H. B. Wehle, *Renoir* (exhib. cat.), Metropolitan Museum (1937), pp. 6f., discusses this portrait // M. Florisoone, *L'Amour de l'art*, XIX (1938), pp. 31, 36, ill. p. 37 // L. Venturi, *Les Archives de l'impressionnisme* (1939), I, p. 47, calls it a masterpiece though artificial in composition // R. H. Wilenski, *Modern French Painters* [c. 1940], pp. 42f., 62, 248, accuses Renoir of compromise in attempting to create a lucrative portrait style // C. Terrasse, *Cinquante Portraits de Renoir* (1941), discusses the picture, ill. pl. 13 // M. Drucker, *Renoir* (1944), pp. 51f., 201, no. 51, pl. 51, reestablishes the identity of the children as a girl and a boy, cites two portraits of Mme Charpentier, regards the portraits of individual members of the family as preparations for our picture, believes that the painting has deteriorated // J. Rewald, *The History of Impressionism* (1946), pp. 338f., 428, ill. p. 340, finds a lack of spontaneity and a deliberate effort to create the stately effect, implies that both the children are girls; (revised and enlarged edition, 1961), pp. 419, 424, 430, 580, ill. p. 420 // E. Jacobson, *Basic Color* (1948), pp. 184–186, analyzes the color // W. Pach, *Renoir* (1950), pp. 18, 66, ill. p. 67 // L. Venturi, *Impressionists and Symbolists* (1950), pp. 105f., fig. 104, comments that the colors do not result from "creative necessity" // [W. Gaunt], *Renoir* (Phaidon ed., 1952), p. 9, pl. 26 // Metropolitan Museum, *Art Treasures* (1952), p. 233, cat. no. 148, pl. 148 // H. B. Wehle, *Figure Painting by Renoir* (*Met. Mus. Miniatures*, 1952), ill. in color, comments on the ease and balance of the composition, the brilliance of the still life, and the masterly handling of black, as in portraits by Hals, Velazquez, and Rubens // M. Sert, *Two or Three Muses, The Memoirs of Misia Sert* (1953), p. 85 // D. Rouart, *Renoir* (1954), p. 46, ill. in color p. 47, details in color pp. 48f., finds the picture conventional but full of pleasing qualities // B. F. Schneider, *Renoir* [c. 1957], p. 50, praises the rendering of the still life // M. Robida, *Le Salon Charpentier et les Impressionnistes* (1958), pp. 55–59, 81, 135, pl. XII (detail), states that Mme Charpentier is wearing a dress designed by Worth and that the setting is her little Japanese salon, quotes Marcel Proust's and Paul Jamot's comments about the painting, publishes a photograph of Paul and Georgette Charpentier (pl. XVI), and reproduces Renoir's portraits of each of them alone (pls. IX, XIV) (much of this information appeared in M. Robida, *Ces Bourgeois de Paris*, 1955, pp. 118, 131f., 135, ill. opp. p. 144; and *Renoir, Enfants*, 1959, pp. 10, 14, 16, ill. opp. p. 9, detail in color) // H. Bünemann, *Renoir* (1959), pp. 151f., 210, 212, fig. 64 (detail), fig. 152 // A. Frankfurter, *Art News Annual*, XXVIII (1959), p. 35, ill. // J. Lethève, *Impressionnistes et Symbolistes devant la presse* (1959), pp. 102, 106, discusses the favorable reception of this picture at the Salon of 1879, quoting the critics Bergerat, Banville, and Bigot, observing that only Bertall criticized it adversely.

07.122

EXHIBITED: Paris, Salon of 1878, no. 2527 (as Mme G . . . C . . . et ses enfants); Brussels, 1886, *Les XX, la troisième exposition annuelle, Renoir*, no. 2 (lent by Georges Charpentier); Durand-Ruel, Paris, 1892, *Renoir*, no. 110 (as *Portrait*, lent by Georges Charpentier); Bernheim-Jeune, Paris, 1900, *Renoir*, no. 19 (as *En Famille*); La Libre Esthétique, Brussels, 1904, *Exposition des peintres impressionnistes*, no. 129 (lent by Georges Charpentier); Metropolitan Museum, 1937, *Renoir*, no. 22.

EX COLL. Georges Charpentier, Paris (1878–1907; sale, Hôtel Drouot, Paris, April 11, 1907, no. 21).

PURCHASE, WOLFE FUND, 1907.

Margot Bérard   61.101.15

Marguerite Bérard, called by her family Margot, was the youngest daughter of Paul Bérard, who held a high post in the French diplomatic

corps. Renoir's friendship with the Bérard family dates from 1879 and was the result of his introduction to the circle of the Charpentiers (see above). The painter visited the Bérards many times in Paris and stayed with them often at their seaside home in Wargemont on the Channel, not far from Dieppe. There he painted not only Margot and her parents but also her sisters Marthe and Lucie, her brother André, and her cousins Thérèse and Alfred Bérard. When Margot grew up she became the wife of Alfred.

At Wargemont Renoir also made some decorations for the dining room and painted a view of the rose garden and one or both of the Museum's two still lifes of peaches (see below).

Signed and dated (at upper left): *Renoir 79*.

Oil on canvas. H. 16⅛, w. 12¾ in. (41 x 32.4 cm.).

REFERENCES: A. Renoir, in letters (Jan. 3–10, 1886), published in L. Venturi, *Les Archives de l'impressionnisme* (1939), II, pp. 227–229, mentions this picture among those to be exhibited in Brussels in 1886 // O. Maus, *Trente Années de lutte pour l'art* (1926), p. 43, note 1, lists it as Margot, étude, among the pictures by Renoir exhibited in 1886 in Brussels // J. L. Allen, *Met. Mus. Bull.*, XXXII (1937), p. 112 // *Vogue* (Mar. 15, 1938), ill. in color p. 103 // M. Bérard, *Renoir à Wargemont* (1938), pl. [7]; *L'Amour de l'art*, XIX (1938), ill. p. 319 // J. W. Lane, *Art News* (Annual), XXXVII (Feb. 25, 1939), p. 133.

EXHIBITED: Brussels, 1886, *Les XX, la troisième exposition annuelle* (lent by Paul Bérard); Metropolitan Museum, 1937, *Renoir*, no. 26 (lent by Stephen C. Clark); Museum of Modern Art, New York, 1939, *Art in Our Time*, no. 51 (lent by Stephen C. Clark), and 1940, *Modern Masters*, no. 7 (lent by Stephen C. Clark); World's Fair, New York, 1940, *Masterpieces of Art*, no. 333 (lent by Stephen C. Clark); Duveen Galleries, New York, 1941, *Renoir*, no. 27 (lent by Stephen C. Clark); Century Association, New York, 1946, *Paintings from the Stephen C. Clark Collection*; Knoedler Galleries, New York, 1954, *A Col-*

lector's Taste: Selections from the Collection of Mr. and Mrs. Stephen C. Clark, no. 15; Museum of Modern Art, New York, 1955, Paintings from Private Collections, no. 127 (lent by Stephen C. Clark); Metropolitan Museum, Paintings from Private Collections, 1958, no. 110, 1959, no. 87, 1960, no. 95 (lent by Stephen C. Clark).

Ex coll.: The Bérard family, Wargemont (near Dieppe); Mme Alfred Bérard (Margot), Paris; [Knoedler, New York, 1937]; Stephen C. Clark, New York (from 1937).

Bequest of Stephen C. Clark, 1960.

56.135.7

View of the Seacoast near Wargemont in Normandy   56.135.7

In the summers of 1879 and the succeeding year Renoir visited the diplomat Paul Bérard at Wargemont, near Berneval, on the Channel coast. This scene, undoubtedly painted during his second visit, shows the soft, free technique of his very impressionistic style during the late seventies and the beginning of the eighties.

Formerly called Landscape, Guernsey.

Signed and dated (at lower right): Renoir. 80.

Oil on canvas. H. 19⅞, w. 24½ in. (50.5 x 62.2 cm.).

Ex coll.: [Durand-Ruel, Paris, bought from Renoir in 1890, and New York, 1895–1906]; Arthur B. Emmons, New York and Newport

(1906–1922); Mrs. Arthur B. Emmons (Julia W.), New York and Newport (1922–1956).

Bequest of Julia W. Emmons, 1956.

Still Life with Peaches and Grapes
56.218

This jardiniere, probably of delftware, filled with peaches, is the subject of two still lifes by Renoir in this Museum, both painted in 1881. Paul Bérard, in his book about Renoir's visits to him, says that it was a frequent decoration on the dining table in his house at Wargemont. See below.

Signed and dated (at lower left): Renoir. 81.

Oil on canvas. H. 21¼, w. 25⅝ in. (54 x 65.1 cm.).

References: M. Bérard, Renoir à Wargemont (1938), pp. 12f., ill., tells of Renoir's painting the peaches in the jardiniere on the dining table at Wargemont // Die Weltkunst, xii (July 3, 1938), p. 4, ill., records the sale of this picture, called Stilleben, with the Pra collection // Art News, xxxviii (1940), p. 3, no. 36, ill. p. 12, publishes a check list of the Detroit exhibition // C. Sterling, La Nature morte (1952), p. 90, pl. 89, considers it perhaps the most personal and beautiful of Renoir's still lifes, completely original but recalling Chardin // F. Daulte (in letters, 1963), gives information about the provenance.

Exhibited: Galerie Durand-Ruel, Paris, 1892, A. Renoir, no. 60 (as Pêches et Raisins, lent by Paul Bérard); Musée de l'Orangerie, Paris, 1933, Renoir, no. 63 (lent by Albert Pra); Detroit Institute of Arts, 1940, Age of Impressionism and Objective Realism, no. 36 (as Still Life, lent anonymously through the Bignou Gallery, New York); Bignou Gallery, New York, 1945, A Selection of 19th-Century French Paintings, no. 9 (lent anonymously); Lefevre Gallery, London, 1948, Renoir, no. 8 (lent anonymously).

Ex coll.: [Durand-Ruel, Paris, 1881]; Paul Bérard, Paris and Wargemont (in 1892, probably from 1881; sale, Galerie Georges Petit, Paris, May 8–9, 1905, no. 27, ill.); [Lucien

56.218

61.101.12

Guérin, Paris, from 1905]; Albert Pra, Paris (by 1933; sale, Galerie Charpentier, Paris, June 17, 1938, no. 51, ill.); [Paul Rosenberg, Paris, 1938]; [Étienne Bignou, Paris, 1939]; William A. Cargill, Carruth, Bridge of Weir, Scotland (1939–1952); [Étienne Bignou, Paris, 1952]; [Sam Salz, New York, 1952–1953]; Edwin C. Vogel, New York (1953–1956).

PURCHASE, MR. AND MRS. HENRY ITTLESON JR. FUND, 1956.

Still Life with Peaches   61.101.12

This still life resembles the Still Life with Peaches and Grapes (see above), but the composition has been changed by the substitution of pears and an apple for the grapes and by the addition of a richly figured wallpaper or screen as background.

Signed and dated (at lower right): *Renoir. 81.*

Oil on canvas. H. 21, w. 25½ in. (53.3 x 64.7 cm.).

REFERENCES: M. Bérard, *Renoir à Wargemont* (1938), pp. 12f. // J. W. Lane, *Art News* (Annual), xxxvii (Feb. 25, 1939), p. 133, ill. p. 146.

EXHIBITED: Metropolitan Museum, 1937, *Renoir*, no. 35 (lent by Stephen C. Clark); Duveen Gallery, New York, 1941, *Renoir*, no. 37 (lent by Stephen C. Clark); Coordinating Council of French Relief Societies, New York,

1944, *Jardin d'Été* (lent by Stephen C. Clark); Century Association, New York, 1946, *Paintings from the Stephen C. Clark Collection*; Paul Rosenberg Gallery, New York, 1948, *Masterpieces by Delacroix and Renoir*, no. 17 (lent by Stephen C. Clark); Knoedler Gallery, New York, 1954, *A Collector's Taste: Selections from the Collection of Mr. and Mrs. Stephen C. Clark*, no. 16; Yale University Art Gallery, New Haven (Conn.), 1956, *Pictures Collected by Yale Alumni*, no. 105 (lent by Stephen C. Clark); Wildenstein Gallery, New York, 1958, *Renoir*, no. 29 (lent by Stephen C. Clark); Metropolitan Museum, *Paintings from Private Collections*, 1958, no. 112, 1959, no. 88, 1960, no. 93 (lent by Stephen C. Clark).

EX COLL.: Possibly Paul Bérard, Paris and Wargemont; [Schoeller, Paris, c. 1920/30]; [Raphael Gérard and Jacques Lindon, Paris]; Haviland Collection; [Mme Paul Guillaume, Paris, 1936]; [Jacques Seligmann, New York, 1936]; Stephen C. Clark, New York (from 1936).

BEQUEST OF STEPHEN C. CLARK, 1960.

The Bay of Naples   56.135.8

In the autumn of 1881 Renoir made a trip to Italy, visiting Venice, Rome, Naples, and Florence, disliking the last intensely. In Rome and Florence he did little except visit museums, but Venice and Naples gave him real pleasure. In giving an account of the trip to Vollard he mentioned among the pictures he had painted in Naples one showing the quay, with Vesuvius in the background. There is at least one other picture with this subject (J. Rewald, *The History of Impressionism*, revised and enlarged edition, 1961, ill. p. 461).

Signed and dated (at lower right): *Renoir. 81*.

Oil on canvas. H. 23½, w. 32 in. (59.7 x 81.3 cm.).

EXHIBITED: Wildenstein Gallery, New York, 1958, *Renoir*, no. 33; California Palace of the Legion of Honor, San Francisco, 1961, *Paintings by the Sea*.

EX COLL.: [Boussod-Valadon, Paris]; Potter Palmer, Chicago (in 1894); [Durand-Ruel, New York, 1894–1911]; Arthur B. Emmons, New York and Newport (1911–1922); Mrs. Arthur B. Emmons (Julia W.) (1922–1956).

BEQUEST OF JULIA W. EMMONS, 1956.

56.135.8

56.135.9

Hills around the Bay of Moulin Huet at Guernsey 56.135.9

Renoir spent the summer of 1883 in Guernsey and wrote from there enchanting letters about the delights of this Channel island. This is one of the very last pictures he painted in the open, impressionistic style, before he changed over to the "sour" or "dry" manner. Another version of this landscape composition, almost exactly the same size, was in a private collection in Washington in 1929 (ill. in J. Meier-Graefe, *Renoir*, 1929, p. 157).

Formerly called Côte du Moulin Huet, Guernsey.

Signed and dated (at lower right): *Renoir. 83*.

Oil on canvas. H. 18⅛, w. 25¾ in. (46.1 x 65.4 cm.).

EXHIBITED: Grafton Galleries, London, 1905, *Pictures by Boudin, Manet. . . .* (exhibited by Durand-Ruel, Paris), no. 273.

EX COLL.: [Durand-Ruel, Paris, 1891–1908, and New York, 1908–1911]; Arthur B. Em-

mons, New York and Newport (1911–1922); Mrs. Arthur B. Emmons (Julia W.), New York and Newport (1922–1956).

BEQUEST OF JULIA W. EMMONS, 1956.

By the Seashore 29.100.125

This picture is a good illustration of the artistic crisis through which Renoir passed in the middle of the eighties. In September of 1883, the year he made this picture, he was staying in Guernsey, and the cliff in the background suggests that he painted it there. A watercolor drawing in the Robert Lehman collection in New York could possibly be related to this picture.

Signed and dated (at lower left): *Renoir. 83*.

Oil on canvas. H. 36¼, w. 28½ in. (92.1 x 72.4 cm.).

REFERENCES: H. B. Wehle, *Met. Mus. Bull.*, xxv (1930), p. 56, notes that this picture was the only one by Renoir in the Havemeyer collection // A. C. Barnes and V. de Mazia, *The Art of Renoir* (1935), pp. 407, 455, no. 133, footnotes pp. 77, 78, 97, ill. p. 274, ana-lyzes it, comparing it to others done about the same time and praising it for its delicacy and unity; finds the relationship between fig-ure and background unconventional // C. Terrasse, *Cinquante Portraits de Renoir* (1941), text and pl. 24, observes that this model re-

29.100.125

calls one in La Fin de Déjeuner of 1879 (Städelsches Kunstinstitut, Frankfort) // M. Drucker, *Renoir* (1944), pp. 62, 203, no. 70, pl. 70, ill. in color, praises the picture, suggests that the sitter appears in several other pictures by Renoir // F. Daulte, in a letter (Apr. 4, 1963), gives the provenance.

EXHIBITED: Pennsylvania Museum of Art, Philadelphia, 1933, *Manet and Renoir* (no catalogue; *Pennsylvania Mus. Bull.*, XXIX, 1933, p. 19); Metropolitan Museum, 1937, *Renoir*, no. 40; Worcester Art Museum (Mass.), 1941, *The Art of the Third Republic*, no. 10.

Ex COLL.: P. de Kuyper (The Hague?; until 1891); [Durand-Ruel, Paris and New York, 1891–1892]; C. Lambert (possibly Catholina Lambert, Paterson, New Jersey, 1892–1899); [Durand-Ruel, New York, 1899]; H. O. Havemeyer, New York (from 1899).

THE H. O. HAVEMEYER COLLECTION. BEQUEST OF MRS. H. O. HAVEMEYER, 1929.

A Young Girl with Daisies 59.21

The young person represented here is somewhat reminiscent of the one in the large feathered hat in the picture called Place Pigalle, that Renoir had painted about 1880.[1] The model who posed for our painting, however, is probably the same one who sat to him for A Girl Reading, which has been dated 1888–1890.[2] A Young Girl with Daisies must be from about this time, as it is rendered in the style of Renoir when he was emerging from the "dry" period, but before reaching the bricky color, the fusion of volumes, and the monumentality of his last phase.

Signed (at lower right): *Renoir*.

Oil on canvas. H. 25⅝, w. 21¼ in. (65 x 54 cm.).

Notes: 1. Ill. in J. Meier-Graefe, *Renoir* (1929), p. 149. 2. Ill. in color in D. Rouart, *Renoir* (1954), p. 79.

REFERENCES: Bernheim-Jeune (ed.), *Renoir*, preface by O. Mirbeau (1913), ill. opp. p. 34, dates this picture 1889–1890 // G. Coquiot, *Renoir* (1925), p. 228, dates it 1889 // *L'Art*

59.21

vivant, IX (1933), p. 288, ill. // A. C. Barnes and V. de Mazia, *The Art of Renoir* (1935), p. 459, no. 179, date it about 1889 (mention it in footnotes to pp. 85, 107) // O. Vinding, *Renoir* (1951), fig. 21, dates it 1889–1890 // F. Daulte (in a letter, 1963), gives information about its provenance.

EXHIBITED: Galerie Bernheim-Jeune, Paris, 1913, *Renoir*, no. 35 (dated 1889); Musée de l'Orangerie, Paris, 1933, *Renoir*, no. 88 (dated 1889, lent by Bernheim-Jeune); Galerie Bernheim-Jeune, Paris, 1938, *Renoir, portraitiste*, no. 14 (dated 1889).

Ex COLL.: Alexandre Rosenberg, Paris (about 1890); Mme Alexandre Rosenberg, Paris (until 1912); private collection of Bernheim-Jeune, Paris (from 1912; coll. cat., *L'Art moderne . . .*, 1919, II, pl. 112); Mme Gaston Bernheim de Villers, Monte Carlo (until 1959).

PURCHASE, MR. AND MRS. HENRY ITTLESON JR. FUND, 1959.

In the Meadow   51.112.4

In style this painting corresponds much more to works made about 1890 than to those from the period around 1895, in which it has sometimes been placed. Both the treatment of the landscape and the handling of the figures are extremely light and delicate, typical of Renoir's work when he was reacting against the exact drawing and hard forms of the so-called "dry" style that he abandoned toward the end of the eighties.

Signed (at lower right): *Renoir.*

Oil on canvas. H. 32, w. 25¾ in. (81.3 x 65.4 cm.).

REFERENCES: *Met. Mus. Bull.*, xv (1920), p. 207, praises Renoir's original use of color in this picture // A. Vollard, *Renoir. An Intimate Record* (1925), appendix II, p. 246, dates the picture 1906 // J. Meier-Graefe, *Renoir* (1929), ill. p. 213, dates it 1890 // W. Georges, *Formes* (1932), nos. XXVIII–XXIX, pp. 306, ill. in color

51.112.4

opp. p. 300 // S. A. Lewisohn, *Art News* (Annual), XXXVII (Feb. 25, 1939), p. 154, ill. p. 69 (hanging in the Lewisohn house), mentions buying it at the Emmons sale, without naming it // R. H. Wilenski, *Modern French Painters* [c. 1940], p. 342, dates it about 1894 // *Renoir Centennial* (exhib. cat.), Duveen Galleries, New York (1941), no. 61, dates it about 1890, considering it to be of the same period as Young Girls Picking Flowers in the Boston Museum of Fine Arts (no. 60, placed about 1889) // R. Frost, *Pierre-Auguste Renoir* (1944), ill. p. 39, dates it about 1894–1895 (this picture in the French edition only) // J. Rewald, *The History of Impressionism* (1946), ill. in color opp. p. 408, dates it about 1895 // W. Pach, *Renoir* (1950), p. 90, ill. p. 91, dates it about 1890, commenting that it recalls Renoir's work of the eighties; analyzes the technique, color, and composition // H. B. Wehle, *Figure Paintings by Renoir* (Met. Mus. Miniatures, 1952), ill. in color, tentatively identifies the sitters as Julie Manet and Jeannie Gobillard, the daughter and niece of Berthe Morisot; dates the picture in the summer of 1891, when Renoir paid a visit to Berthe Morisot in Mézy // Mme Julie Manet-Rouart, in a letter (Feb. 18, 1952), states that she and her cousin did not pose for this picture, suggests that the models were the ones who posed for the painting of two girls at the piano // D. Rouart, *Renoir* (1954), p. 78, places this painting between Renoir's "iridescent" period, about 1890, and his last period, observing that he reverts here to the less rich textures and "acrid" colors of the 1880's, compares it to ivory miniatures or porcelain decorations // B. F. Schneider, *Renoir* [c. 1957], p. 45, ill. in color, dates it 1890–1894 // H. Bünemann, *Renoir* (1959), pp. 95f., 214, no. 95, ill.

EXHIBITED: Metropolitan Museum, 1920, *Fiftieth Anniversary Exhibition*, listed p. 10 (lent by Adolph Lewisohn), and 1937, *Renoir*, no. 55 (dated c. 1894–1895, lent from the Adolph Lewisohn collection); Duveen Galleries, New York, 1941, *Renoir Centennial*, no. 61 (dated c. 1890, lent from the Adolph Lewisohn collection); Paul Rosenberg Gallery, New York,

1948, *Delacroix and Renoir*, no. 19 (dated c. 1890, lent by Mr. and Mrs. Sam A. Lewisohn); Metropolitan Museum, 1951, *The Lewisohn Collection*, no. 69; Los Angeles County Museum and San Francisco Museum of Art, 1955, *Pierre Auguste Renoir*, no. 53 (dated c. 1894–1895).

EX COLL.: [Durand-Ruel, Paris, 1892]; Mrs. Potter Palmer, Chicago (1892–1894); [Durand-Ruel, New York, 1894–1906]; Arthur B. Emmons, New York and Newport (1906–1920; sale, American Art Association, New York, Jan. 14, 1920, no. 46); Adolph Lewisohn, New York (1920–1938; Cat., 1928, p. 136, dated c. 1894–1895); Samuel A. Lewisohn, New York (1938–1951).

BEQUEST OF SAMUEL A. LEWISOHN, 1951.

53.171

Odalisque 53.171

During the nineties Renoir painted a number of pictures showing young women in exotic dress. The Spanish Girl Playing the Guitar (Dr. Gustave Schweitzer collection, Berlin) and the so-called Oriental Woman, formerly belonging to Durand-Ruel, show girls wearing heavily encrusted jackets similar to the one in which the model of our picture is dressed. Our painting represents a very young person, almost a child, with rounded cheeks and short-lipped profile.

Signed (at upper left): *Renoir*.

Oil on canvas. H. 16⅛, w. 12¾ in. (41 x 32.4 cm.).

Notes: 1. M. Drucker, *Renoir* (1944), pl. 121. 2. *Renoir* (Phaidon, 1952), pl. 49.

REFERENCE: R. Frost, *Pierre-Auguste Renoir* (1944), p. 33, ill., dates this picture 1895 and calls it Dancer in a Turkish Costume.

EXHIBITED: Grafton Galleries, London, 1905, *Pictures by Boudin, Manet . . .* (exhibited by Durand-Ruel, Paris), no. 247 (Young Girl) or no. 264 (Young Lady); Wichita Art Museum (Kansas), 1954.

EX COLL.: Private collection of Durand-Ruel, Paris (until c. 1940); [Jacques Seligmann, New York, c. 1940–1945]; [Van Diemen-Lilienfeld Galleries, New York, 1945]; James A. Moffett II, Glen Head, New York (until 1953).

GIFT OF JAMES A. MOFFETT II IN MEMORY OF GEORGE M. MOFFETT, 1953.

A Girl with a Basket of Flowers
64.165.3

In proportions and the general effect of the single figure this painting and its companion, which follows, resemble a pair of decorative pictures in the Barnes Foundation at Merion, Pennsylvania (A. C. Barnes and V. De Mazia, *The Art of Renoir*, 1935, ill. p. 296). The Barnes pictures are thought to have been painted about 1889; the Museum's have been placed by Vollard about six years later. Although the girl carrying flowers wears a hat, her costume in other respects and the basket closely resemble those of another youthful female figure by Renoir in the Barnes Foundation (Barnes and De Mazia, *ibid.*, ill. p. 297;

64.165.3   64.165.4

A Girl Picking Fruit   64.165.4

This painting was left unfinished. The peasant model in her simple costume of blouse and skirt is surely the same as the young woman with a basket of fish in the Barnes Foundation (A. C. Barnes and V. De Mazia, *The Art of Renoir*, 1935, ill. p. 296). See also A Girl with a Basket of Flowers, above.

Oil on canvas. H. 50¼, w. 15¾ in. (127.6 x 40 cm.).

REFERENCE: A. Vollard, *Tableaux, Pastels, et Dessins de Pierre Auguste Renoir* (1918), I, p. 141, no. 562, ill.

EX COLL.: [Mouradian and Vallotton, Paris, in 1950]; Henry Pearlman, New York (1950–1952); [Knoedler, New York, 1952–1953]; George N. Richard, New York (1953–1964).

GIFT OF GEORGE N. RICHARD AND HELEN M. RICHARD, SUBJECT TO A LIFE ESTATE IN THE DONORS, 1964.

A Woodland Pool with Bathers and Washerwomen   59.106

The treatment of the tree at the right, which is rendered in soft, tufted masses, and the sketchy character of the figures are both typical of Renoir's landscape style in the years around the turn of the century.

Formerly called Bathers and Washerwomen.

dated in the early 1890's). See also A Girl Picking Fruit, below.

Oil on canvas. H. 50⅛, w. 15¾ in. (127.3 x 40 cm.).

REFERENCE: A. Vollard, *Tableaux, Pastels, et Dessins de Pierre Auguste Renoir* (1918), I, p. 141, no. 563, ill.

EX COLL.: [Mouradian and Vallotton, Paris, in 1950]; Henry Pearlman, New York (1950–1952); [Knoedler, New York, 1952–1953]; George N. Richard, New York (1953–1964).

GIFT OF GEORGE N. RICHARD AND HELEN M. RICHARD, SUBJECT TO A LIFE ESTATE IN THE DONORS, 1964.

59.106

Signed and dated (at lower left): *Renoir/01.*

Oil on canvas. H. 18⅛, w. 22 in. (46 x 55.8 cm.).

EXHIBITED: Galerie Durand-Ruel, Paris, 1910, *Tableaux par Monet, C. Pissarro, Renoir et Sisley*, no. 41 (Baigneuses et laveuses, 1901; possibly this picture).

EX COLL.: [John Levy Gallery, New York]; Mrs. Walter Sachs (Edna H.), New York (between 1930 and 1939–until 1959).

GIFT OF MRS. EDNA H. SACHS, SUBJECT TO A LIFE ESTATE IN THE DONOR, 1959.

Tilla Durieux 61.101.13

Tilla Durieux is an actress of considerable reputation. She was born in Vienna and was destined as a child to become a musician, but in early youth began to attend a school for acting. At the time when Renoir painted her she was married to Paul Cassirer, a picture dealer in Berlin. In the summer of 1914, just before the outbreak of the first World War, she and her husband went to Paris expressly to have this portrait painted. She sat to Renoir morning and afternoon for two weeks, dressed in the costume by Poiret that she had worn in the next-to-last act of *Pygmalion*.[1] Renoir was seventy-three, and according to Tilla Durieux's memoirs, so crippled that he painted from a wheel chair, his brush strapped into his arthritic hand.[2] The picture nevertheless shows the breadth and monumental poise that characterize the creations of his very latest, classic style.

Signed and dated (at lower left): *Renoir/1914.*

Oil on canvas. H. 36¼, w. 29 in. (92.1 x 73.4 cm.).

Notes: 1. T. Durieux, *Eine Tür steht offen: Erinnerungen* (1954), pp. 94–97. 2. Cf., however, J. Renoir, *Renoir, My Father* (1962), p. 449, who denies this.

REFERENCES: J. Meier-Graefe, *Renoir* (1929), p. 424, ill. p. 436 (photograph of Renoir working on this picture), tells of seeing the portrait in Renoir's studio in Paris // M. Morsell, *Art News*, XXXIV (Dec. 7, 1935), pp. 4f., ill. // J. L. Allen, *Met. Mus. Bull.*, XXXII (1937), p. 114 // J. W. Lane, *Art News* (Annual), XXXVII (Feb. 25, 1939), p. 132, ill. p. 138 // M. Wheeler, *Twentieth Century Portraits* (1942), pp. 12, 142, ill. in color (frontis.), compares the painting to a lithograph of Tilla Durieux by Kokoschka and a bust by the sculptor Barlach // M. Drucker, *Renoir* (1944), pp. 96, 190, ill. opp. p. 58 (Renoir at work on this picture) // J. Rewald, *The History of Impressionism* (1946), ill. in color p. 428; (revised and enlarged edition, 1961), ills., pp. 585 (this picture in color), 584 (photograph of Renoir with Tilla Durieux posing for him in his studio, 1914) // W. Pach, *Renoir* (1950), pp. 120f., ill. in color // H. B. Wehle, *Figure Paintings by Renoir* (Met. Mus. Miniatures, 1952), no. 22, ill. in color // R. J. Goldwater, *Art in America* (Spring, 1958), p. 60, ill. in color p. 62.

EXHIBITED: Bignou Gallery, New York, 1935, *Renoir*, no. 14 (lent anonymously); Metropolitan Museum, 1937, *Renoir*, no. 60 (lent by Stephen C. Clark); World's Fair, New York, 1940, *Masterpieces of Art*, no. 337 (lent by Stephen C. Clark); Duveen, New York, 1941, *Renoir*, no. 81 (lent by Stephen C. Clark); Museum of Modern Art, New York, 1942, *Twentieth Century Portraits*, cat. p. 142 (lent by Stephen C. Clark); Century Association, New York, 1946, *Paintings from the Stephen C. Clark Collection*; Paul Rosenberg Gallery, New York, 1948, *Delacroix and Renoir*, no. 28 (lent by Stephen C. Clark); Century Association, New York, 1949, *Trends in European Painting*, no. 18 (lent by Stephen C. Clark); Yale University Art Gallery, New Haven (Connecticut), 1950, *French Paintings of the Latter Half of the Nineteenth Century*, no. 17 (lent by Stephen C. Clark); Knoedler, New York, 1954, *A Collector's Taste: Selections from the Collection of Mr. and Mrs. Stephen C. Clark*, no. 17, Musée de l'Orangerie, Paris, 1955, *De David à Toulouse-Lautrec*, no. 49

(lent by Stephen C. Clark); Wildenstein Gallery, New York, 1958, *Renoir*, no. 67 (lent by Stephen C. Clark); Yale University Art Gallery, New Haven (Connecticut), 1960, *Paintings, Drawings and Sculpture Collected by Yale Alumni*, no. 60 (lent by Stephen C. Clark); Baltimore Museum of Art, 1964, *1914; An Exhibition of Paintings, Drawings, and Sculpture Created in 1914*, no. 202.

EX COLL.: Tilla Durieux, Berlin; [Étienne Bignou, New York, 1935]; Stephen C. Clark, New York (from 1935).

BEQUEST OF STEPHEN C. CLARK, 1960.

Morisot

Berthe Morisot. Born in Bourges in 1841; died in Paris in 1895. Berthe Morisot's father was a high government official, who held posts in Caen and Rennes before settling, when Berthe was about eleven, in Paris. When she was sixteen, the early interest she and her sister Edma had shown in drawing, led her parents to send them for lessons to a little-known painter named Chocarne. They soon transferred to Joseph Alexandre Guichard, a painter who had studied with Ingres and was able to give them a solid training in drawing. Under his direction Berthe Morisot began copying in the Louvre. There she especially admired the work of landscape painters. Wishing to work out of doors herself, she began in 1860 to take some lessons from Corot, who became a regular guest in her family circle. After several summers of painting under his direction she took lessons with one of his pupils, Achille François Oudinot and about the same time made the acquaintance of Daubigny and Daumier.

In 1864 Berthe Morisot made her debut at the Salon with two landscapes and in the following decade exhibited there frequently. During these years she worked steadily, in the winters in her studio in Paris and in the vacations with her family in Normandy and Brittany. It was in 1868 that she was formally introduced to Édouard Manet, who had already noticed her work. From this time on she enjoyed a lively friendship with him, posing for him, submitting to his influence in her painting, and in turn exerting some influence on his. The two families also established a warm social relationship, and in 1874 Berthe Morisot was married to Manet's younger brother Eugène. This was also the year of the first Impressionist exhibition, to which Berthe Morisot, resolving never again to contribute to the official Salon, sent nine pictures.

The world of artists in which she lived both before and after her marriage was of the greatest importance to her work and to her intellectual development, bringing her into frequent friendly contact with the best painters of the time and also with many writers and musicians, including Zola, Baudelaire, Chabrier, and Rossini. Renoir, Degas, and Monet saw her frequently, and the poet Mallarmé became one of her greatest admirers and friends. She traveled widely in France and also visited Spain, England,

Italy, and the Low Countries. After Manet's death in 1883 she took an active part in the organization of an exhibition and sale of his works.

The form-destroying light that makes early Impressionist paintings so brilliant was Berthe Morisot's major preoccupation during most of her career. In her last years, however, she gave a new attention to drawing, as Renoir had done in the eighties, in an effort to strengthen her modeling and emphasize plasticity, especially in her paintings of the human figure, for which her daughter Julie and her young niece were frequent models. Short separate staccato brush-strokes were replaced by longer sinuous curving ones, which give a linear definition to form. Berthe Morisot's subject matter creates an image of the pleasant serene life that she and her family led, and her very feminine attitude and style are admirably adapted to the themes she treated. Had she lived beyond the three decades that encompass her short career she might have carried her late style even farther in the direction of strength and solidity, but it is improbable that she would have adopted the most drastic of Post-Impressionist developments.

The Seine below the Pont d'Iéna
64.149.4

This is one of the sensitive views of familiar sites in Paris that Berthe Morisot painted in the early years of her career. Daubigny influenced her at this time, and the Museum's picture of the Seine recalls the kind of quiet landscape he was painting at the beginning of the sixties.

Signed (at lower right): *B. M.*

64.149.4

Oil on canvas. H. 20, w. 31½ in. (50.8 x 80 cm.).

REFERENCES: M. Angoulvent, *Berthe Morisot* [1933], pp. 21, 118 (no. 13), catalogues the painting, comments on the manner in which the artist evokes the exact sensations she has received from landscape // M. L. Bataille and G. Wildenstein, *Berthe Morisot* (1961), p. 23, no. 11, pl. 4, catalogue it under the year 1866.

EXHIBITED: Paris, Salon of 1867, no. 1100 (Vue prise en aval du pont d'Iéna); Musée de l'Orangerie, Paris, 1941, *Berthe Morisot*, no. 6 (La Seine au point du jour, lent by M. Octave Thomas); Musée Toulouse-Lautrec, Albi, 1958, *Berthe Morisot*, no. 3 (La Seine au point du jour, lent by M. Octave Thomas); Wildenstein Gallery, New York, 1960, *Berthe Morisot*, no. 2; Musée Jacquemart André, Paris, 1961, *Berthe Morisot*, no. 2; Wildenstein Gallery, London, 1961, *Berthe Morisot*, no. 2.

EX COLL.: Octave Thomas (by 1941, in 1958); [Wildenstein, New York, 1960–1961]; Mary V. T. Eberstadt, New York.

GIFT OF MARY V. T. EBERSTADT, SUBJECT TO A LIFE ESTATE IN THE DONOR, 1964.

Henri Rousseau

Henri Julien Félix ("le Douanier") Rousseau. Born in Laval (Mayenne) in 1844; died in Paris in 1910. Henri Rousseau was the son of a tinsmith at Laval. He studied law, but he never received any formal instruction in art. According to his own account he worked without any master but nature, asserting, however, that he had gotten some advice from two of the most popular teachers of his day, Gérôme and Clément.

He appears to have served twice in the army, from 1864 to 1868, and again as a sergeant for about five months during the war of 1870. It has frequently been reported, without proof, that during his earlier term of service he accompanied the French expedition to Mexico. For twenty-two years (1871–1893) he held a post at the toll office of Paris, and, though he was nicknamed "le Douanier," or Customs Inspector, by Jarry, he was actually only a minor inspector at the city limits. Besides painting he had numerous other talents and interests, playing the violin, the flute, and other instruments. He wrote little pieces for the theater and supplemented his small income by opening a school, where he taught, for a very low fee, painting, music, diction, and solfeggio.

Rousseau had been painting for many years and had copied old masters in the Louvre when he retired in 1893 and devoted himself entirely to being an artist. He had exhibited four paintings at the Salon des Indépendants in 1886 and from then on showed there regularly; he also contributed three times to the Salon d'Automne. Gauguin and Pissarro noticed his work and from about 1906 on he was much admired by other painters, including Picasso, Derain, and Vlaminck. Poets and literary men as well as art critics made much of him, and Alfred Jarry, the author of *Ubu Roi*, introduced him to artistic circles. Guillaume Apollinaire, Max Jacob, Georges Duhamel, and Jules Romains became his admirers. During the last years of his life he participated eagerly in the bohemian amusements of this lively group, acting as host at evening parties, where he offered as entertainment musical performances by his pupils. In 1908 he was the guest of honor at a now famous banquet in the studio of Picasso. Soon after his death a serious appreciation of his work began, marked by Wilhelm Uhde's monograph that was published in 1911. In that year there was a retrospective exhibition of his paintings at the Salon des Indépendants and in 1912 another at the Galerie Bernheim-Jeune.

Henri Rousseau's pictorial range was great, and it was also exceptionally varied. He painted landscapes, portraits, still life, scenes from real life, and allegories. The most original and probably the finest of his works were his imaginary compositions, which often had exotic themes. He made trips to the zoo and the botanical gardens, gathered bouquets of flowers, and sketched from nature to provide the realistic basis for his fantastic inventions, which probably accounts for their extraordinary vigor. His inspiration was powerfully poetic rather than naïve, and his vision, though innocent of convention, was refined and completely personal. Neither a "Sunday painter" nor a folk painter, he eludes classification and must be thought of as a great master who was self-taught. In spite of his non-involvement in the artistic currents of his time and his complete independence of them, he did not play an isolated historic role. His attitude was opposed to the sensuous approach of the Impressionists, but because of his desire to give expression to subjective poetry and to create forms with freedom, Gauguin, the Fauves, and Picasso prized his work.

The Repast of the Lion   51.112.5

This is one of a number of pictures by Rousseau showing the wild mysterious life of the jungle as he imagined it. From 1891, when he painted The Storm in the Jungle, he delighted in creating these vivid exotic scenes, which he himself found credible and threatening. This one shows a lion in the act of devouring a smaller wild beast with spotted skin, probably a jaguar. A similar animal appears in a picture in the Kunstmuseum in Basel dated 1907, which is so like also in the arrangement of the plant forms that it suggests that the Museum's painting was done in the same year (Ref., Bouret, 1961, pl. 31). Rousseau indeed exhibited at the Salon d'Automne of 1907, along with three others, a painting that he himself described, in conversations with Vollard, as A Combat of a Lion with a Jaguar, which could well be our picture.

Although the circle of light behind the little

51.112

hills in the middle of the horizon is very pale, more like the moon than the sun, the sky is as blue as if it were day. The dreamlike unreality is increased by the disproportion between the size of the beasts and the huge flowers. The sharply defined, motionless stems and leaves compose, with extreme refinement, a monumental tapestry.

Signed (at lower right): *Henri Rousseau.*

Oil on canvas. H. 44¾, w. 63 in. (113.7 x 160 cm.).

REFERENCES: W. Uhde, *Henri Rousseau* (1914), ill. (unnumbered plate), as Urwaldlandschaft, in the collection of Julius Keller, Aachen // C. Einstein, *Die Kunst des 20. Jahrhunderts* (1926), ill. p. 241, dates it 1904 // P. Soupault, *Henri Rousseau le Douanier* (1927), pl. 19, wrongly calls it Le Lion ayant faim se jette sur l'antilope // S. Bourgeois, *The Adolph Lewisohn Collection of Modern French Paintings . . .* (1928), pp. 196f., ill., identifies the lion's prey wrongly as a crocodile // S. Bourgeois and W. George, *Formes*, XXVIII–XXIX (1932), pp. 301, 306, ill. after p. 304 // A. Vollard, *Recollections of a Picture Dealer* (1936), pp. 216f., relates a dream Rousseau had about his picture of a lion and a jaguar shown in the Salon d'Automne of 1907 (possibly to be identified with this painting) // R. Grey, *Henri Rousseau* (1943), p. 51, pl. 123 // R. H. Wilenski, *Modern French Painters* (1944), pp. 206, 363 // Metropolitan Museum, *Art Treasures* (1952), p. 234, cat. no. 153, pl. 153 // J. Bouret, *Henri Rousseau* (1961), p. 259, no. 160, ill. p. 219 // H. Certigny, *La Vérité sur le douanier Rousseau* (1961), pp. 281f., quotes Vollard (see Ref. 1936) // D. Vallier, *Henri Rousseau* (1961), ill. in color p. 101 with the date 1907.

EXHIBITED: Paris, Salon d'Automne, 1907, no. 1493 or 1494 (as Paysage exotique, possibly this picture); Kunstmuseum, Winterthur, 1921; Bourgeois Gallery, New York, 1923; Union League Club, New York, 1924, "*Modern*" Pictures, no. 30 (as Lion and Crocodile, but probably this picture); Metropolitan

Museum, 1951, *The Lewisohn Collection*, no. 75.

EX COLL.: Julius Keller, Aachen (c. 1914); [Stephan Bourgeois, New York, 1923]; Adolph Lewisohn, New York (probably from 1923–1938; Cat., 1928, p. 196, ill.); Samuel A. Lewisohn, New York (from 1938).

BEQUEST OF SAMUEL A. LEWISOHN, 1951.

The Banks of the Bièvre near Bicêtre
39.15

In a signed note pasted on the back of the stretcher of this picture, the artist identifies it as a view of the banks of the Bièvre near Bicêtre in springtime.[1] The Bièvre is a little stream that rises near Versailles and, running underground, empties into the Seine in Paris. It formerly skirted the Jardin des Plantes, which Rousseau frequently visited. Bicêtre is today a suburb of Paris, where since the early nineteenth century there has been an asylum, workhouse, and prison. Although Rousseau dated his note February 23, 1909, the foliage represented in the painting is too far advanced for February in the Île de France, where the season was especially slow that year, according to newspaper accounts. It is probable that the date on this sticker, as on a number of others Rousseau attached to his paintings, records the time when the annotation, not the picture, was made.

In style this little landscape is related to the works made two or three years before the turn of the century, like the landscape in a private collection in Paris dated 1897, which shows sharply defined paths through the grass like those in the Museum's picture, and also a railway viaduct (Ref., Bouret, 1961, fig. 107).

Formerly called Spring in the Valley of the Bièvre.

Signed (at lower right): *H. Rousseau.*

Oil on canvas. H. 21½, w. 18 in. (54.6 x 45.7 cm.).

Note 1. "Une Vue de Bords de la Bièvre près

39.15

Bicêtre Printemps. 23 Février 1909. H. Rousseau."

REFERENCES: H. B. Wehle, *Met. Mus. Bull.*, XXXIV (1939), pp. 64f., ill., comments on the disciplined talent shown in this picture // D. C. Rich, *Henri Rousseau* (1942), ill. p. 57, dates it tentatively 1908–1910 // D. Cooper, *Burl. Mag.*, LXXXIV–LXXXV (1944), p. 164, ill. opp. p. 159, dates it tentatively 1908 and

lists it as one example showing the diversity of the artist's landscape themes after 1895 // W. Uhde, *Rousseau (le Douanier)* (1948), pl. 40, dates it 1908–1910, calls it Landschaft vor Paris mit Viadukt // D. Cooper, *Rousseau* (1951), p. 12, ill. (unnumbered plate), dates it 1908 // J. Bouret, *Henri Rousseau* (1961), p. 251, no. 38, ill. p. 135 in color // D. Vallier, *Henri Rousseau* (1961), fig. 92, dated around 1904 // *De Lusthof der Naïeven* (exhib. cat.), Museum Boymans-van Beuningen, Rotterdam (1964), no. 21, dates it c. 1903/04.

EXHIBITED: Art Institute of Chicago and Museum of Modern Art, New York, 1942, *Henri Rousseau*; Wildenstein Gallery, 1942, *Six Masters of Post-Impressionism*, no. 43 (with the date 1908–1910); XXV Biennale, Venice, 1950, Sala LVII, *Il Doganiere Rousseau*, no. 19 (on p. 242 of cat.); Casino Communale, Knokke-Le Zoute, 1958, *Les Peintres naïfs*, no. 5; Galerie Charpentier, Paris, 1961, *Henri Rousseau*, no. 63; Museum Boymans-van Beuningen, Rotterdam, 1964, *De Lusthof der Naïeven*, no. 21.

EX COLL.: Private collection, France (from 1901); [Alex Reid and Lefevre, London, until 1936]; [Étienne Bignou, Paris and New York, in 1936]; Marshall Field, New York (from 1936).

GIFT OF MARSHALL FIELD, 1939.

Gauguin

Eugène Henri Paul Gauguin, called Paul Gauguin. Born in Paris in 1848; died in 1903 in the village of Atuana on the island of Hiva-Oa in the Marquesas. Gauguin's father was a journalist and his mother the daughter of a writer who had been an early partisan in the labor movement in France. As a small child he spent four years with his mother's Spanish-Peruvian family in Lima and later, between the ages of seventeen and twenty-three, sailed as a member of the crew to Rio de Janeiro, Bahia, and other distant ports. The impression made on Gauguin by these early contacts with exotic countries was not erased during the eleven years he spent in the brokerage firm of Bertin in Paris. He proved adept in financial speculation and married and established a family, but he was also an enthusiastic "Sunday" painter and had a landscape in the style of Jongkind accepted by the Salon of 1876. Through Pissarro he met the other Impressionists, bought pictures by them, and imitated their technique in his own works. In 1883 during a business depression he decided to resign from Bertin's in order to devote himself entirely to painting. After failing in Paris and Rouen to earn enough to support his wife and children, he took them to Copenhagen, where his wife's family lived. He soon left them in Denmark and returned to Paris. Poverty forced him at this time to part with most of his own collection of pictures. In 1886 he made his first trip to Pont-Aven in Brittany, where he met Émile Bernard. In the same year in Paris he made the acquaintance of Degas and also met Van Gogh, who admired him and became his friend.

In the spring and summer of 1887, in the company of Charles Laval, Gauguin visited Panama and Martinique. This was his first voyage to the tropics since his early youth and the beginning of a significant alteration in his style of painting. In the three following years he made long stays in Brittany. He joined Van Gogh for a short time in Arles in 1888, but this brief visit and their friendship were terminated by Van Gogh's first attack of madness and the well-known gruesome episode when Vincent slashed his own ear.

Gauguin held a one-man show in Paris in 1888 and the next year had pictures in a group exhibition at the Café Volpin, but he did not manage to sell a single work. Finally in 1891, yearning for an utterly simple life, which he believed he could lead in a strange natural world surrounded only by primitive people, Gauguin set out for Tahiti.

For two years, enchanted by the country and the people, he painted some of his finest pictures and put together in an illustrated manuscript, *L'Ancien Culte mahorie*, the native myths that he found so interesting and attractive. Even in Tahiti, however, his lack of money became acute, and he returned in 1893 to France. Durand-Ruel gave him a one-man show, and a small, unexpected inheritance enabled him to enjoy a brief period of freedom from cares. But his eccentric and restless personality made life in France impossible; once more disgusted with Western civilization and longing for the tropics, he returned to Tahiti in 1895.

Sickness, recurrent poverty, and loneliness made his self-chosen exile in the South Seas a miserable one for most of the eight remaining years of his life. With increasing success, however, he translated into paint all his discontent and his compensating dreams. In 1897 he summarized his beliefs in the large allegory of human life now in the Boston Museum, which he entitled "D'où venons-nous? Que sommes-nous? Où allons-nous?" (Where do we come from? What are we? Where are we going?).

In 1901, still in pursuit of an earthly paradise, Gauguin moved to Hiva-Oa, the largest of the Marquesan islands, and settled in the remote village of Atuana. Here he painted some of his most remarkable pictures and devoted much time to reflection and writing, producing a study of religion and the church and also *Avant et Après*, a book of memoirs combined with imagined episodes. He died in the house he had built for himself in Atuana.

The style of Gauguin's paintings at the beginning of his career was based on the work of the Barbizon painters and later on that of the Impressionists. But he very early arrived at Cézanne's belief that the purely visual sensations on which the Impressionists concentrated could not produce a strong expression of emotion. He was convinced that intelligence and discipline must be the basis for composing a picture. He avoided the direct imitation of nature and searched for purity in color, for strength and rhythm in line, and for simplified form. To his childhood familiarity with Peruvian idols he added an interest in Egyptian and Indian art and in Japanese prints. Folk art in general attracted him, especially the peasant art of Brittany. At Pont-Aven in 1888 he discussed his ideas with Émile Bernard, who had drawn from the study of medieval stained glass certain theories about style. They formulated a new doctrine about painting and founded a school in which many admiring young artists looked to Gauguin for leadership. He then began to paint in a new way, with flat areas of intense color surrounded by heavy outlines. This was the compartmented style that came to be known as *Synthétisme*, or, because of the heavy outlines, as *Cloisonnisme*. This kind of painting, deliberately primitive and decorative, strove to express poetic ideas in simplified plastic terms and embodied the essence of the artistic and literary movement of Symbolism.

The pictures that Gauguin painted between 1891 and 1893 on his first trip to Tahiti mark his emergence as a great imaginative painter. He filled them with the richness of the tropical world around him and the mystery that he detected beneath the happy, child-like attitudes of the island people. During his second stay in the South Seas he achieved a remarkable combination of monumentality, serenity, and moving poetry. His last pictures, made in Atuana, were painted with a new palette, rich in pastel rose and violet tones, and they are distinguished by their strange, dreamlike beauty.

Along with Cézanne and Van Gogh, Gauguin is one of the most influential artists of the twentieth century. Less powerful than they, he exerted, nevertheless, a much more impressive and widespread influence. His revaluation of primitive and folk art and of the archaic art of Asia created a taste that has continued into the present time. His intellectuality anticipated surrealism. With extraordinary courage he renounced all the time-honored conventions of Western art, shunning classical perspective, tactile modeling, and transitions between light and shadow. He concentrated on making the picture's surface both decorative and expressive, the problem that has obsessed the artists of the twentieth century. By insisting that color and line alone, regardless of their representational values, can make a powerful emotional impact, Gauguin cleared the way for abstract art and theory.

Ia Orana Maria   51.112.2

This is the first important picture that Gauguin painted in Tahiti and the most impressive of the group made during his first stay there. It shows the new style that he had developed, less abstract than the compartmented *(cloisonné)* style of his Brittany period. The title, which was inscribed on the painting by the artist himself, means, in the

IA ORANA MARIA

language of the Maori, "I hail thee, Mary," —the opening words of the angel's salutation to the Virgin Mary at the moment of the Annunciation. Well before he painted this picture, Gauguin had already tried in France to revive Christian themes, interpreting them according to the strong and ingenuous feelings of the very old civilization of Brittany, which still bore the marks of paganism. The angel, his words, and the halos around the heads of the Mother and Child are the only elements that Gauguin has taken from traditional representations of the Annunciation. Everything else in the picture has been rendered in the Tahitian idiom: the types of the divine beings as well as those of the worshipers, the costumes, the landscape, and the fruit in the foreground that resembles the offerings Tahitians lay at the feet of their idols. The picture, furthermore, is enriched with the colors of Tahiti. It has been pointed out that the flowering tree and the two worshipers with their hands folded in the attitude of prayer were directly inspired by a bas-relief in the Javanese temple of Boro-Budur, which Gauguin knew from a photograph he had with him in Tahiti (Ref., Dorival, 1951, p. 118, fig. 15).

Gauguin subsequently reused many of the motifs from this painting in other works. The figures of the Virgin and Child appear again with some variations in a water color,[1] a charcoal drawing,[2] two monotypes,[3] and zinc engravings.[4] The angel and the woman with the flowered skirt are in the water color inscribed Te Faruru;[5] the woman alone reappears in Parau Parau (Words, Words)[6] and in Haere Pape (Bather by the River).[7] Bernard Dorival recognized several studies for the Ia Orana Maria in a Gauguin notebook that he published in facsimile (Ref., 1954).

Gauguin offered this picture, which he considered one of his best, as a gift to the Luxembourg, but the curator Léonce Bénédite refused it (Ref., Perruchot, 1961). When a reproduction of it was published in Figaro illustré he cut it out, retouched it with water color, and pasted it in his manuscript of Noa Noa.

Signed and dated (at lower right): P. Gauguin, 91.

Inscribed (at lower left): IA ORANA MARIA.

Oil on canvas. H. 44¾, w. 34½ in. (113.7 x 87.7 cm.).

Notes: 1. In 1933 in the coll. of Frederic C. Bartlett, Chicago, ill., Bull. of the Art Institute of Chicago, 19 (1925), p. 85. 2. J. Rewald, Gauguin Drawings (1958), p. 30, no. 51, ill. 3. Ibid, p. 29, nos. 48, 50, ill. 4. M. Guérin, Oeuvre gravé de Gauguin (1927), 1, pl. 51. 5. Gaz. des B.-A., XLVII (1956), ill. p. 123. 6. Ref., Goldwater, 1957, ill. in color p. 113. 7. Ref., Malingue, 1948, p. 180.

REFERENCES: P. Gauguin, Lettres ... à Georges Daniel de Monfreid (1920), p. 86 (Mar. 11, 1892), describes this picture and implies that it is the only finished work made up to this date in Tahiti // A. Delaroche, D'Un Point de vue esthétique (1893), reprinted in P. Gauguin, Intimate Journals (1921), p. 41, interprets the picture // C. Morice, Preface to Oeuvres récentes de Paul Gauguin (exhib. cat.), Durand-Ruel, Paris (Nov. 1893), pp. 14f., interprets the religious character of the picture // A. Jarry, in guestbook of the pension of Marie-Jeanne Le Gloanec at Pont-Aven (July 1, 1894), a poem dedicated to Gauguin, inspired by this picture (reprinted in Gauguin et le groupe de Pont-Aven, exhib. cat. by G. Martin-Méry, Musée des Beaux-Arts, Quimper, 1950, no. 24) // P. Gauguin, Lettres ... à Georges Daniel de Monfreid (1920), p. 254 (June, 1899), indicates his wish to have the picture exhibited at Vollard's gallery; p. 281 (Apr., 1900), expresses the desire to have it shown in an exhibition at Durand-Ruel's gallery in connection with the World's Fair // P. Gauguin, Letters to Ambroise Vollard and André Fontainas (1943), p. 39 (Sept. 1900, to Vollard), tells of selling it to Michel Manzi for 2000 francs // C. Morice, in P. Gauguin and C. Morice, Noa Noa (1901), p. 19, repeats with variations his interpretation of the picture published in the catalogue of the 1893 exhibition at Durand-Ruel's; Paul Gauguin

(1919), pp. 171, 183, 201, ill. opp. p. 184 (monotype) // C. Chassé, *Gauguin et le groupe de Pont-Aven* (1921), pp. 50f., reports that the husband of Marie Henry, who kept the inn at Le Pouldu, found in the head of the Virgin a great likeness to the portrait of Marie painted by Meyer de Haan // M. Denis, *Journal*, III (1959), p. 83, entry dated Oct. 3, 1927, notes that he had restored the picture // W. Barth, *Paul Gauguin* (1929), p. 144 // A. Alexandre, *Paul Gauguin* (1930), pp. 135f., 140, 161, 263, ill. pp. 133, 261 (monotype), analyzes the classic qualities of this picture, compares the composition with that of the Yellow Christ and pictures Gauguin made later // R. H. Wilenski, *French Painting* (1931), pp. 289, 294 // Pola Gauguin, *My Father, Paul Gauguin* (1937), pp. 171f., connects this picture with the pleasure Gauguin felt in learning that Juliette Huet, back in Paris, had borne him a daughter // R. J. Goldwater, *Primitivism in Modern Painting* (1938), p. 65, pl. v, fig. 10, suggests that Gauguin tried to restore the original human simplicity to this subject by representing it in terms of everyday primitive life // S. A. Lewisohn, *Art News* (Annual), XXXVII (Feb. 25, 1939), p. 154, ill. p. 69 (hanging in the Lewisohn house) // M. Malingue, *Gauguin* (1948), pl. 192, ill. in color // H. Perruchot, *Gauguin* (1948), pp. 188–191, ill. opp. p. 97, compares this picture with the Yellow Christ, stresses the paganism and primitivism that underlie its Christian subject matter // J. Leymarie, *Gauguin* (exhib. cat.), Musée de l'Orangerie, Paris (1949), no. 25, pl. VIII, observes that the figure of the woman at the left was used again in Haere Pape, emphasizes the importance Gauguin accorded the Museum's picture; no. 98 (zincograph), no. 108 (letter to Monfreid, Mar. 11, 1892), no. 110 and appendix IV (unpublished letter, 1894–1895), mentions the illustration in *Figaro Illustré* // L. van Dovski [H. Lewandowski], *Paul Gauguin* (1950), p. 347, no. 245, pl. 22 // B. Dorival, *Burl. Mag.*, XCIII (1951), p. 118, fig. 16, traces the source of various elements in this picture to the frieze at Boro-Budur (fig. 15) // R. Huyghe, *Présentation de*

l'ancien culte mahorie (1951) (bound with facsimile reproduction of the manuscript), p. 14, relates a still life on p. 25 of the manuscript to the one in the foreground of this painting // H. Dorra, *Met. Mus. Bull.*, X (1952), pp. 255–260, ill. p. 254, discusses the stylistic relations between this picture and the Breton works that Gauguin had made earlier, does not regard the Tahitian milieu as a decisive influence on his new style, which had already evolved before he left France // Metropolitan Museum, *Art Treasures* (1952), p. 234, cat. no. 152, pl. 152 // H. Dorra, *Gaz. des B.-A.*, XLI (1953), p. 189, ill. p. 191 // B. Dorival, text accompanying facsimile reproduction of Paul Gauguin's *Carnet de Tahiti* (1954), pp. 26, 36, identifies drawings on pp. 72 verso and 73 recto and verso of the notebook as studies for the worshipper in the light skirt, the feet of the Virgin, and the foliage // J. Rewald, *Post-Impressionism* (1956), pp. 502, 506, 509, ill., with a detail of the frieze of Barabudur (Boro-Budur) // R. Goldwater, *Gauguin* [1957], pp. 100f., ill. in color // A. Frankfurter, *Art News Annual*, XXVIII (1959), p. 43 // R. Huyghe, H. Perruchot, et al., *Gauguin* (1960), pp. 87, 90, [196f.], ill. // H. Perruchot, *La Vie de Gauguin* (1961), pp. 271, 275, tells how this picture was rejected when Gauguin offered it as a gift to the Luxembourg; notes that Manzi's willingness to pay 2,000 francs for it was exceptional among purchasers of pictures by Gauguin // G. Wildenstein, *Gauguin* (1964), pp. 167f., no. 428, ill. p. 167, fig. 428, catalogues it in great detail with many relevant quotations.

EXHIBITED: Durand-Ruel, Paris, 1893, *Oeuvres récentes de Paul Gauguin*, no. 1; Metropolitan Museum, 1920, *Fiftieth Anniversary Exhibition*, cat. p. 10 (lent by Adolph Lewisohn), and 1921, *Impressionist and Post-Impressionist Paintings*, no. 47 (lent by A. Lewisohn); Union League Club, New York, 1924, *"Modern" Pictures*, no. 16 (lent by A. Lewisohn); Durand-Ruel Gallery, New York, 1928, *French Masterpieces of the Late Nineteenth Century*, no. 8 (lent by A. Lewisohn); Knoedler Gallery, New York, 1928, *A Century of French Painting*, no. 29 (lent by A. Lewisohn); Museum of Modern Art, New York, 1930, *Summer Retrospective*, no. 39 (lent by A. Lewisohn); Royal Academy, London, 1932, *French Art, 1200–1900*, no. 540, commemorative catalogue, 1933, no. 382 (lent by A. Lewisohn); Art Institute of Chicago, 1933, *A Century of Progress*, no. 366 (lent by A. Lewisohn); Museum of Modern Art, New York, 1934–1935, *Modern Works of Art*, no. 12 (lent by A. Lewisohn); Pennsylvania Museum of Art, Philadelphia, 1935, *Post-Impressionism* (lent by A. Lewisohn); Toledo Museum of Art, 1935, *Cézanne—Gauguin* (lent by A. Lewisohn); Wildenstein Gallery, New York, 1936, *Paul Gauguin*, no. 17 (lent from the Adolph Lewisohn collection); Cleveland Museum of Art, 1936, *Twentieth Anniversary Exhibition*, no. 276 (lent from the Adolph Lewisohn collection); Palais National des Arts, Paris, 1937, *Chefs-d'oeuvre de l'art français*, no. 326 (lent from the Adolph Lewisohn collection); Museum of Modern Art, New York, 1939, *Art in Our Time*, no. 67 (lent from the Lewisohn collection); World's Fair, New York, 1940, *Masterpieces of Art*, no. 355 (lent from the Lewisohn collection); Wildenstein Gallery, New York, 1946, *Paul Gauguin*, no. 19 (lent by Mr. and Mrs. Samuel A. Lewisohn); Museum of Modern Art, New York, 1946, *New York Private Collections*; Musée de l'Orangerie, Paris, 1949, *Gauguin*, no. 25 (lent by Mr. and Mrs. Samuel A. Lewisohn); Paul Rosenberg Gallery, New York, 1950, *Nineteenth-Century Heritage*, no. 8 (lent by Mr. and Mrs. S. A. Lewisohn); Metropolitan Museum, 1951, *The Lewisohn Collection*, no. 34; Musée National d'art Moderne, Paris, 1952, *L'Oeuvre du XXe siècle*, no. 31; Wildenstein Gallery, New York, 1956, *Gauguin*, no. 22; Art Institute of Chicago and Metropolitan Museum, 1959, *Gauguin*, no. 28.

EX COLL.: Michel Manzi, Paris (purchased at the Durand-Ruel exhibition, Nov., 1893; sale, Galerie Manzi et Joyant, Paris, Mar. 13–14, 1919, no. 56, to Knoedler); [Knoedler, New York, 1919]; Adolph Lewisohn, New York

(1919–1938; Cat., 1928, p. 161, ill.); Samuel A. Lewisohn, New York (1938–1951).

BEQUEST OF SAMUEL A. LEWISOHN, 1951.

Tahitian Landscape   39.182

The date on this picture, though difficult to read, is without doubt 1891, the year Gauguin arrived in Tahiti for the first time. This date is supported by the fact that several of its motifs are linked to drawings in a notebook (Ref., Dorival, 1954) used by Gauguin in Tahiti in 1891 and 1892. This notebook contains a sketch of a horse and some trees (p. 39 recto) and several figures wearing round hats that are similar to those in this painting. In style and color this landscape still recalls Gauguin's work of the Brittany period. It is also related to paintings made in Tahiti in 1891, like the Haere Temai, a landscape with two black hogs, now in the collection of J. K. Thannhauser in New York (ill. in color in J. Rewald, *Gauguin*, 1938, p. 105). It may well be one of the "studies" that Gauguin, writing to his friend George Daniel de Monfreid, men-

39.182

tioned having done before he painted the Ia Orana Maria (see below), his first major work in Tahiti (*Lettres . . . à Georges Daniel de Monfreid*, 1920, p. 86, letter of Mar. 11, 1892).

Signed and dated (at lower left): *P. Gauguin* 9[*1*].

Oil on canvas. H. 25⅜, w. 18⅝ in. (64.5 x 47.3 cm.).

REFERENCES: H. B. Wehle, *Met. Mus. Bull.*, xxxv (1940), pp. 56f., ill., accepts the date of 1891, finds in this picture a continuation of Gauguin's Parisian method as well as the vividness of color characteristic of his South Sea paintings // M. Malingue, *Gauguin* (1948), p. 175, ill., dates it 1892 // L. van Dovski [H. Lewandowski], *Paul Gauguin* (1950), p. 348, no. 259, dates it 1892 // B. Dorival, text accompanying facsimile reproduction of Paul Gauguin's *Carnet de Tahiti* (1954), pp. 23f., regards the drawings on page 39 recto of the notebook as studies for this painting // G. Wildenstein, *Gauguin* (1964), p. 175, no. 442, ill. fig. 442, catalogues it with the title *Cheval au pâturage*.

EXHIBITED: Art Institute of Chicago and Metropolitan Museum, 1959, *Gauguin*, no. 32.

EX COLL.: Private collection, France (from 1897; bought from the artist); [Étienne Bignou, Paris and New York, until 1935]; Marshall Field, Chicago (1935).

ANONYMOUS GIFT, 1939.

A Farm in Brittany 54.143.2

This picture must have been painted around 1894, which is the year inscribed on another landscape (Hugo Perls coll., New York) showing the same place but with more of the tree trunk at the right and with only two houses at the left-hand margin of the painting. In the summer of 1894, between his two stays in Tahiti, Gauguin worked at Le Pouldu and Pont-Aven in Brittany, and in one of these places he probably found the subject of the two pictures. Most of the Brittany landscapes that Gauguin painted in the late eighties before his first departure for Tahiti are very

54.143.2

different in style, much less simplified in composition and pattern and with separate brush strokes in the Impressionist manner.

Signed (at lower left): *P. Gauguin*.

Oil on canvas. H. 28½, w. 35⅝ in. (72.4 x 90.5 cm.).

REFERENCES: F. Burger, *Cézanne und Hodler* (1913), I, pp. 95f., II, pl. 83, analyzes the composition of this picture // H. Perruchot, *Gauguin* (1948), ill. opp. p. 80, places it wrongly in the Hugo Perls collection // G. Wildenstein, *Gauguin* (1964), pp. 215f., no. 526, ill. p. 216, fig. 526, catalogues it, dating it in the same year as the painting in the Perls collection.

EXHIBITED: Metropolitan Museum, 1921, *Impressionist and Post-Impressionist Paintings*, no. 49 (dated 1892, lent by Joseph Stransky); Museum of Modern Art, New York, 1934–1935, *Modern Works of Art*, no. 11 (lent from the Adolph Lewisohn collection); San Francisco Museum of Art, 1936, *Gauguin*, no. 2 (lent by Mr. and Mrs. Sam Lewisohn); Wildenstein Gallery, New York, 1946, *Paul Gauguin*, no. 9 (dated 1889, lent by Mr. and Mrs. Samuel A. Lewisohn); Metropolitan Museum, 1951, *The Lewisohn Collection*, no. 33; Art Institute of Chicago and Metropolitan Museum, 1959, *Gauguin*, no. 59; Arkansas Arts Center, Little Rock, 1963, *Five Centuries of*

European Painting, cat. p. 48; Tate Gallery, London and Kunsthaus, Zurich, 1966, *Gauguin and the Pont Aven Group*.

EX COLL.: [J. K. Thannhauser, Munich]; Joseph Stransky, New York (in 1921); Adolph Lewisohn, New York (until 1938; Cat., 1928, pp. 158f., ill.); Samuel A. Lewisohn, New York (1938–1951); Margaret S. Lewisohn, New York (1951–1954).

BEQUEST OF MARGARET S. LEWISOHN, 1954.

Two Tahitian Women   49.58.1

This picture was painted in 1899 during Gauguin's second stay in Tahiti and is notable among the works of his late style for its ease and grace. In addition to the strength and animal health that Gauguin usually stressed in his paintings of Maori women, he has given these two a subtle feminine beauty. This was a quality the European public could accept and appreciate, and it doubtless explains the ready praise with which the picture was received at the Salon d'Automne of 1906.

The woman at the left has been identified as Pahura, a young Tahitian who lived with Gauguin at this time and bore him two children. The pose of the figure on the right with flowers clasped between her hands appears many times in works Gauguin made between 1896 and 1899 (ill. in Ref. Wildenstein, 1956). The position of the hands was inspired by the Javanese relief at Boro-Budur.

This picture is also called *Les Seins aux Fleurs Rouges* and *Tahitian Women with Mango Blossoms*.

Signed and dated (at lower left): 99 / *P. Gauguin*.

Oil on canvas. H. 37, w. 28½ in. (94 x 72.4 cm.).

REFERENCES: P. Jamot, *Gaz. des B.-A.*, XXXV (1906), p. 471, ill. opp. p. 470, relates this picture to the Three Tahitians of 1897 // A. Alexandre, *Paul Gauguin* (1930), p. 259, ill. p. 185 (with wrong title) // R. H. Wilenski, *Modern French Painters* [c. 1940], pp. 133, 138, pl. 45A, considers this and the Three

Tahitians more European than earlier works // H. Perruchot, *Gauguin* (1948), p. 298 // J. Leymarie, *Gauguin* (exhib. cat.), Musée de l'Orangerie, Paris (1949), no. 54, pl. XXI, relates it to other paintings by Gauguin // L. van Dovski [H. Lewandowski], *Paul Gauguin* (1950), p. 353, no. 357 // B. Dorival, *Burl. Mag.*, XCIII (1951), p. 121, notes in this picture Gauguin's dependence on the relief at Boro-Budur (fig. 15) // H. Dorra, *Met. Mus. Bull.*, X (1952), p. 259, ill. p. 257, finds it an example of the later mature style, notes the borrowing of Eastern elements of stylization // J. Rewald, *Paul Gauguin* (1952), p. 24, ill. in color on cover // F. Novotny, *Die grossen französischen Impressionisten* (1952), p. 60, pl. 37 // L. and E. Hanson, *The Noble Savage* (1954), pp. 253, 266, ill. opp. p. 256, identify the woman on the left as Pahura, one of Gauguin's native wives // B. Dorival, text accompanying facsimile reproduction of Paul Gauguin's *Carnet de Tahiti* (1954), p. 62, note for p. 39, quotes the opinion held by Mme Thirion in an unpublished manuscript that Gauguin took his inspiration for this picture from a drawing by H. Gray, illustrated in the *Courrier français*, no. 30, 1884 // H. Read, *Art News Annual*, XXV (1955), p. 144, ill. p. 123 in color // G. Wildenstein, *Gaz. des B.-A.*, XLVII (1956), pp. 137, 157, fig. 25, finds the same figures and poses in several other paintings (figs. 19, 23, 26–28) // R. Goldwater, *Gauguin* [1957], pp. 152f., ill. in color // R. Huyghe, H. Perruchot, et al., *Gauguin* (1960), pp. 60, 254, ill., state that the idea was suggested by the drawing in the *Courrier français* // G. Wildenstein, *Gauguin* (1964), p. 246, no. 583, ill. fig. 583, catalogues it in detail, citing drawings and other paintings with similar figures.

EXHIBITED: Grand Palais, Paris, 1906, *Salon d'Automne: Oeuvres de Gauguin*, no. 14 (Deux Tahitiennes, lent by G. Fayet); Metropolitan Museum, 1932, *Taste of Today* (lent by William Church Osborn); Royal Academy, London, 1932, *French Art, 1200–1900*, no. 536, commemorative catalogue, 1933, no. 387 (lent by William Church Osborn); Art Institute of

Chicago, 1933, *A Century of Progress*, no. 364; Durand-Ruel Gallery, New York, 1934, *Great French Masters*, no. 19 (lent anonymously); Pennsylvania Museum of Art, Philadelphia, 1935, *Post-Impressionists* (lent by W. C. Osborn); Wildenstein Gallery, New York, 1936, *Paul Gauguin*, no. 41 (lent by Mr. and Mrs. W. C. Osborn); Fogg Art Museum, Cambridge (Mass.), 1936, *Gauguin*, no. 40 (lent by Mr. and Mrs. William Church Osborn); Cleveland Museum of Art, 1936, *Twentieth Anniversary Exhibition*, no. 281 (lent by W. C. Osborn); Palais National des Arts, Paris, 1937, *Chefs-d'oeuvre de l'art français*, no. 327 (lent by W. C. Osborn); World's Fair, New York, 1940, *Masterpieces of Art*, no. 354 (lent by W. C. Osborn); Museum of Modern Art, New York, 1944, *Art in Progress*, cat. p. 27 (lent by W. C. Osborn); Wildenstein Gallery, New York, 1946, *Paul Gauguin*, no. 35 (lent by Mr. and Mrs. W. C. Osborn); Musée de l'Orangerie, Paris, 1949, *Gauguin*, no. 54; Kunstmuseum, Basel, 1949/50, *Paul Gauguin*, no. 61; Musée Cantonal des Beaux-Arts, Lausanne, 1950, *Paul Gauguin*, no. 17; Art Institute of Chicago and Metropolitan Museum, 1959, *Gauguin*, no. 64.

EX COLL.: Gustave Fayet, Igny, France (after 1925); [Wildenstein, New York, c. 1925–1930]; William Church Osborn, New York (1930–1949).

GIFT OF WILLIAM CHURCH OSBORN, 1949.

Lebourg

Albert Lebourg. Born in Montfort-sur-Risle (Eure) in 1849; died in Rouen in 1928. Lebourg began his career at about the age of seventeen, when he was sent to Rouen to study architecture under Alexis Drouin. In the Museum at Rouen he saw and admired the works of Ruysdael and Van Goyen and also landscapes by Corot, Ziem, and Daubigny, which the museum had recently acquired. Soon he too began to draw and paint landscapes, especially the scenery along the banks of the Seine, which became his favorite theme. In 1872 Laperlier, a collector and the president of the Société des Beaux-Arts in Algeria, offered him a position teaching drawing. Lebourg accepted, traveling to Africa in the fall of that year and remaining until 1877. In Algeria, where he painted decorations for the palace of the archbishop, he came to know another French painter, Jean Seignemartin, whose pictures impressed him deeply with their light and color. Concentrating in his own work on light and shadow and the effects of atmosphere, Lebourg began to paint studies, as Monet and Pissarro also did later, of the same subject at different times of day.

   Though established as an artist when he returned to Paris, Lebourg, seeking further instruction, worked for two years in the studio of J. P. Laurens, drawing from the antique. He soon came in contact with the Impressionist painters and contributed to their exhibitions in 1878 and 1880. He especially respected Claude Monet, whose aims in painting were similar to his own.

   During the eighties Lebourg painted at various seasons of the year in the region of the Auvergne. From 1895 to 1897 he lived in Holland, and in 1900 he made a short trip to England, renewing an interest that he had felt for some years in the English painters. Most of his time after his return from Algeria, however, was divided between Paris and Rouen. During the last seven years of his life, Lebourg, paralyzed, was unable to paint.

He was a prolific artist and very popular in his own day. His works were seen in many one-man exhibitions, which were well received by the critics. His gentle and sensitive landscapes were easily overshadowed by the splendid productions of the great Impressionist painters, but these artists felt a certain regard, as we do today, for his technique and the effects he achieved.

View of Rouen in Winter   60.55.3

60.55.3

Lebourg painted a number of views of Rouen similar to this one. They were apparently done from the northern bank of the Seine, facing the Île Lacroix and showing the Pont Corneille, which connects the island with the Quai de Paris.

This picture seems to have been painted about 1895. In technique and color it shows the influence of the Impressionists.

Signed (at lower right): *A. Lebourg*.

Oil on canvas. H. 19¾, w. 28⅝ in. (50.1 x 72.7 cm.).

Formerly called French River View.

REFERENCE: L. Bénédite, *Albert Lebourg* (1923), p. 356, no. 1369, ill. p. 141, publishes it as Vue de Rouen, en hiver, par temps clair, dating it c. 1895.

Ex COLL.: [Graat et Madoulé, Paris, in 1923]; Rupert L. Joseph, New York.

BEQUEST OF RUPERT L. JOSEPH, 1959.

Van Gogh

Vincent van Gogh. Born at Groot-Zundert in the Netherlands in 1853; died at Auvers-sur-Oise in France in 1890. Vincent van Gogh was the son of a Protestant clergyman and grew up in a religious atmosphere. He had some familiarity with painting at an early age, as three of his uncles were picture dealers, and at the age of sixteen he began to work for the Goupil Gallery in its various branches in The Hague, London, and Paris. When emotional instability led to his dismissal in the spring of 1876, he determined to devote his life to the poor. After some time spent in England holding minor

posts in schools and as assistant to a clergyman, he decided to study theology in Amsterdam but after a period of preparation found himself unable to take the examinations
for admission to the university. With continuing determination he went next to the
mining district of the Borinage in Belgium, where he shared the wretched existence of
the workmen he was trying to help. This too ended in failure, and in 1879 he entered
on a period of vagabondage and deep unhappiness.

After a few months he realized that his true destiny lay in painting, and he began
to study drawing in Brussels. He copied many works by Millet, whose subject matter
and humanitarian concepts influenced him deeply. Later at The Hague his cousin, the
painter Mauve, gave him some advice about painting, and the work of other Dutch
artists, such as Israels and Breitner, also impressed him. From 1883 to 1885 he lived
with his parents in Nuenen and spent his time wandering about the country sketching
the peasants and their surroundings. His first important painting, The Potato-Eaters,
dates from this period. It is somber in color and mood and completely unacademic in
its power of expression and its broad, personal technique.

In 1885 Vincent spent several months in Antwerp, where he discovered the amaz-
ing vitality of Rubens. This experience, along with his response to the light color range
of the Japanese prints so popular at the time, produced a startling effect, almost a shock,
on his personal way of seeing. Already well aware of his emotional imbalance, he now
dreamed of restoring his equilibrium by immersing himself in the creation of glowing
paintings. Early in 1886 he went to Paris, where his brother Theo, who worked at the
Goupil Gallery, took Vincent to live with him, and from this time until the end of his
life provided him with moral as well as financial support. In Paris he met Pissarro,
Degas, Gauguin, Seurat, Signac, and Toulouse-Lautrec and became identified with the
Impressionist movement. Under the influence of Impressionist painting Vincent's color
changed completely. He adopted a very light palette and applied the paint in vibrant
strokes. Within twenty months he painted more than two hundred pictures.

After he had absorbed all that Impressionism offered him, he felt the need of fresh
stimulation and a change of scene and light. The excitement of life in Paris, furthermore,
had proved a great strain. He therefore set off in 1888 for Arles in Provence. There he
achieved pure, brilliant color and vigorous, incisive drawing, and with these means
expressed his passionate feelings about the living quality in a human face or the play
of the wind and sun across the Provençal landscape. Vincent soon mastered this new
style completely and rendered his daring visions with increasing success. In his feverish
productiveness he turned out two hundred pictures in fifteen months, most of them
masterpieces. He never managed to sell anything, however, and he lived in great
poverty and misery. Worst of all, his mental illness began to cause him genuine anguish.
He quarreled bitterly with his friend Gauguin, who had joined him in Arles, tried to
kill him, and, driven beyond control, slashed one of his own ears. His hallucinations
and the crises to which he was subject were rendered even more harrowing because he
retained the ability to analyze his trouble with complete lucidity.

After a term in the hospital at Arles in 1889 Van Gogh entered the asylum of Saint Paul at Saint-Rémy. There, in spite of repeated attacks, he produced one hundred and fifty paintings and hundreds of drawings, working feverishly against his fear of total madness and his obsession with the idea of death. His painting at this time became wildly lyrical. Though his vision was inflamed by his unbalanced emotions, his expression continued to be precise and masterly.

After a year in Saint-Rémy Van Gogh went to Auvers-sur-Oise, near Paris, where he was placed in the care of Dr. Gachet, who was to become a faithful and devoted friend. At Auvers he painted his last works—poignantly tormented pictures in a style that betrayed occasional hesitations. There, in ultimate despair and with the knowledge that madness was inescapable, he shot himself at the age of thirty-seven.

Misjudged in its own day except by a few friends and superior artists, the art of Vincent van Gogh is recognized today as a development of the greatest significance for the twentieth century. He gave fresh life to the pictorial elements of painting by making color more radiant and, in contrast to the Impressionists, by strengthening drawing. His vigorously defined contours, his intense hues, his meaningful distortions, created a new style, alongside that of Gauguin. Van Gogh's work, however, is not only more powerful and richer in technical invention, it is also less stylized, more spontaneous and subjective. This is especially apparent in his drawings, which are among the most remarkable in all of Western art. His painting, which was an expression of his personal turbulence, paved the way for the violence of the Expressionists and the Fauves and gave direction to troubled spirits like Utrillo and Soutine. His deep compassion for suffering mankind, his obsession with light, his mystical vision, always firmly rooted in reality, relate Van Gogh to the greatest of his countrymen, Rembrandt. Since Impressionism was the determining influence on his work and he attained his artistic maturity in the atmosphere of France, Van Gogh is classified with the French as well as the Dutch. His numerous letters, among the most beautiful ever written by an artist, give evidence that he always held on to a deeply reasoned conception of his art.

Sunflowers   49.41

From the time when he became aware that his true destiny was to be a painter Van Gogh was obsessed with the possibilities of sunflowers as a theme. With their complex structure they seemed to him particularly well adapted to interpretation in direct and multiple strokes. He always saw these flowers as symbols of the sun's energy, dazzling stars rotating about a hidden force. In Paris, where he adopted as his own the Impressionist's way of seeing, he did many still lifes. Our picture, which was painted at this time, shows the dried flowers, cut from their stalks as they were going to seed, against a blue background slashed with brush strokes that extend the impression of cosmic force. Later in Arles he was to paint at least seven other pictures of sunflowers, in vases, but still fresh and vivid, glorifying the power of their growth and the intensity of their radiance.

Two pictures, similar to ours except in the color of the ground, date from the same time in Paris. One in the Hahnloser collection in Winterthur, has a ground hatched with vermilion, the other, owned by the artist's nephew Vincent W. van Gogh, shows the flowers against dark green. There is one more painting of this type with four rather than two clustered flowers. (All three ill. in Ref. La Faille, 1939, cat. nos. 279, 275, 280.)

Note: A. Tellegen has recently brought to the Museum's attention her article in *Museumjournaal*, X (1964–65), pp. 51f., ill. p. 43c, identifying the Museum's painting as one of three by Van Gogh owned by Gauguin in 1893.

Signed and dated (at lower left): *Vincent 87*.

Oil on canvas. H. 17, w. 24 in. (43.2 x 61 cm.).

REFERENCE: J. B. de la Faille, *L'Oeuvre de Vincent van Gogh* (1928), I, p. 105, cat. no. 375, II, pl. CIII, no. 375; (1939), p. 215, cat. no. 278, ill.

EXHIBITED: Kunsthaus, Zurich, 1917, *Französische Kunst des XIX und XX Jahrhunderts*, no. 109 (lent by A. K.); Kunstmuseum, Winterthur, 1922, *Meisterwerke aus Schweizer Privatbesitz*, no. 52 (lent by E. Richard Bühler); Kunstmuseum, Basel, 1932; Galerie Thannhauser, Paris, 1938; Carnegie Institute, Pittsburgh (Pa.), 1943, *Modern Dutch Art and Paintings by Vincent van Gogh*, cat. suppl. (lent by J. K. Thannhauser); Montreal Museum of Fine Arts, 1944, *Five Centuries of Dutch Painting*, no. 120 (lent by J. K. Thannhauser);

Metropolitan Museum and Art Institute of Chicago, 1949–1950, *Van Gogh*, no. 60; Houston Contemporary Arts Museum (Texas), 1951, *Vincent van Gogh*, no. 5; Wildenstein Gallery, New York, 1955, *Van Gogh*, no. 12.

EX COLL.: M. C. Hoogendijk, The Hague (sale, Frederick Muller, Amsterdam, May 21–22, 1912, no. 31); Alphonse Kann, Paris (in 1917); E. Richard Bühler, Winterthur (in 1922, until 1937/1938); [J. K. Thannhauser, New York, by 1938, until 1949].

PURCHASE, ROGERS FUND, 1949.

The Flowering Orchard   56.13

Vincent left Paris for Arles toward the end of February 1888. Even in the south of France the winter still held, but early in March he was able to write back to his brother Theo that the weather had changed. When the orchards began to bloom he delightedly started making pictures of the flowering trees: ". . . every day is a good day now—not meaning the weather . . . but those orchards in bloom that there are to paint! I find painting hard work because of the wind, but I fasten my easel to pegs driven into the ground and work in spite of it, it is too lovely." And later, "I'm up to my ears in work, for the trees are in blossom and I want to paint a Provençal orchard of astounding gaiety" (Letters 472, 473).

He felt guilty as usual about the large amount of paint his work consumed and Theo's outlay for it but hoped that the popularity of the subject would at last lead to sales (Letter 474). He conceived the idea of making decorative groups of three pictures, a vertical flanked by two horizontal orchard scenes, and he sketched one such triptych in a letter written during April (Letter 477). Our picture, a vertical, was probably intended to be the center of such a triptych. One concludes from Vincent's various allusions that he made in all twelve paintings of orchards and three small studies, one of which he destroyed.

Signed (at lower left): *Vincent*.

Oil on canvas. H. 28½, w. 21 in. (72.4 x 53.3 cm.).

49.41

REFERENCES: J. B. de la Faille, *L'Oeuvre de Vincent van Gogh* (1928), I, p. 157, cat. no. 552, II, pl. CLI, records this picture as a work not mentioned in Van Gogh's letters // W. Scherjon and J. de Gruyter, *Vincent van Gogh's Great Period* (1937), p. 54, ill., identifies this painting with pictures mentioned in letters to Theo and to Émile Bernard (*The Complete Letters*, 1958, II, p. 549, letter no. 478 of Apr. 20, 1888; and III, p. 482, letter no. B4 [4]) // J. B. de la Faille, *Vincent van Gogh* (1939), p. 401, cat. no. 577, ill., agrees that this is the cherry tree mentioned in letter no. 478 // W. Uhde, *Vincent van Gogh* (1941), no. 19, ill. // F. Elgar, *Van Gogh* (1958), p. 307, no. 105, ill. p. 271 // A. Kuhn-Foelix, *Vincent van Gogh, eine Psychographie* (1958), p. 140, fig. 34.

EXHIBITED: Städtische Ausstellungshalle, Cologne, 1912, *Internationale Kunst-Ausstellung des Sonderbundes Westdeutscher Kunstfreunde und Künstler*, no. 20 (Obstgarten, signed Vincent, 1887 [*sic*]; lent by H. P. Bremmer, The Hague); Gemeentemuseum, The Hague, 1950, *Verzameling H. P. Bremmer*, no. 35 (as Boomgaard); Palazzo Reale, Milan, 1952, *Vincent van Gogh*, no. 94 (as Frutteto, lent by Bremmer); E. J. van Wisselingh & Co., Amsterdam, 1955, *Maîtres français, XIX et XX siècles*, no. 14.

EX COLL.: [Oldenzeel Art Gallery, Rotterdam, before 1912]; H. P. Bremmer, The Hague (by 1912–1955); [E. J. van Wisselingh & Co., Amsterdam, 1955]; [Wildenstein, New York, 1955–1956].

PURCHASE, MR. AND MRS. HENRY ITTLESON JR. FUND, 1956.

Oleanders 62.24

In a letter to his brother from Arles in August of 1888 Vincent announced his intention "one of these days . . . to make a study of oleanders" (Letter 524), and before their blooming season had come to an end in the next month he had painted this jugful of the pink flowers. The bouquet fairly bristles with a vital energy that Vincent felt was characteristic of the plant. He described a row of oleander bushes

56.13

to Theo as "raving mad; the blasted things are flowering so riotously they may well catch locomotor ataxia. They are loaded with fresh flowers, and quantities of faded flowers as well, and their green is continually renewing itself in fresh, strong shoots, apparently inexhaustibly" (Letter 541).

In placing Zola's novel *La Joie de Vivre* next to the bouquet in this still life, Van Gogh may have intended to give a title to the growing force he felt in the oleander. He had included this novel in a still life once before, in Nuenen in 1885, posing it then next to a big open Bible (ill., Ref. La Faille, 1939, cat. no. 121). These two still lifes, one solemnly philosophical and the other full of light and vitality, summarize the difference between the religious and social concerns that had occupied Vincent in the north, and his new and more purely artistic interests in the south.

Vincent painted one other picture of cut

oleanders. Vertical in composition, it shows the flowers standing in the same jug, but it does not show the book, nor does it have the exuberance of the Museum's picture (ill., Ref. La Faille, cat. no. 605).

Oil on canvas. H. 23¾, w. 29 in. (60.3 x 73.6 cm.).

REFERENCES: J. B. Manson, *Apollo*, III (1926), p. 143, ill. in color opp. p. 156 // J. B. de la Faille, *L'Oeuvre de Vincent van Gogh* (1928), I, p. 167, cat. no. 593, II, pl. CLXIV, no. 593 // J. B. Manson, *Apollo*, VIII (1928), p. 280 // W. Scherjon and J. de Gruyter, *Vincent van Gogh's Great Period* (1937), p. 106, no. 80, ill. // J. B. de la Faille, *Vincent van Gogh* (1939), p. 411, cat. no. 594, ill. // W. Uhde and L. Goldscheider, *Vincent van Gogh* (1941), pl. 22 // P. James, *Van Gogh* [1948], pl. 16, color pl. 5 // M. Schapiro, *Vincent van Gogh* (1950),

pp. 66f., ill. in color // J. Seznec, *Mag. of Art*, XLIII (1950), p. 284, ill. p. 282 // J. Leymarie, *Van Gogh* (1951), pp. 27, 98, mentions this picture in a discussion of the artist's Still Life: Open Bible (Van Gogh, Laren), in which Zola's *Joie de Vivre* also appears // F. Elgar, *Van Gogh* (1958), p. 309, no. 130, ill. p. [276].

EXHIBITED: Stedelijk Museum, Amsterdam, 1905, *Tentoonstelling Vincent van Gogh*, no. 122; Lefevre Galleries, London, 1923, *Gauguin, Van Gogh, Toulouse-Lautrec, Renoir*, no. 20; Galerie d'Art Marcel Bernheim, Paris, 1925, *Exposition rétrospective d'oeuvres de Vincent van Gogh*, no. 25; National Gallery of British Art (Tate Gallery), London, 1926, *List of Loans at the Opening Exhibition of the Modern Foreign Gallery*, cat. p. 7 (lent by Mrs. R. A. Workman); Knoedler Galleries, New York, 1928, *A Century of French Painting*, no. 31; and 1948, *Van Gogh—Fourteen Master-*

62.24

pieces, no. 9; Paul Rosenberg Gallery, New York, 1948, *21 Masterpieces by 7 Great Masters*, no. 11 (lent by Mrs. C. Suydam Cutting); Metropolitan Museum and Art Institute of Chicago, 1949–1950, *Van Gogh Paintings and Drawings*, no. 90; Newark Museum (New Jersey), 1950, *Flower Paintings by European Masters of the 19th and 20th Centuries*, no. 12 (lent by Mrs. C. Suydam Cutting); and 1954, *From the Collection of Mrs. C. Suydam Cutting*, no. 12.

Ex coll.: [Ambroise Vollard, Paris]; Mme Redlich, Vienna (until c. 1924); [Barbazanges, Paris, c. 1924–c. 1925]; Sir Michael E. Sadler, Oxford (from c. 1925); Mrs. R. A. Workman, London (in 1926, until 1928); [a London gallery, 1928]; [Knoedler, New York, 1928]; Mrs. William Andrews Clark, New York (1928–1947); [Knoedler, New York, 1947]; Mrs. Charles Suydam Cutting, New York (1947–1961); [Knoedler, New York, 1962].

Gift of Mr. and Mrs. John L. Loeb, 1962.

The Arlésienne (Madame Ginoux)

51.112.3

We know from Van Gogh's letters to his brother that in November of 1888 in Arles he painted a portrait of Madame Ginoux, who, with her husband, kept the Café de la Gare. This was during the time of Gauguin's stay, and the two artists are said to have tricked her into posing by inviting her to take coffee with them. Once Madame Ginoux was seated, Vincent "slashed out" this portrait in an hour (Letter 559), while Gauguin kept repeating, "Madame Ginoux, Madame Ginoux, your portrait will be placed in the Louvre in Paris" (Ref., Coquiot, 1923). While Van Gogh painted furiously, Gauguin, viewing her from a different angle, made a sketch of Madame Ginoux in the same pose.[1] Gauguin was at that time full of enthusiasm for the aesthetics of "synthetism" as a result of conversations with Émile Bernard at Pont-Aven, and he gave Van Gogh the idea of treating this portrait as a "synthesis" of the

Arlésienne. A second version shows the same pose but with gloves and an umbrella on the table instead of books. This picture, as Gauguin prophesied, has recently been acquired by the Louvre (ill. in color in Ref. La Faille, 1939, pl. xi, opp. p. 368). Our version with books is much more spontaneous than the one with the gloves and more convincing in its vitality and vigorous and sure in its stylization. The Louvre example, therefore, is very probably a repetition. In 1889 and 1890 at Saint-Rémy Van Gogh used Gauguin's drawing of the Arlésienne as the basis for several painted versions turned toward the right (Ref., La Faille, 1939, nos. 710–713). It may have been one of these that he is supposed to have been taking from Saint-Rémy to Arles to give to Madame Ginoux, when he was seized with one of his worst attacks. It is not known what became of this picture.

The Arlésienne is one of the first modern pictures with the extreme simplification of a poster. In spite of the treatment of the color in flat areas, this picture does give some effect of depth and volume, due to the way the drawing builds and defines the form and also to the bold alternation of light and dark tones.

Oil on canvas. H. 36, w. 29 in. (91.4 x 73.7 cm.).

Note 1. T. E. Hanley coll., Bradford, Pa.; ill. in J. Rewald, *Gauguin Drawings* (1958), pl. 15.

References: V. van Gogh, *The Complete Letters* (1958), iii, p. 100, no. 559 (Nov. 1888), p. 128, no. 573 (Jan. 23, 1889), p. 182, no. 595 (June 19, 1889) // R. Walser and K. Scheffler, *Kunst und Künstler*, x (1912), pp. 442–444, ill. p. 435, interprets the picture // J. Meier-Graefe, *Vincent van Gogh* (1922), i, pp. 126–128; ii, p. 24, compares the composition to a Japanese print of an actor's head by Sharaku // G. Coquiot, *Vincent van Gogh* (1923), pp. 187f., reports how the Arlésienne came to be painted // L. Piérard, *The Tragic Life of Vincent van Gogh* (1925), p. 104, quotes Mme Ginoux herself on the subject of the portrait // *Kunst und Künstler*, xxiv (1925–1926), pp.

417f. // *Art News*, xxiv (Mar. 27, 1926), p. 1 // J. B. de la Faille, *L'Oeuvre de Vincent van Gogh* (1928), i, cat. no. 488; ii, pl. cxxxv, no. 488 // R. H. Wilenski, *French Painting* (1931), pp. 296, 303, pl. 122, considers it "perhaps Van Gogh's most notable achievement" // S. Bourgeois and W. George, *Formes* (1932), nos. 28–29, pp. 301, 305, ill. in color opp. p. 302 // D. C. Rich, *Bull. of the Art Institute of Chicago*, xxix (1935), pp. 5f., ill. p. 36, discusses the possible influence of Sharaku on Van Gogh in this painting // L. Vitali, *Vincent van Gogh* (1936), pp. 12f., discusses the influence of Gauguin on Van Gogh at the time the picture was painted // W. Scherjon and J. de Gruyter, *Vincent van Gogh's Great Period* (1937), pp. 147f., no. 118, ill., quotes the letters to Theo about the Arlésienne but includes two (nos. 582 and 590) that may not refer to it // J. B. de la Faille, *Vincent van Gogh* (1939), p. 365, cat. no. 515, ill. // S. A. Lewisohn, *Art News* (Annual), xxxvii (Feb. 25, 1939), p. 155, ill. p. 69 (hanging in the Lewisohn house) // R. H. Wilenski, *Modern French Painters* [c. 1940], p. 80, asserts that Van Gogh based this painting on Gauguin's Hospital Garden at Arles, pl. 23 A // L. Venturi, *Painting and Painters* (1945), pp. 172f., fig. 39, analyzes the picture, comparing its color harmony, based on contrast, with that of fifteenth-century painting; comments on the union here of the abstract character with the realistic image // A. Meyerson, *Konsthistorisk Tidskrift*, xv (1946), pp. 143–146, ill., discusses its relationship to Gauguin's work and publishes connected pictures by the two artists // F. Kimball and L. Venturi, *Great Paintings in America* [c. 1948], pp. 204f., color pl. 95 // M. Schapiro, *Vincent van Gogh* (1950), pp. 21, 34, 88, ill. in color, analyzes Van Gogh's use of color in it, commenting on its sophistication and subtlety // L. Venturi, *Impressionists and Symbolists* (1950), pp. 193f., fig. 192, discusses the technique and Van Gogh's discarding of the impressionist style // J. Leymarie, *Van Gogh* (1951), pp. 44f., 90, 109, cat. no. 73, pl. 73, discusses the Louvre version, catalogues our picture, reports that the authenticity of the Louvre

version is contested by some authors // W. Weisbach, *Vincent van Gogh*, ii (1951), pp. 100–102, pl. 55, believes that our version is the earlier and better one // R. Huyghe, *Le Carnet de Paul Gauguin* (1952), i, pp. 75, 77, cites the picture as an example of Van Gogh's greatest effort to follow the precepts of Gauguin // Metropolitan Museum, *Art Treasures* (1952), p. 234, cat. no. 151, pl. 151 // A. Kuhn-Foelix, *Vincent van Gogh, eine Psychographie* (1958), p. 120 // F. Elgar, *Van Gogh* (1958), p. 311, no. 153, ill. p. 280 // K. Badt, *Die Farbenlehre van Goghs* (1961), pp. 76, 127, pl. 21 (detail in color).

EXHIBITED: Galerie de Le Barc de Boutteville, Paris, 1892/1893, *Van Gogh*, no. 13 (possibly ours; see A. Vollard, *Lettres de Vincent van Gogh à Émile Bernard*, 1911, pl. 1, for reproduction of catalogue); Bernheim-Jeune, Paris, 1901, *Van Gogh*, no. 50 (possibly ours); Ausstellunghaus am Kurfürstendamm, Berlin, 1912, *XXIV Ausstellung der Berliner Secession*, no. 81 (no lender listed but according to K. Scheffler in Ref., *Kunst und Künstler*, 1912, lent by Bernt Grönvold); Paul Cassirer, Berlin, 1914, *Ausstellung von Werken van Goghs*, no. 80 (lent by Bernt Grönvold); Kunsthalle, Basel, 1924, *Van Gogh*, no. 43; Kunsthaus, Zurich, 1924, *Vincent van Gogh*, no. 41 (lent by a private collector, Basel); Paul Cassirer, Berlin, 1925, *Impressionisten*, no. 22 (lent by a German private collector); Reinhardt Galleries, New York, 1927, *Paintings from El Greco and Rembrandt to Cézanne and Matisse*, no. 24 (lent by Adolph Lewisohn); Fogg Art Museum, Cambridge (Mass.), 1929, *Nineteenth and Twentieth Century French Art*, no. 92 (lent by Adolph Lewisohn); Museum of Modern Art, New York, 1929, *First Loan Exhibition*, no. 73 (lent by Adolph Lewisohn); Knoedler, New York, 1931, *Pictures of People*, no. 2 (lent by Adolph Lewisohn); Metropolitan Museum, 1932, *Taste of Today* (lent by Adolph Lewisohn); Museum of Modern Art, New York, 1933, *Modern European Art* (lent by Adolph Lewisohn), and 1934–1935, *Modern Works of Art*, no. 16 (lent by Adolph Lewisohn), and *Vincent van Gogh*, no. 39 (lent by Adolph Lewisohn); Cleveland Museum of Art, 1936, *Great Lakes Exposition*, no. 318 (lent by Adolph Lewisohn); Wildenstein Gallery, New York, 1938, *Great Portraits from Impressionism to Modernism*, no. 47 (lent from the Adolph Lewisohn collection); Boston Institute of Modern Art, 1939, *The Sources of Modern Art*, no. 71 (lent by Sam A. Lewisohn); Museum of Modern Art, New York, 1939, *Art in Our Time*, no. 69 (lent from the Adolph Lewisohn collection); and 1940, *Modern Masters from European and American Collections*,

51.112.3

no. 11 (lent from the Lewisohn collection);
World's Fair, New York, 1940, *Masterpieces
of Art*, no. 358 (lent from the Lewisohn collection); Wildenstein Gallery, New York,
1943, *Art and Life of Vincent van Gogh*, no. 36
(lent by Sam A. Lewisohn); Metropolitan
Museum and Art Institute of Chicago, 1949–
1950, *Van Gogh*, no. 87 (lent by Sam A. Lewisohn); Metropolitan Museum, 1951, *The Lewisohn Collection*, no. 37; Musée de l'Orangerie,
Paris, 1955, *De David à Toulouse-Lautrec*,
no. 33.

Ex coll.: Bernt Grönvold, Berlin (by 1912,
until after 1914); Fritz Schön, Berlin-Grunewald and Basel (by 1924, until 1926); [Stephan
Bourgeois, New York, 1926]; Adolph Lewisohn, New York (1926–1938; Cat., 1928, pp.
151f., ill. frontis. in color); Samuel A. Lewisohn, New York (1938–1951).

Bequest of Samuel A. Lewisohn, 1951.

49.30

Cypresses   49.30

Like sunflowers, cypress trees with their flame-
shaped form gave Van Gogh an opportunity
to express dynamic vitality. In his letters there
are many enthusiastic allusions to their form
and color. Our picture was painted in June of
1889, when he was at the Asylum of Saint
Paul in Saint-Rémy. At this time he wrote to
his brother at length about his interest in
cypresses, which he found "as beautiful in
line and proportion as an Egyptian obelisk"
(Letter 596). He referred particularly to two
studies on which he was working and told
how he had prepared the foregrounds with
heavy layers of white lead, which he supposed
was the technique often used by Monticelli,
an artist he admired. The same letter includes
a little sketch and a full description of our
picture, which he expected to be the better
one. He had also made an important preparatory drawing for it, now in the Brooklyn
Museum (Ref., La Faille, 1928, IV, pl. CLXXVI,
no. 1525). The second painting mentioned in
the letter has a very different composition,
and is the one Van Gogh gave to the critic
Albert Aurier in recognition of an article he
had written in praise of the artist's work. It is
now in the Kröller-Müller Museum at Otter-
loo, and a reduced repetition of it belongs to
Vincent W. van Gogh at Laren (Ref., La
Faille, 1939, cat. nos. 617, 618).

Our picture's arrangement of two cypress
trees, the taller at the right and the shorter
close beside it, forming a triangle, was used
again in October of the same year in three
similar pictures showing the trees set behind
a field of yellow corn. Later still, in May 1890
at Auvers, he used the motif again in a picture that in 1939 was in the collection of S.
van Deventer in Wassenaer. This example is
painted in the curling, tortured style of his
latest work. For some time its authenticity
was questioned, but it has been validated as
a genuine work. (All four ill. in Ref., La Faille,
1939, cat. nos. 611, 633, 634, 816.) Still another picture very similar to ours, once regarded by La Faille as genuine, has been pub-

lished by him as a forgery (La Faille, *Les Faux van Gogh*, 1930, pl. VII).

Oil on canvas. H. 36¾, w. 29⅛ in. (93.3 x 74 cm.).

REFERENCES: V. van Gogh, *The Complete Letters* (1958), III, pp. 185f., no. 596, ill. sketch of this composition (June 25, 1889), p. 218, no. 608 // J. B. de la Faille, *L'Oeuvre de Vincent van Gogh* (1928), I, pp. 172f., cat. no. 613; II, pl. CLXXI, no. 613 // A. Bader, *Künstler-Tragik* (1932), pp. 89f., fig. 47 // W. Scherjon and J. de Gruyter, *Vincent van Gogh's Great Period* (1937), p. 212, no. 10 // J. B. de la Faille, *Vincent van Gogh* (1939), p. 425, cat. no. 616, ill. // I. H. Perry, *Bulletin of the History of Medicine*, XXI (1947), no. 2, p. 169, comments on the rhythm and movement in this painting and observes that Van Gogh's brush strokes had always been evidence of his impulsive nature // G. Schmidt, *Van Gogh* (1947), p. 26, pl. 38, observes in it the influence of Monticelli // M. Pease, *Art News Annual*, XIX (1950), pp. 91–96, ill. in color, publishes the results of a technical analysis of this painting and detail photographs of the brush strokes // J. Leymarie, *Van Gogh* (1951), pp. 91, 125, no. 116, pl. 116 // M. M. Van Dantzig, *Vincent?* [c. 1953], pp. 89f., 95f., fig. 6, argues that the similar composition of cypresses (F. 614) is a forgery modeled after this picture // J. Rewald, *Post-Impressionism* (1956), p. 335, ill. in color // A. Kuhn-Foelix, *Vincent van Gogh, eine Psychographie* (1958), p. 146, fig. 37.

EXHIBITED: Galerien Thannhauser, Munich, 1907, *Van Gogh*, no. 43; Galerie d'Art Druet, Paris, 1908, no. 4; Städtische Ausstellungshalle, Cologne, 1912, *Internationale Kunst-Ausstellung des Sonderbundes Westdeutscher Kunstfreunde und Künstler*, no. 108 (lent by Fritz Meyer, Zurich); Kunsthalle, Basel, 1924, no. 60 (lent by J. K. Thannhauser); Künstlerhaus, Berlin, 1927, *Erste Sonderausstellung in Berlin* (organized by Galerien Thannhauser, Munich), no. 119; Galerie Bernheim-Jeune, Paris, 1927, *Van Gogh* (no cat. published); Museum of Modern Art, New York, 1929,

First Loan Exhibition, no. 85 (lent by Justin Thannhauser, Berlin); Cleveland Museum of Art, 1948, *Works by Vincent van Gogh*, no. 18 (lent anonymously); Metropolitan Museum and Art Institute of Chicago, 1949–1950, *Van Gogh*, no. 112.

EX COLL.: Maurice (?) Fabre, Paris; [E. Druet, Paris, c. 1907/1908]; Fritz Meyer-Fierz, Zurich (1908–1923); [Justin K. Thannhauser, Berlin, Paris, and New York, 1923–1949].

PURCHASE, ROGERS FUND, 1949.

The Olive Pickers
56.14

Letters written in the summer of 1888 during Vincent's first months in Provence relate his dissatisfaction with a picture he was painting of Christ in the Garden of Olives, which he twice scraped out. More than a year later, when he was living at the Asylum of Saint Paul, near Saint-Rémy, he wrote of his irritation with studies of the same subject by Émile Bernard and Gauguin, noting that he himself had worked for a month painting in the olive groves because of his annoyance with their pictures, which he called "abstractions," finding in them nothing "really observed." In the same letter he said that the olive and the

56.14

cypress have the same significance in Provence as the willow in the north and commented on the changing quality of olive trees (Letters 505, 540, 615). Following his custom of treating one theme many times in an effort to express his inner vision more accurately, Van Gogh painted more than a dozen studies of olive trees. Four of these pictures show the gathering of olives: ours, one in the collection of Ira Haupt, New York, and one in the Chester Dale collection, all with the same composition, and a fourth, with a different arrangement, in the Kröller-Müller Museum, Holland (Ref., La Faille, 1939, cat. nos. 665, 661, 650). It is difficult to say which is the painting known to have been made from nature, but the vigor and freshness of ours suggest that it was made on the spot.

Oil on canvas. H. 28¾, w. 36½ in. (73 x 92.7 cm.).

REFERENCES: V. van Gogh, *The Complete Letters* (1958), III, pp. 236f., no. 617, describes a painting of this composition made for his mother and sister after a study of the same dimensions done from nature; p. 240, no. 619 (to his mother); p. 243, no. 621, lists this among pictures sent to Theo // J. B. de la Faille, *L'Oeuvre de Vincent van Gogh* (1928), I, p. 185, cat. no. 654, dates it Nov. 1889, Saint-Rémy; cat. nos. 655, 656, catalogues the other versions; II, pl. CLXXXIII, figs. 654, 655, 656 // W. Scherjon and J. de Gruyter, *Vincent van Gogh's Great Period* (1937), p. 266, no. 69, ill., quote letters 617, 619, and 621; publish other versions as nos. 70, 71 // J. B. de la Faille, *Vincent van Gogh* (1939), p. 458, cat. no. 664, ill.; cat. nos. 661, 665 (other versions) // W. Weisbach, *Vincent van Gogh* (1951), II, pp. 162f.

EXHIBITED: Stedelijk Museum, Amsterdam, 1905, *Tentoonstelling van schilderijen en teekeningen door Vincent van Gogh*, no. 203 (probably ours); Galerie Thannhauser, Munich, 1910, an exhibition of the work of Dutch artists; Städtische Ausstellungshalle, Cologne, 1912, *Internationale Kunst-Ausstellung des Sonderbundes Westdeutscher Kunstfreunde und*

Künstler, no. 95 (lent by Dr. Alfred Wolff); Württembergischer Kunstverein, Stuttgart, 1924, no. 39 (see Ref., La Faille); Glaspalast, Munich, 1926, *Allgemeine Kunst-Ausstellung*, no. 2093 (lent anonymously).

EX COLL.: [Ambroise Vollard, Paris]; Dr. Alfred Wolff, Munich (in 1912); [J. K. Thannhauser, c. 1948]; Vincent Astor, New York (until 1955); [M. Knoedler, New York, 1955–1956].

PURCHASE, MR. AND MRS. RICHARD J. BERNHARD FUND, 1956.

First Steps   64.165.2

In the late autumn of 1889 Vincent van Gogh, at the asylum of St. Rémy, received from his brother a package of paints, some canvas, and some reproductions of Millet's works. In his letter acknowledging them (Letter 611) he alluded to the fact that Theo was soon to become a father, and, associating this circumstance with one of the Millets, he exclaimed, "How beautiful that Millet is, 'A Child's First Steps!'"

In the same letter he also noted that he thought "it might be interesting to try to do Millet's drawings in painting" and not long afterward wrote (Letter 623) that he felt there was "justification for trying to reproduce some of Millet's things which he himself had no time to paint in oil." This second letter dealing with Millet is undated, but was probably written at the beginning of 1890; in it he

64.165.2

also announced his intention of starting that week "on the snow-covered field and Millet's 'The First Steps.' "

Millet made several drawings which, with minor differences, treat the theme of a child's learning to walk. Although we do not know certainly which one Theo sent to St. Rémy, Van Gogh's painting is closest to a drawing by Millet that belonged in 1911 to Moulton and Ricketts in Chicago. Since Vincent is known to have owned a copy of Alfred Sensier's book on Millet, he must also have been familiar with the drawing reproduced in it on page 345, which belonged at that time to Georges Petit.

Oil on canvas. H. 28½, w. 35⅞ in. (72.4 x 91.2 cm.).

REFERENCES: I. Querido, *Op de Hoogte*, 11 year, no. 8 (Aug. 1905), ill. p. 480 // K. Pfister, *Vincent van Gogh* (1922), pl. 43 // J. B. de la Faille, *L'Oeuvre de Vincent van Gogh* (1928), I, p. 190, no. 668, II, pl. CLXXXI, no. 668 // W. Scherjon and J. de Gruyter, *Van Gogh's Great Period* (1937), p. 288, pl. 93 // J. B. de la Faille, *Vincent van Gogh* (1939), p. 472, no. 685.

EXHIBITED: Stedelijk Museum, Amsterdam, 1905, *Tentoonstelling van schilderijen en teekeningen door Vincent van Gogh*, no. 173; Kunsthaus, Zurich, 1924, *Vincent van Gogh*, no. 63 (lent by Paul Vallotton); Museum of Modern Art, New York, 1929, *First Loan Exhibition*, no. 88 (lent by Julius Oppenheimer); Art Institute of Chicago, 1933, *A Century of Progress*, no. 378 (lent by Julius Oppenheimer); Metropolitan Museum and Art Institute of Chicago, 1949–1950, *Van Gogh Paintings and Drawings*, no. 127.

EX COLL.: Mme J. van Gogh-Bonger, Amsterdam; [Thannhauser Gallery, Munich]; Karl-Ernst-Osthaus Museum, Hagen (by 1905, in 1917); [Alfred Flechtheim Gallery, Berlin]; W. Russ Young, Serrières, near Neufchâtel (until 1924); [Galerie Paul Vallotton, Lausanne, 1924–1926]; Julius Oppenheimer, New York (in 1926, until 1935); Frank Oppenheimer, San Francisco (by 1945); [Dalzell

Hatfield Gallery, Los Angeles, in 1955]; Mr. and Mrs. George N. Richard, New York (1955–1964).

GIFT OF GEORGE N. AND HELEN M. RICHARD, SUBJECT TO A LIFE ESTATE IN THE DONORS, 1964.

Irises   58.187

In May 1890, during the last days of his stay at the hospital in Saint-Rémy, Van Gogh enjoyed a period of relative tranquillity. "As soon as I got out into the park, I got back all my lucidity for work; I have more ideas in my head than I could ever carry out, but without its clouding my mind. The brush strokes come like clockwork." In a subsequent letter he stated that his latest horrible attack had "disappeared like a thunderstorm," and that he was working with "a calm and steady enthusiasm" (Letters 630, 633). It was at this time that he made two pictures of iris in vases, ours and the one with a strong yellow background that belongs to his nephew, Vincent W. van Gogh, at Laren (Ref., La Faille, 1939, cat. no. 700). He left both pictures in Saint-Rémy to dry, and an attendant sent them on to Auvers in June. The year before he had painted two pictures of iris growing in the earth, one done in Arles, showing a single plant (in 1939 in coll. of Mme J. H. Le Cosquino de Bussy), the other in his first days at Saint-Rémy, showing a garden patch of iris (Payson coll., New York; Ref., La Faille, 1939, cat. nos. 591, 606.)

Oil on canvas. H. 29, w. 36¼ in. (73.7 x 92.1 cm.).

REFERENCES: V. van Gogh, *The Complete Letters* (1958), III, p. 269, no. 633 (May 1890), p. 288, no. 644 (June 24, 1890) // J. Meier-Graefe, *Vincent van Gogh* (1922), II, pp. 76f., compares this and the other iris picture of 1890 with the sunflowers, finds the iris "lighter and gayer" // J. B. de la Faille, *L'Oeuvre de Vincent van Gogh* (1928), I, p. 194, cat. no. 680; II, pl. CXC, no. 680 // A. Bader, *Künstler-Tragik* (1932), p. 92, finds in this picture and

58.187

the other flower pictures of the same time the last clear and joyful expression of Van Gogh's art and spirit // W. Scherjon and J. de Gruyter, *Vincent van Gogh's Great Period* (1937), p. 302, no. 111 // J. de Beucken, *Vincent van Gogh* [c. 1937/38], p. 108, mentions the iris paintings and the circumstances under which they were made // J. B. de la Faille, *Vincent van Gogh* (1939), p. 484, cat. no. 701, ill. // J. Rewald, *Post-Impressionism* (1956), pp. 380, 383, 394, ill., notes that this and the three

other flower pictures done at the same time were the only still lifes painted at Saint-Rémy.

EXHIBITED: Brussels, 1891, *Les XX; La Huitième Exposition annuelle*, no. 4 (Bouquet d'iris, possibly ours); Nationalgalerie, Berlin, 1921; Galerie Bernheim-Jeune, Paris, 1927, *Van Gogh* (no catalogue published; see letter from Bernheim-Jeune, Jan. 28, 1960); Künstlerhaus, Berlin, 1927, *Erste Sonderausstellung in Berlin* (organized by Galerien Thannhauser, Munich), no. 114; Galerie Matthiesen, Berlin, 1927, *Das Stilleben*, no. 120 (lent by Sammlung M., Berlin); Paul Cassirer, Berlin, 1928, *Vincent van Gogh*, no. 70 (lent by a private collector, Berlin-Grunewald); Wildenstein Gallery, New York, 1955, *Van Gogh*, no. 68 (lent by Dr. and Mrs. David M. Levy); Metropolitan Museum, 1957, *Impressionist and Modern Paintings from Private Collections* (lent by Dr. and Mrs. David M. Levy); and *Paintings from Private Collections*, 1958, no. 71, 1959, no. 55 (lent by Dr. and Mrs. David M. Levy); Museum of Modern Art, New York, 1961, *Mrs. Adele R. Levy Collection, a Memorial Exhibition*, cat. p. 21.

Ex COLL.: Mme Giulietta von Mendelssohn-Bartholdy, Grunewald; Dr. and Mrs. David M. Levy, New York.

GIFT OF ADELE R. LEVY, 1958.

Seurat

Georges Pierre Seurat. Born in Paris in 1859; died there in 1891. Seurat, who was the son of a bailiff, took drawing lessons as a school boy. Between 1878 and 1880, he studied at the École des Beaux-Arts. There, through the teaching of Henri Lehmann, who carried on the tradition of Ingres, he became acquainted with the art of line and stylized draughtsmanship. He also copied works of older masters and paid frequent visits to the museums. From 1879 to 1880 his studies were interrupted by his term of military service at Brest. On his return to Paris he investigated with great interest the scientific theories of color and juxtaposed contrasts set forth by the chemist Chevreul and other theoreticians, and he read the works of physicists who had concerned themselves with the theory of vision. The scientific research of his friend Charles Henry was also to be extremely important for the development of his own theories about the expressive values of line, color, and light. He sought examples illustrating these color theories in the paintings of various masters and was especially enthusiastic about the color in the work of Delacroix. In the highly original drawings of Seurat's maturity form, although partly defined by line, is actually constructed by a vaporous play of light and shadow. With extraordinary sensitiveness the artist subtly freighted the forms in these drawings with spiritual meaning, merging external and inner life in a way not realized in Western art since the time of Leonardo da Vinci.

Seurat came into contact with the work of the Impressionists at the end of the 1870's, as a progressive artist could hardly have avoided doing in Paris, and in 1879 he attended the Fourth Impressionist Exhibition. His attention was also directed to Impressionist painting by his friend Signac, an admirer of Monet, and he was soon making small oil sketches in the Impressionist manner. The curious butterfly brush stroke that became the dominant characteristic of these sketches shows his response to the technique of the Impressionists, which he adopted with a much more methodical approach than theirs. Seurat's first great picture was Bathing at Asnières, painted in 1883–1884 and now in the National Gallery, London. In this very smooth and linear work he strove for solid construction and made a liberal use of preliminary drawings— an intention and a procedure at complete variance with Impressionism.

Sunday at the Grande Jatte, which was finished in 1886, is the first of Seurat's works to reveal his clear formulation of the "divisionist" pictorial system, for which he has become famous. According to this system, color, both in light and shadow, was applied in small strokes of pure tones, complementary or contrasted, side by side, which, though separate on the canvas, would merge in the eye of the spectator to give the impression that the artist wanted. By making his strokes small and regular Seurat was able to avoid the dissolution and confusion of forms that result from the Impressionist technique and to preserve both the volume and the linear design of the silhouette. When the Grande Jatte was exhibited in 1886 it raised a storm of criticism because of the novelty of its sparkling color and its rigid figures, the very qualities that heralded the daring stylization of the twentieth century. Seurat had now established the important characteristics of the style in which he was to paint during the remaining six years of his life.

Seurat's other major paintings are The Models of 1887–1888 in the Barnes Foundation at Merion, Pennsylvania, Invitation to the Side-Show, 1888 (see below), Le Chahut of 1890 in the Kröller-Müller Museum at Otterlo, and The Circus of 1891 in the Louvre. These important works, as well as his landscapes and harbor scenes of the northern coast of France, are refined and harmonious compositions in which delicate, luminous color is combined in an unusual way with subtle patterns and rhythms. Seurat thus substituted for Impressionism a calculated style, which was soon labeled Neo-Impressionism. The circle of followers who continued to work in this style after Seurat's early death was led by Signac and included for a brief time the aging Pissarro.

Though he lived to be only thirty-one, Seurat developed an original and highly personal form of expression, characteristic of a new tendency in painting. Very different contemporary innovators such as Puvis de Chavannes, Redon, Gauguin, and Cézanne followed the same trend, which impelled them all to search in a highly intellectual way for an individual style exactly adapted to their subject matter and desired emotional effect.

View of the Seine   59.16.5

This rapid notation of a river scene, painted on one of the small cigar-box panels often used by Seurat *(croquetons)*, was taken from the opposite bank but at just about the same part of the river as a sketch called The Bridge at Courbevoie (Ref., Dorra and Rewald, 1959, no. 85, ill.). Both sketches were probably made during Seurat's explorations of the region around Asnières in preparation for the painting Bathing at Asnières, which Seurat worked on in 1883 and completed in 1884 (Une Baignade, Asnières, National Gallery, London; for a detailed discussion of this painting see W. I. Homer, *Seurat and the Science of Painting*, 1964, pp. 54–111).

Formerly called Study for the Bathers (Scene on the Seine).

Oil on wood. H. 6¼, w. 9¾ in. (15.9 x 24.8 cm.); with added strip, h. 6½, w. 10 in. (16.5 x 25.4 cm.).

REFERENCES: H. Dorra and J. Rewald, *Seurat* (1959), p. 75, cat. no. 78, ill., call this picture Pêcheurs près d'un pont, date it about 1883, assert that it was exhibited as no. 49 *bis* in

1908–1909 at Bernheim-Jeune // J. Dauberville (in a letter, May 5, 1960), states that in the archives for the exhibition of 1908–1909 at Bernheim-Jeune there is a photograph of this painting inscribed on the back in the hand of Félix Fénéon, who drew up the catalogue for this exhibition: "No. 49 bis – Croqueton – Vers 1883 – Famille Appert (?)," but says this is not necessarily proof that the picture was actually exhibited // C. M. de Hauke, *Seurat* (1961), I, pp. 44f., 237, cat. no. 77, ill., dates it about 1883, calls it Le Pont, identifying it wrongly with a picture of this title lent by H[enry] V[an] d[e] V[elde] as no. 25 to the Bernheim-Jeune exhibition of 1908–1909; identifies the site as the bank of the Seine opposite that shown in Seurat's Bathing at Asnières.

EXHIBITED: Galerie Bernheim-Jeune, Paris, 1908–1909, *Georges Seurat*, no. 49 *bis* (this number is not included in the printed catalogue; see above under Refs., Dorra and Rewald, 1959, and Dauberville, 1960).

EX COLL.: Possibly the Appert family; [Bernheim-Jeune, Paris]; [Valentine Gallery, New York]; Mabel Choate, New York.

BEQUEST OF MABEL CHOATE IN MEMORY OF HER FATHER, JOSEPH HODGES CHOATE, 1959.

A Sunday Afternoon at the Grande Jatte   51.112.6

The Grande Jatte is an island in the Seine lying opposite Courbevoie, a northwestern suburb of Paris, where the working people of Paris used to go to fish, row, and stroll, particularly on Sundays. In 1884, after finishing his first large picture, Bathing at Asnières,[1]

59.16.5

now in the National Gallery, London, which showed the landscape at Asnières near the Grande Jatte, Seurat got the idea of doing another large composition with a similar theme, the pleasures of summer that city people enjoy. He called the painting Un Dimanche d'été à la Grande Jatte.[2] This large picture, now in the Art Institute of Chicago, was shown in the Eighth Impressionist Exhibition, which opened in May, 1886. Our picture, a sketch for the final painting, must date from sometime in the preceding year.

Seurat prepared for the final composition with especial care. Probably as a result of his academic training he composed his pictures from a variety of carefully chosen single studies, unlike the Impressionists, who usually did not invent compositions in this way but preferred to select them in their entirety from nature. Seurat made a great many drawings and small oil studies for individuals, groups, and animals and at least two large studies, our picture and a landscape of the scene without any figures that he exhibited in December 1884 at the newly founded Society of Independent Artists.[3] Félix Fénéon, a great admirer of Seurat, once owned our sketch and also collected other sketches and drawings for the Grande Jatte.

The Museum's picture is the study that was carried farthest, and, of all the ones known, is nearest to the final work. It differs from the final version chiefly in its smaller size, its smaller number of figures, and its more intense color. In spirit also it differs greatly from the picture in Chicago, preserving in the coloring and the light the richness due to direct observation of nature. There is here more shifting in the shadows, the brush strokes that form the lights are extremely free and delicate, and the outlines of form are vague. The manner in which the river is rendered is still very impressionistic. The stylization of light, shadow, and silhouette in the Chicago picture, on the other hand, is much more systematic, the "divisionist" stroke is small and regular, the landscape is deeper and more clearly constructed, and the entire composition has a rigid, static effect. In short, our picture is more sensitive and more intimate, whereas the Chi-

51.112.6

cago picture is more imposing, exhibiting indeed much of the grandeur and majesty of a fresco. In the Bathing at Asnières and The Grande Jatte, his two masterpieces, Seurat contrived to endow scenes drawn from daily life with the epic quality that characterized the works of Paolo Uccello and Pieter Bruegel.

The border of dotted strokes around our picture, as Henri Dorra has pointed out, was painted later than the scene itself (Ref., 1959). The artist obtained an unpainted area on all four sides of the picture by restretching the original canvas on a slightly larger stretcher, which is proved by the irregular wavy edges of the added border, due to the give of the fabric in response to the pull of the original nails. To provide a transition between this pointillist border and the criss-cross brushwork of the picture itself he painted a sprinkling of yellow dots irregularly on the previously painted areas just within the border.

Oil on canvas. H. 27¾, w. 41 in. (70.5 x 104.1 cm.).

Notes: 1. Ill., Ref., Dorra and Rewald, 1959, cat. no. 98, p. 101. 2. Ill. in color, *ibid.*, cat. no. 139, opp. p. LXIV. 3. Ill. in color, *ibid.*, cat. no. 116, opp. p. XLVIII; in coll. of Ambassador and Mrs. John Hay Whitney, New York.

REFERENCES: W. Pach, *Georges Seurat* (1923), p. 22, contrasts the technique of this study with that of the finished work and observes in the sketch "a tendency to brush together the colors" // S. Bourgeois, *The Adolph Lewisohn Collection* (1928), p. 186, ill., catalogues it // A. H. B[arr] Jr., *First Loan Exhibition* (cat.), Museum of Modern Art, New York (1929), p. 25, analyzes its organization // S. Bourgeois and W. George, *Formes* (1932), nos. 28–29, pp. 301, 306, ill. after p. 304, prefer our picture to the final version because of its greater spontaneity // D. C. Rich, *Seurat and the Evolution of La Grande Jatte* (1935), pp. 17, 24f., 58, no. 49, pl. XLIV, describes our picture as the "definitive sketch, chiefly concerned with the color harmony," observes that the colors are more intense than in the finished painting but that there are only hints of the line, volume, and space devel-

oped in the final work // S. A. Lewisohn, *Art News* (Annual), XXXVII (Feb. 25, 1939), p. 155, ill. p. 69 (hanging in the Lewisohn house) // J. Rewald, *Georges Seurat* (1943), pp. 20–26, fig. 71, discusses the evolution of the composition // L. Venturi, *Gaz. des B.-A.*, XXVI (1944), p. 426, fig. 5, compares the treatment of landscape in our picture with that in the study once owned by Chester Beatty (now owned by John Hay Whitney) // H. Huth, *Gaz. des B.-A.*, XXIX (1946), p. 239, note 21, suggests that this may be the study for the Grande Jatte that was exhibited in 1886 in New York at the American Art Association and the National Academy of Design (*Works in Oil and Pastel by the Impressionists of Paris*, no. 112) // M. Breuning, *Art Digest*, XXIII (Apr. 15, 1949), p. 14, ill. // L. Venturi, *Impressionists and Symbolists* (1950), p. 145, fig. 147, comments on the atmosphere and the phantom quality of the figures // J. de Laprade, *Seurat* (1951), p. 49, ill. // Metropolitan Museum, *Art Treasures* (1952), pp. 233f., no. 150, pl. 150, in color // D. C. Rich, *Seurat, Paintings and Drawings* (exhib. cat.), Art Institute of Chicago and Museum of Modern Art, New York (1958), pp. 14, 31, no. 100 // H. Dorra and J. Rewald, *Seurat* (1959), pp. LXXVI (note 59d), LXXXV (note 15), 150f., cat. no. 138, ill. // C. M. de Hauke, *Seurat* (1961), I, pp. 94f., ill. (cat. no. 142), 197, 200–209, 231, 234, 238 // J. Rewald, *The History of Impressionism* (revised and enlarged edition, 1961), ill. p. 513 // W. I. Homer, *Seurat and the Science of Painting* (1964), pp. 123, 125, ill. p. 124, comments on the importance of this sketch and its effect of light and shade // J. F. Revel, *L'Oeil*, 119 (Nov. 1964), pp. 25, 44, discusses the effects achieved by a combination of line and color and their relation to the theoretical writings of Charles Henry.

EXHIBITED: Société des Artistes Indépendants, Paris, 1892, *VIIIᵉ Exposition*, no. 1088 (probably ours); Bureau de la Revue Blanche, Paris, 1900, *Exposition Seurat*, no. 16 (probably ours; lent anonymously); Société des Artistes Indépendants, Paris, 1905, *21ᵐᵉ Exposition, Serre*

B (Aval-Alma), *Exposition Rétrospective, Georges Seurat*, no. 5 (lent by Félix Fénéon); Germany, *Pariser Künstler Wanderausstellung*, 1906–1907, no. 99; Galerie Bernheim-Jeune, Paris, 1908–1909, *Georges Seurat*, no. 45 (lent by M. F. F.); Bourgeois Gallery, New York, 1918; Metropolitan Museum, 1921, *Impressionist and Post-Impressionist Paintings*, no. 113 (lent by A. Lewisohn); Union League Club, New York, 1924, *"Modern" Pictures*, no. 32 (as La Promenade, lent by A. Lewisohn); Museum of Modern Art, New York, 1929, *First Loan Exhibition*, no. 56 (lent by A. Lewisohn); and 1930, *Summer Exhibition: Retrospective*, no. 96 (lent by A. Lewisohn); Burlington House, Royal Academy, London, 1932, *French Art, 1200–1900*, no. 523 (lent by A. Lewisohn) (*Commemorative Cat.*, no. 503); Metropolitan Museum, 1932, *Taste of Today* (lent by A. Lewisohn); Albright Art Gallery, Buffalo (New York), 1932, *Nineteenth-Century French Art*, no. 56 (lent by A. Lewisohn); Museum of Modern Art, New York, 1933, *Summer Exhibition*; Durand-Ruel Gallery, New York, 1934, *Great French Masters*, no. 48 (lent by A. Lewisohn); Museum of Modern Art, New York, 1934–1935, *Modern Works of Art*, no. 27 (lent by A. Lewisohn); Renaissance Society, University of Chicago, 1935, *24 Paintings and Drawings by Georges Pierre Seurat*, no. 15 (lent by A. Lewisohn); Museum of Modern Art, New York, 1937, *Summer Exhibition*, and 1939, *Art in Our Time*, no. 74 (lent from the Lewisohn collection); Knoedler Gallery, New York, 1939, *Views of Paris*, no. 37 (lent from the Lewisohn collection); World's Fair, New York, 1940, *Masterpieces of Art*, no. 369 (lent by Mr. and Mrs. S. A. Lewisohn); Colorado Springs Fine Arts Center, 1943; Museum of Modern Art, New York, 1946, *Paintings from New York Private Collections* (lent by S. A. Lewisohn); Wildenstein Gallery, New York, 1948, *Six Masters of Post-Impressionism*, no. 50 (lent by Mr. and Mrs. S. A. Lewisohn); Knoedler Gallery, New York, 1949, *Seurat*, no. 7 (lent by Mr. and Mrs. S. A. Lewisohn); Durand-Ruel Gallery, New York, 1949, *"What They Said"—Postscript to Art Criticism*, no. 7 (lent by Mr. and

Mrs. S. A. Lewisohn); Metropolitan Museum, 1951, *The Lewisohn Collection*, no. 79; Musée de l'Orangerie, Paris, 1955, *De David à Toulouse-Lautrec*, no. 51; Art Institute of Chicago and Museum of Modern Art, New York, 1958, *Seurat*, no. 100.

Ex coll.: Léon Appert, Paris; Félix Fénéon, Paris (in 1905–after 1909); [Stephan Bourgeois, New York, 1918]; Adolph Lewisohn, New York (by 1921–1938; Cat., 1928, p. 186); Samuel A. Lewisohn, New York (1938–1951).

Bequest of Samuel A. Lewisohn, 1951.

Invitation to the Side-Show (La Parade) 61.101.17

A *parade* is a free sample of entertainment played at the entrance of a traveling theater in order to attract a crowd and whet their enthusiasm to pay for the performance offered within.[1] Seurat painted this picture, one of his major works, in about six months during the winter of 1887–1888, while he was also working on The Models (now in the McIlhenny collection, Philadelphia). In each of his large and carefully planned compositions Seurat attacked new aesthetic problems. The two most notable features of this picture are the lighting and the deliberate avoidance of an effect of depth. The scene takes place out of doors in the evening, and the picture is lit by the yellow glow of gaslight. Seurat's attention is said to have been drawn to the problems of representing artificial light by a lecture that Whistler gave, which was published in French by Mallarmé (*Revue Indépendante*, 1888). The composition is extremely flat and is geometrical in scheme, with a pattern of calculated vertical and horizontal divisions. A similar patterned background and a row of silhouetted heads appear in an illustration of the same subject by Gavarni, published in *Le Diable à Paris* in 1846 (ii, p. 161, top), which Seurat could very well have known.

Seurat seems to have been influenced in the Museum's picture, as he was in The Models, by the theories of Charles Henry concerning the relationship between aesthetics and the physiology and psychology of the senses. There are quotations from the writings of Henry on a preliminary drawing for the architectural background of this picture.[2] In contrast to his earlier major works, the Baignade and the Grande Jatte, for which he made many preliminary studies, this painting seems to have been preceded by very few preparatory works. Although three *croquetons* and four drawings in conte crayon were listed in the inventory of Seurat's studio after his death, only one small oil study and the four drawings are extant (Ref., Dorra and Rewald, 1959, pp. LXXV, 222–224; Ref., Homer, 1960, p. 229, note 8). Seurat himself appears to have added the painted border around the picture but not the narrow wooden frame.

Oil on canvas. H. 39¼, w. 59 in. (99.2 x 149.9 cm.).

Notes: 1. D. Panofsky, *Gaz. des B.-A.*, XXXIX (1952), p. 325, note 19. 2. In the unpublished Signac archives belonging to Mme Ginette Cachin-Signac.

REFERENCES: Néo [Signac], *Le Cri du peuple* (Mar. 29, 1888) // G. Geffroy, *La Justice* (Apr. 11, 1888) // P. Adam, *La Vie moderne* (Apr. 15, 1888), pp. 228f. // F. Fénéon, *L'Art moderne* (Apr. 15, 1888), p. 122 // J. Meier-Graefe, *Entwicklungsgeschichte der modernen Kunst* (1904), I, p. 232; trans., *Modern Art* (1908), I, p. 314 // *Apollon*, II (1911), part 2, no. 7, ill. opp. p. 24 // L. Cousturier, *L'Art décoratif*, XXVII (1912), pp. 361, 368, ill. p. 357 (reprinted in *Georges Seurat*, 1926, pp. 12, 21) // W. Pach, *Georges Seurat* (1923), pp. 27f., pl. 14 // G. Coquiot, *Seurat* (1924), pp. 134, 227f., 248, ill. opp. p. 80 // [F. Fénéon], *Bulletin de la vie artistique*, V (1924), pp. 359f., ill. (detail) // H. Focillon, *Gaz. des B.-A.*, LXVIII (1926), pp. 260f., ill. // F. Fels, *A B C, Magazine d'art* (Nov. 3, 1927), ill. p. 282 // A. H. Barr Jr., *First Loan Exhibition* (cat.), Museum of Modern Art, New York (1929), pp. 25f., 43, no. 55, pl. 55 // R. Fry, *Burl. Mag.*, LV (1929), pp. 289–293, ill. in color // K. Niehaus, *Elsevier's Geïllustreerd Maandschrift*, LXXIX (1930), pp. 299, 309, ill. opp. p. 301 // R. Rey, *La Renaissance du sentiment*

classique (1921, error for 1931), pp. 123f., 144 // A. Lhote, *Encyclopédie française* (1935), p. 16.30-7, ill. p. 16.30-6 (fig. 2), p. 16.31-7 (fig. 1) // J. W. Lane, *Art News* (Annual), XXXVII (Feb. 25, 1939), pp. 133f., ill. in color p. 130 // R. J. Goldwater, *Art Bull.*, XXIII (1941), pp. 121–125, 127, 130, fig. 16 (the painting), figs. 14, 15 (studies) // B. Dorival, *Les Étapes de la peinture française* (1943), I, pp. 245f. // J. Rewald, *Georges Seurat* (1943), pp. 58, 70, 72, pl. 77 // J. de Laprade, *Georges Seurat* (1945), pp. IV, VII, pl. 48 // G. Seligman, *The Drawings of Georges Seurat* (1947), pp. 17, 19–21, 23–25, 57–60, pls. XVI–XX, catalogues and illustrates associated drawings, discusses the development of Seurat's conception of the picture // J. Rewald, *Georges Seurat* (1948), p. 137, ill. p. 107; and *Art News*, XLVIII (Apr. 1949), p. 62, ill. in color p. 26 // J. de Laprade, *Georges Seurat* [1951], pp. 81–83, 87, ill. p. 63 // J. Rewald, *Post-Impressionism* (1956), pp. 141f., 427, 516, ill. p. 420 // R. L. Herbert, *Burl. Mag.*, C (1958), p. 152, note 24 // H. Dorra and J. Rewald, *Seurat* (1959), pp. XXII (note 23), XXIV, LXII–LXIV, LXXV f. (note 59), LXXVIII, 225–227, cat. no. 181, ill., discuss, analyze, and catalogue the painting; quote critics; publish a pen sketch as a study by Seurat after the painting (no. 181A) // A. Frankfurter, *Art News Annual*, XXVIII (1959), ill. p. 39 // W. I. Homer, *Art Bull.*, XLII (1960), pp. 229, 231, notes 5, 8, questions the attribution of the pen study to Seurat // C. M. de Hauke, *Seurat* (1961), I, pp. XXIX–XXX, 150–153, cat. no. 187, pp. 197, 211, 222, 228f., 231, 239, 246, ill., publishes fourteen drawings that he relates to the picture, including the pen sketch (II, pp. 262f., no. 681, ill.), which he calls a study for this painting // R. L. Herbert, *Seurat's Drawings* (1962), pp. 127f., 131, 174, 180f. (no. 71), ill. p. 115, pl. VIII, comments on its flatness, mentions a study for it, made in 1886, in a private collection in Paris, and concludes from the palette and brushwork that it was reworked in 1890, finds that the drawing of the Acrobat (de Hauke no. 671) is not related to this picture // W. I. Homer, *Seurat and the Science of Painting* (1964), pp.

164, 175, 177–179, 183, 188, 219f., 223, 229, 240, 246, 298 (note 42), 300 (note 53), 303 (note 81), ill. p. 176, observes that the brushwork is unrelated to actual texture, and that Seurat in this picture expressed a feeling of calmness by uniting color, line, and value, and comments also on his dependence on the theories of Charles Henry and Ogden Rood // J. F. Revel, *L'Oeil*, 119 (Nov. 1964), p. 58 // A. Blunt, *Seurat* (1965), pp. 7f., 83f., color pls. 39, 40 (detail) // J. Russell, *Seurat* (1965), pp. 78, 216–219, fig. 194, in color.

EXHIBITED: Société des Artistes Indépendants, Pavillon de la Ville de Paris, 1888, *Quatrième Exposition*, no. 614 (marked for sale); Musée Moderne, Brussels, 1892, *Les XX, neuvième exposition annuelle*, no. 10 (lent by Mme Seurat); Société des Artistes Indépendants, Pavillon de la Ville de Paris, 1892, *Exposition commémorative Seurat*, no. 1084; Bureau de la Revue Blanche, Paris, 1900, *Georges Seurat*, no. 32; Galerie Bernheim-Jeune, Paris, 1908–1909, *Georges Seurat*, no. 69 (lent by MM. J. and G. B-J.); and 1917, *Essai d'une collection*, no. 30; and 1920, *Georges Seurat*, no. 28; Thé-

âtre de La Cigale, Paris, 1923–1924, *Soirées de Paris . . . l'art au music-hall, au théâtre et au cirque*, no. 38; Galerie Bernheim-Jeune, Paris, 1925, *Oeuvres du XIXe et XXe siècles, exposition au bénéfice de l'Hôpital Saint-Michel*, no. 116; and 1926, *Les Dessins de Seurat*; Grand Palais, Paris, 1926, *Trente Ans d'art indépendant*, no. 3216 (lent by MM. Bernheim-Jeune); Lucerne, 1929, *Peintures de l'école impressionniste et néo-impressionniste*, no. 20; Lefevre Gallery, Glasgow, 1929, *Masterpieces by XIXth Century French Painters*, no. 8; Lefevre Gallery, London, 1929, *Ten Masterpieces by Nineteenth-Century French Painters*, no. 7; Museum of Modern Art, New York, 1929, *First Loan Exhibition*, no. 55 (lent by Knoedler); Rhode Island School of Design, Providence, 1930, *Modern French Art*, no. 36 (lent by Knoedler); Galerie Georges Petit, Paris, 1930, *Cent Ans de peinture française*, no. 31; Knoedler, New York, 1930, *Masterpieces by Nineteenth-Century French Painters*, no. 11; Royal Academy, London, 1932, *French Art*, no. 552, commemorative catalogue, no. 509 (lent by Roland F. Knoedler); California Palace of the Legion of Honor, San Francisco, 1934, *French Painting*,

61.101.17

no. 148 (lent by Stephen C. Clark); Museum of Modern Art, New York, 1934–1935, *Modern Works of Art*, no. 29 (lent by Stephen C. Clark); Cleveland Museum of Art, 1936, *Twentieth Anniversary Exhibition*, no. 313 (lent by Stephen C. Clark); Museum of Modern Art, New York, 1939, *Art in Our Time*, no. 76 (lent by Stephen C. Clark); and 1940, *Modern Masters*, no. 13 (lent by Stephen C. Clark); World's Fair, New York, 1940, *Masterpieces of Art*, no. 366 (lent by Stephen C. Clark); Museum of Modern Art, New York, 1944, *Art in Progress*, cat. p. 30 (lent by Stephen C. Clark); The Century Association, New York, 1949, *Trends in European Painting*, no. 3 (lent by Stephen C. Clark); Knoedler Gallery, New York, 1949, *Seurat*, no. 22 (lent by Stephen C. Clark), and 1954, *A Collector's Taste: Selections from the Collection of Mr. and Mrs. Stephen C. Clark*, no. 20; Museum of Modern Art, New York, 1955, *Paintings from Private Collections*, no. 139 (lent by Stephen C. Clark); Metropolitan Museum, *Paintings from Private Collections*, 1958, no. 124, 1959, no. 101, 1960, no. 112 (lent by Stephen C. Clark).

Ex coll.: Mme Seurat, Paris (in 1892); Émile Seurat and Léon Appert, Paris (until 1900?; sold at the exhibition at La Revue Blanche in 1900 according to Fénéon, Ref., 1924, and C. M. de Hauke, Ref., 1961, but according to Dorra and Rewald, Ref., 1959, sold soon after the exhibition to Bernheim-Jeune); Bernheim-Jeune, private collection, Paris (by 1908–1928 or 1929; Cat., *L'Art moderne . . .*, 1919, II, pl. 151); [Alex Reid and Lefevre, London, in 1929]; [Knoedler, New York, 1929–1933]; Stephen C. Clark, New York (from 1933).

BEQUEST OF STEPHEN C. CLARK, 1961.

Signac

Paul Signac. Born in Paris in 1863; died there in 1935. Signac's family intended him to be an architect. He was enrolled for regular studies at the Collège Rollin but left without graduating and began to study painting. He worked first at the École Nationale Supérieure des Arts Décoratifs and then at Bing's Academy.[1] He greatly admired the works of Monet and became a close friend of the painter Guillaumin, working often at his side and through him coming into contact with other Impressionist painters. He also had a chance to see their works at the painters' supply shop of Père Tanguy, who exhibited pictures by Van Gogh, Gauguin, Cézanne, and Bernard. In 1884 Signac took part in the exhibition of a group of independent artists who banded together and founded the Society of Independents. Signac always remained in close contact with the organization and much later, in 1908, became its president. It was at their first exhibition that he saw Seurat's earliest large composition, Bathing at Asnières, and from this time on the two painters were closely associated. Together they perfected the system of painting that came to be known as divisionism, or pointillism. Like Seurat he was deeply indebted to the aesthetic theories of Charles Henry.

Signac was always attracted by the sea, and his favorite subjects were marines and views of ports. He was an enthusiastic yachtsman and spent much of his time on the

French coast, often, during the eighties, at Port-en-Bessin in Normandy and after 1892 in his villa at St. Tropez. He also traveled extensively, visiting Italy and the Low Countries, and made a trip to Constantinople.

His working method began with annotations made on the spot, drawings in flowing, calligraphic line and brush strokes of water color wash. These free and spontaneous sketches were the basis for his carefully planned and constructed oil paintings, which were always carried out indoors in the studio. He gave great attention to the construction and organization of his pictures. His intention, according to his own statement, was to "give color the greatest possible brilliance," and to this end he used pure pigments, refraining from mixing them on the palette but placing them side by side on the canvas so that the combining might take place in the eye of the beholder. Unlike Pissarro, who, under the influence of Seurat and Signac adopted the dot technique, but for a short time only, Signac continued all his life to paint in the small regular brush strokes that characterize divisionism, making them circular at first and later square.

Signac, who had known Vincent van Gogh when he was in Paris, and later at Arles, influenced him to try the dot technique and to experiment with juxtaposed contrasting colors. He was a passionate propagandist, the chief theorist of the group of Neo-Impressionists, and with a pronounced talent for expository writing wrote a book on Jongkind and one called *D'Eugène Delacroix au Néo-Impressionnisme*. After Seurat's early death in 1891 Signac was the chief apostle of the Neo-Impressionists, dedicated to carrying on Seurat's work and to making their theories generally known.

Note 1. According to W. I. Homer in *Seurat and the Science of Painting* (1964), p. 266, note 13, the artist who ran the academy was named Bin.

View of the Port of Marseilles

55.220.1

Signac must have painted this view of Marseilles from the north bank of the old port of the city, looking south toward the steep limestone peak upon which stands the basilica of Notre Dame de la Garde. This church was constructed by Espérandieu and consecrated in 1864. It was built on the site of a thirteenth-century chapel and is surrounded by the ramparts of a sixteenth-century fort. It is crowned by a gilded statue of the Virgin, almost thirty feet high, that is familiarly called by the people of Marseilles La Bonne Mère (The Good Mother), a title by which this picture has been known.

Four years before painting this picture Signac made a somewhat smaller version, signed and dated 1901, that is pastel in color. It belongs to Mr. and Mrs. William Mazer of New York City (ill. in *Modern French Painting*, exhib. cat., Wildenstein, New York, 1962, no. 60). Signac showed Notre Dame de la Garde perched on its high hill in the background of several other pictures of the port of Marseilles, some painted as late as the 1930's.

Signed and dated (at lower right): *P. Signac/ 1905.*

Oil on canvas. H. 35, w. 45¾ in. (88.9 x 116.2 cm.).

REFERENCES: G. Besson, *Signac* (1935), pl. 10 // *The Studio*, CLIV (1957), ill. p. 135.

55.220.1

EXHIBITED: Société des Artistes Indépendants, Paris, 1906, *22me Exposition*, no. 4626 (La Bonne Dame, Marseille, lent by M. Druet; possibly this picture); La Libre Esthétique, Brussels, 1908, *Salon jubilaire*, no. 182 (La Bonne Mère; possibly this picture); and 1910, *L'Evolution du paysage*, no. 170 (La Bonne Dame, Marseille; possibly this picture); Public Art Gallery, Brighton, 1910, *Exhibition of Modern French Artists*, no. 151 (La Bonne Mère—Notre Dame de la Garde, Marseille, lent by Bernheim-Jeune; possibly this pic-

ture); Bernheim-Jeune, Paris, 1911, *Les Ponts de Paris, nouvelle série d'aquarelles de Paul Signac; Tapisserie d'Aristide Maillol*, no. 79 (Marseille, La Bonne Mère; possibly this picture); Galerie E. Druet, Paris, 1911, *Henri Edmond Cross & Paul Signac*, no. 17 (La Bonne Dame, Marseille; possibly this picture); New York, 1913, *International Exhibition of Modern Art ("The Armory Show")*, no. 396 (La Bonne Mère, lent by Bernheim-Jeune; possibly this picture); Galerie Bernheim-Jeune, Paris, 1913, *Paul Signac*, no. 12 (La Bonne Mère, 1907; possibly this picture); and 1923, *Paul Signac*, no. 5 (La Bonne Mère, Marseille; possibly this picture); and 1930, *Paul Signac*, no. 28 (La Bonne Mère, Marseille, 1906); Musée National d'Art Moderne, Paris, 1951, *P. Signac*, no. 25 (lent by a private collector, Paris); Arkansas Arts Center, Little Rock, 1963, *Five Centuries of European Painting*, cat. p. 46; Musée du Louvre, Paris, 1963–1964, *Signac*, no. 66; Paul Rosenberg, New York, 1966, *Seven Decades of Modern Art*.

EX COLL.: Paul Signac, Paris (until 1928); Gaston Lévy, Paris (1928–1952; sale "Mme S. et divers amateurs," Galerie Charpentier, Paris, May 9, 1952); Robert Lehman, New York (from 1952).

GIFT OF ROBERT LEHMAN, 1955.

Toulouse-Lautrec

Henri Raymond de Toulouse-Lautrec-Monfa. Born in Albi (Tarn) in 1864; died at the Château of Malromé (Gironde) in 1901. Toulouse-Lautrec was a descendant of one of France's oldest aristocratic families and was never in his life oppressed by poverty. He was carefully educated, and he began to draw at an early age, displaying great skill in expressing liveliness in portraits and in pictures of horses, his favorite subjects. At adolescence in 1878 and 1879, two falls, resulting probably from congenitally weak bone structure, left him permanently deformed. His arms and legs remained abnormally short, contrasting with a normally developed torso, so that he had the appearance of a grotesque dwarf. If he had not suffered these accidents that prevented his leading an ordinary life, Lautrec would perhaps have remained only a talented amateur artist like his father and uncles and other members of the family. He now concentrated, however, on learning to be a painter. He got his first instruction from another handicapped artist, a deaf mute, the academic animal painter René Princeteau, who helped him to acquire a rapid and flexible technique. In 1882–1883 he worked also in the studios of the academicians Bonnat and Cormon, but with little profit. At Cormon's, however, he got to know Émile Bernard and Vincent van Gogh, and he soon met the other leading artists of the time, Pissarro, Gauguin, Seurat, and Degas. He admired the works of Manet, who had died in 1883. As a result of his contact with Impressionism his palette lightened. The decisive influence on his way of seeing, however, came from the art of Degas and from the popular Japanese prints, which had been so important in Degas's own formation, and through these mediums he learned how to create an effect of intense vitality, resulting from his use of linear arabesques and shrill accents of color.

About 1886 he became a resident of Montmartre, the favorite haunt of innumerable artists and the Parisian center for night life and pleasure-seeking. From its cabarets, music halls, and the circus he drew the subject matter for his prolific outpouring of drawings and paintings and for his famous lithograph posters and illustrations. He portrayed the celebrities, always with an incisive perception of individuality, immortalizing among others the dancers Jane Avril, La Goulue, the female clown Cha-U-Kao, and Valentin le Désossé, and the singers Aristide Bruant and Yvette Guilbert. The force of his repressed vitality, his aristocratic scorn for bourgeois convention, and a deep interest in the strange and cruel aspects of life often determined his choice of sordid subject matter. For several years, about 1892–1896, he spent a great deal of time painting and sketching in brothels, drawing his motifs from the daily life there.

During the last two years of his short life Toulouse-Lautrec produced little, spending part of his time being treated for severe alcoholism in a sanitarium. His artistic activity, though extremely intense, was brief, lasting scarcely twenty years. His work became known early, for his posters often appeared as decorations in the lobbies of music halls and cabarets. Although he belonged to no group and always preserved his personal integrity and freedom, he exhibited frequently at the Salon des Indépendants. In 1893 a showing of his works at the Goupil Gallery attracted a great deal of attention and brought him the acclamation of all the important artists of the time, especially that of Degas. This exhibition had been arranged by his devoted life-long friend Maurice Joyant, who later founded the Toulouse-Lautrec Museum at Albi.

The style of Toulouse-Lautrec, which crystallized into its final form about 1887, is characterized by extreme refinement and, regardless of the nature of his subject matter, always showed surprising dignity and brilliance. He not only extracted from the life of Montmartre all that it could offer of the grotesque and picturesque, but with astonishing penetration uncovered depths of moral degeneration and tragic loneliness beneath the laughter and excess. The portraits that he painted of entertainers and prostitutes as well as those of members of the aristocratic circle in which he was born are all distinguished by an acute perception of individuality and human qualities. Toulouse-Lautrec played a dominant part in the development of the art of the poster, and he made an important contribution to the formulation of aesthetic attitudes in the period that followed Impressionism, when great stress was being laid on subjective interpretations of life expressed by pure and intense line and color. His art was a source of inspiration for the Fauves and captured the imagination of Picasso at the beginning of his career.

The Sofa   51.33.2

This painting is one of a large series of pictures and studies that Toulouse-Lautrec made between 1892 and 1896 on themes drawn from his observation of houses of prostitution. He carried out the most important examples in his studio in Montmartre, which was in a building at the corner of the Rue Caulain-court and the Rue Tourlaque. It is possible, however, that our painting could have been done on the spot in one of the Parisian brothels in which he lived between 1894 and 1896. It is a rapid sketch in oil on cardboard, a favorite medium with Toulouse-Lautrec, and has the spontaneity of a study from nature.

The nearer figure reappears in an oil sketch in the Musée d'Albi (*Toulouse-Lautrec*, Collection Génies et Réalités, 1962, ill. p. 137,

51.33

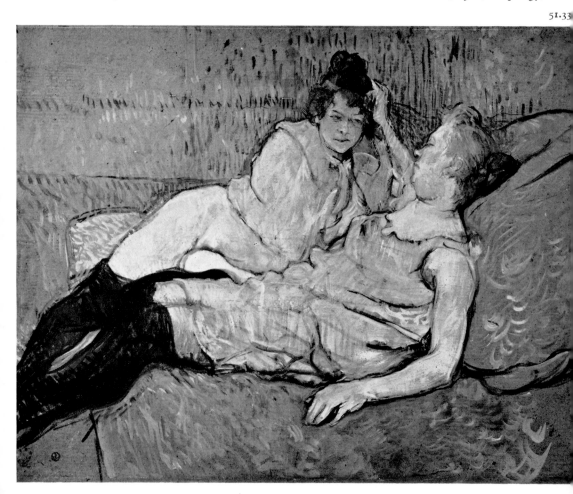

fig. 4). The same two women seem to have served as models for a picture called Rue des Moulins in the Chester Dale collection (exhibited at the Philadelphia Museum of Art, 1943, cat. pl. 10).

This picture is a perfect example of Toulouse-Lautrec's unsparing analysis, which observed the cruel deterioration of the women's bodies. It also reveals his sympathy for their profound spiritual disillusionment.

Stamped (at lower left): HTL (monogram).

Oil on cardboard. H. 24¾, w. 31⅞ in. (62.9 x 81 cm.).

REFERENCES: *L'Amour de l'art*, XII (1931), p. 138, fig. 8, calls this picture Femmes au lit, states that it has not been previously published // M.-L. Dortu, M. Grillaert, and J. Adhémar, *Toulouse-Lautrec en Belgique* (1955), p. 35, no. 92, pl. 32 (a gallery view of the exhibition in 1935 in Brussels, showing this picture) // M. Rheims, in *Toulouse-Lautrec*, Collection Génies et Réalités (1962), p. 224, comments upon the price this picture brought at the sale of the Soubies collection in 1928.

EXHIBITED: Musée des Arts Décoratifs, Paris, 1931, *Henri de Toulouse-Lautrec*, no. 114 (as done in 1894; lent by Henraux); Palais des Beaux-Arts, Brussels, 1935, *L'Impressionnisme*, no. 92 (lent by Henraux); Knoedler Gallery, Paris, 1938, *Toulouse-Lautrec*, no. 23 (as Le Sopha, 1894; lent by Albert S. Henraux); Philadelphia Museum of Art, 1955, and Art Institute of Chicago, 1956, *Toulouse-Lautrec*, no. 49; Museum of Modern Art, New York, 1956, *Toulouse-Lautrec*, no. 28 (as painted in 1894); Wildenstein Gallery, New York, 1964, *Toulouse-Lautrec*, no. 37; Palais de la Berbie, Albi, and Petit-Palais, Paris, 1964, *Centenaire de Toulouse-Lautrec*, no. 56.

EX COLL.: Dr. Soubies, Paris (sale, Hôtel Drouot, Paris, June 14, 1928, no. 90, as Le Sopha); Albert S. Henraux, Paris (from 1928, until after 1938); Chabert, Switzerland; [a Paris dealer]; [Wildenstein, New York, in 1951].

PURCHASE, ROGERS FUND, 1951.

(left part)   64.153

Madame Thadée Natanson at the Theater   64.153

Misia Godebska, a beautiful Polish woman, was married the first time to Thadée Natanson, who with his brother Alexandre founded the magazine *La Revue Blanche*. She subsequently became the wife of Alfred Edwards, the founder of the paper *Le Matin*, and finally of the Spanish painter José Maria Sert y Badia. She was a lively and lavish hostess and a sympathetic friend of a large circle of poets and artists, including Verlaine, Mallarmé, Bonnard, and especially Vuillard. Toulouse-Lautrec, another of her favorites, made many likenesses of her. This sketch, showing her in elegant evening dress at the theater, was a preparation for a large lithograph (L. Delteil, *Le Peintre-Graveur Illustré*, X, 1920, no. 127, ill.). The print was used as the cover for the final number (March 1895) of *L'Estampe Originale*, a periodical that reproduced original prints. The portrait of Misia appeared on the back of the magazine, and the other half of the design, taken from the right side of the Museum's drawing, appeared on the front. This part of the drawing, which is not illustrated, shows a stage hand busy with the pulleys that work the curtains and a statue of an elephant on a pedestal, on which, in the lithograph, the names of the contributors to the final issue of the magazine were inscribed.

Gouache on cardboard. H. 24½, w. 29½ in. (62.2 x 73.6 cm.).

Signed, dated, and inscribed (at lower right): *à Mme Th. Natanson./ Hommages de / T. Lautrec 95.*

REFERENCES: M. Joyant, *Toulouse-Lautrec— Peintures* (1926), p. 292 // G. Mack, *Toulouse-Lautrec* (1938), p. 264, discusses Toulouse-Lautrec's likenesses of Misia Natanson, including the cover for *L'Estampe Originale* and posters // J. Lassaigne, *Toulouse-Lautrec* (1939), p. 167, ill. p. 117 // G. Mack (in a letter, 1950), gives information about the sketch and the finished lithograph // M. Sert, *Two or Three Muses, the Memoirs of Misia*

Sert (1953), discusses the circumstances under which it was made, and says that she preferred it to all other portraits of herself by Toulouse-Lautrec // L. and E. Hanson, *The Tragic Life of Toulouse-Lautrec* (1956), pp. 175, 178, call the lithograph portrait of Misia Natanson perhaps the best of Toulouse-Lautrec's characterizations of her, mistakenly referring to it as a cover for the first rather than the last number of *L'Estampe Originale*.

EXHIBITED: Musée des Arts Décoratifs, Paris, 1931, *H. de Toulouse-Lautrec*, no. 138 (lent by Marcel Guérin); Knoedler, Paris, 1938, *Toulouse-Lautrec*, no. 26 (lent by Marcel Guérin); Wadsworth Atheneum, Hartford (Conn.), 1959, *The Music Makers*, no. 18 (lent by Mr. and Mrs. Richard Rodgers).

EX COLL.: Marcel Guérin, Paris (by 1931, in 1938); [Jacques Lindon, New York, until 1950]; Mr. and Mrs. Richard Rodgers, New York (1950–1964).

GIFT OF MR. AND MRS. RICHARD RODGERS, SUBJECT TO A LIFE ESTATE IN THE DONORS, 1964.

Bonnard

Pierre Bonnard. Born in 1867 at Fontenay-aux-Roses; died in 1947 at Le Cannet, near Cannes. At the insistence of his father, who held an important post in the Ministry of War, Bonnard began the study of law. He failed the oral examinations, however, and studied drawing and painting at the École des Beaux-Arts, and, more importantly for him, at the Académie Julian. There he met and became friendly with a number of other young artists, including Édouard Vuillard, Maurice Denis, and Paul Sérusier. They learned from Sérusier, who had visited Pont-Aven, of Gauguin's convictions about representing nature symbolically in strong patterns and colors, and Gauguin's exhibition at the Café Volpini in 1889 impressed them deeply. Drawn together by a common interest in art and methods, they became a loosely organized little circle. This group, who called themselves "Nabis," from the Hebrew word for prophet, included, besides the painters, the musician Hermant, the writer Percheron, and the actor producer Lugné-Poë. The Nabis held as their aim the expression of meaning and emotion in a way that should be symbolic but at the same time simpler and less literary than the "Symbolism" of Gauguin and his followers.

Bonnard's first one-man show was held in 1896 at the gallery of Durand-Ruel in Paris. For several years before that, however, he had exhibited in group shows with the Indépendants and also at the gallery of the dealer Le Barc de Boutteville. Thadée Natanson, who, with his brother Alexandre, had founded in 1891 a new periodical in Paris called *La Revue Blanche*, became an early patron of Bonnard's painting. For Thadée Natanson's first wife, Misia Godebska, Bonnard designed a set of four large decorative panels that were shown at the Salon d'Automne in 1910. The following year he showed a set of three made for a collector in Moscow. The making of lithographs also absorbed him, and he contributed many illustrations to the *Revue blanche*. Ambroise Vollard commissioned him to provide prints for several books, including Verlaine's *Parallèlement* and a modern edition of *Daphnis and Chloë*, two of the earliest and finest of the great illustrated books of the twentieth century. Bonnard was much influenced in his print-making by Toulouse-Lautrec, with whom he also collaborated. In addition to all these pursuits he made designs for furniture, rugs, theatrical sets, and costumes.

Between 1907 and 1911 Bonnard took a number of short trips on the Continent, in 1910 visiting the south of France for the first time. He went also to North Africa. In 1912 he bought a small country house at Vernonnet, near Vernon, and until about 1938 he divided his time between this village on the Seine and the French Mediterranean region. He acquired a house at Le Cannet, near Cannes, in 1925. He was there when the second World War broke out and remained until his death.

Bonnard painted many different kinds of subjects, enlivening all of them with rich paint textures and with color that is surprisingly fresh and bright, though never harsh. He achieved especial success with his interiors, glimpses of cheerful rooms with their occupants. His landscapes are characterized by original observation and are rendered in a peculiarly personal way. His original manner of painting was based on Impressionism but dependent also on the theories of the Nabis. In his early years Bonnard's style bore a close resemblance to that of his friend Vuillard. Both artists liked to render simple, everyday subject matter decoratively but with a gentle human atmosphere that earned for them the name "Intimists." Toward the end of his life Bonnard approached abstraction, subordinating the subject more and more in order to obtain the desired effects of color and light.

Vase with Anemones   64.152

Bonnard often included bowls of fruit or bouquets of flowers as incidental elements and complements to his main motif. Here, however, he has used a vase of anemones as his central theme. It is painted with the rich thick pigment and strong stroke characteristic of his work in the first decade of the twentieth century. These qualities make the picture significantly different from the few, more delicate, flower pieces of later years.

Signed (at lower left): *Bonnard.*

Oil on wood. H. 15¾, w. 12½ in. (40 x 31.8 cm.).

64.152

63.64

EXHIBITED: Wadsworth Atheneum, Hartford (Conn.), 1959, *The Music Makers*, no. 2 (Flowers, 1900–1904; lent by Mr. and Mrs. Richard Rodgers); Wildenstein Gallery, New York, and Rose Art Museum, Brandeis University, Waltham (Mass.), 1962, *Modern French Painting*, no. 1 (lent by Mr. and Mrs. Richard Rodgers).

EX COLL.: [Ambroise Vollard, Paris]; Gustave Lévy, Paris; Jacob Israel, Paris; [Wildenstein, New York, until 1951]; Mrs. Richard Rodgers, New York (1951–1964).

GIFT OF MRS. RICHARD RODGERS, SUBJECT TO A LIFE ESTATE IN THE DONOR, 1964.

The Green Blouse   63.64

This picture, probably painted in 1919, is one of Bonnard's earliest formulations of a motif which he used frequently during the two ensuing decades—a figure with a table and still life in front of a window.

In this picture the intensely clear, bright colors of the blouse, the fruit, the sky, and the foliage contrast with the shadowy figure on the left and the melancholy stare of the seated woman.

Signed (at lower left): *Bonnard.*

Oil on canvas. H. 40⅛, w. 26⅞ in. (101.9 x 68.3 cm.).

REFERENCES: C. Roger-Marx, *Pierre Bonnard* (1924), ill. p. 37, calls this picture Serre (Conservatory), dates it 1915 // M. Denis, *Gaz. des B.-A.*, XI (1934), p. 176, fig. 11.

EXHIBITED: Carnegie Institute, Pittsburgh (Pa.), 1924, *23rd Annual International Exhibition of Paintings*, no. 26 (as The Cup of Coffee, lent by Bernheim-Jeune); Wildenstein Gallery, New York, 1934, *Bonnard*, no. 25 (as The Cup of Coffee, with the date 1924).

EX COLL.: Gaston Bernheim de Villers, Paris; Abbé Philippe de la Chapelle, Paris (until 1962); [Sam Salz, New York, 1962–1963].

PURCHASE, MR. AND MRS. HENRY ITTLESON JR. FUND, 1963.

Interior   64.127

Painted a few years later than The Green Blouse (above), this picture is one of many variants of the same theme, a table with a seated woman in front of a window. The partial view of the woman and the glimpse of the painter's dachshund at the extreme right are characteristic features of many of Bonnard's works. Although the woman and dog are immobile, they suggest a witty rapport that enlivens the inanimate surroundings.

Signed (at lower right): *Bonnard*.

Oil on canvas. H. 50½, w. 47 in. (127 x 119.5 cm.).

Ex coll.: Jacques de Chollet, Lausanne; [Durand-Ruel, Paris, until 1960]; Mr. and Mrs. David Rockefeller, New York (1960–1964).

GIFT OF MR. AND MRS. DAVID ROCKEFELLER, SUBJECT TO A LIFE ESTATE IN MR. ROCKEFELLER, 1964.

64.127

The Seine at Vernon   59.168

In 1912 Bonnard bought and made over a country house called Ma Roulotte ("My Gypsy Caravan") at Vernonnet on the Seine, near Vernon and not far from Giverny, where Monet, a frequent visitor of Bonnard's, was living. This view of the river glimpsed through lush vegetation is one of a number that Bonnard painted, probably from a window of Ma Roulotte. It was done in 1928 and is much less linear and more impressionistic than his work at the beginning of the twenties.

Signed (at bottom, right of center): *Bonnard*.

Oil on canvas. H. 19¾, w. 26⅞ in. (50.2 x 68.2 cm.).

EXHIBITED: Carnegie Institute, Pittsburgh (Pa.), 1930, *Twenty-Ninth Annual International Exhibition*, no. 213 (lent by Bernheim-Jeune); Cleveland Museum of Art, 1931, *Exhibition of the Foreign Section of the 29th Carnegie International*, no. 39 (lent by Bernheim-Jeune); Art Institute of Chicago; Wil-

59.168

denstein Gallery, New York, 1934, *Paintings by Bonnard*, no. 34 (lent by Bernheim-Jeune); Society of the Four Arts, Palm Beach (Florida), 1957, *Bonnard*, no. 23.

Ex coll.: [Bernheim-Jeune, Paris, until after 1935]; [Sam Salz, New York, 1948/1949]; Nate B. Spingold, New York (1948/1949–1958); Mrs. Nate B. (Frances) Spingold, New York (1958–1959).

GIFT OF FRANCES SPINGOLD, SUBJECT TO A LIFE ESTATE IN THE DONOR, 1959.

Roussel

Ker Xavier Roussel. Born in 1867 at Chênes (Lorry-lès-Metz); died in 1944 at Étang-la-Ville. Roussel began his education at the Lycée Condorcet, where in 1884 he met Édouard Vuillard, who became his friend and later his brother-in-law. Roussel influenced Vuillard in making his decision to adopt painting as a career. They both entered the École des Beaux-Arts, studying under Gérôme from 1886 to 1888. They then entered the Académie Julian, where Bouguereau and Lefebvre were their masters, and came to know Maurice Denis, Sérusier, Bonnard, and Vallotton. With these friends, who called themselves Nabis (see biography of Bonnard), Roussel showed his works at the Café Volpini and at the gallery of Le Barc de Boutteville. Most of his works at the beginning of his career were still lifes and landscape in oil or pastel.

The style of the pictures painted by Roussel during the late eighties and early nineties is characterized by tight composition, thick impasto, and somber color, all reflections of his admiration for the work of Cézanne. Then, like his friends Vuillard and Bonnard, he came under the influence of Impressionism, which led him to use a looser technique and to lighten his palette. His subject matter changed too, and he began painting decorative pictures, related in spirit to those of Vuillard and Bonnard. They, however, continued as Intimists, searching for beauty in casual everyday settings, while Roussel, a lifelong admirer of Poussin, turned to classical subject matter, illustrating antique themes with depictions of nymphs and gods in landscape settings suggested by the countryside around Paris.

In 1905, the year before Cézanne's death, Roussel and Maurice Denis visited him at Aix. The significance of this meeting with an artist whom he had long admired combined with his first experience of Mediterranean light and color to make this visit one of great importance for Roussel, who worked throughout the rest of his career from the pastels and studies he had made at Aix.

His large panels decorated with antique themes were well liked, and he was called on to decorate public buildings and private houses, such as that of Jos Hessel at Clayes, which was destroyed by fire during the liberation of Paris. In 1912 he was asked to paint the curtain for the theater of the Comédie des Champs-Élysées. He was also an accomplished illustrator, providing among other things the designs to go with Maurice de Guérin's prose poem "La Centaure" and drawings to accompany an edition of Virgil's *Bucolics*.

Faun and Nymphs   64.307

The figure reclining in the center of a group of blossoming trees and shrubs near a pool is probably a symbol of the fountain of youth. Roussel painted this subject many times and it was the theme of one of the two decorative panels, now destroyed, that he made for the château of Jos Hessel. The light colors of the vegetation and the verdant landscape are typical of the style Roussel developed for his decorative paintings.

Oil on canvas. H. 41¾, w. 55½ in. (106 x 141 cm.).

Ex coll.: Jacques Roussel, Paris; [Sam Salz, New York, until 1964].

Gift of Nineteenth and Twentieth Century French Art, Inc., through Sam Salz, 1964.

64.307

Vuillard

Édouard Vuillard. Born at Cuiseaux (Saône-et-Loire) in 1868; died at La Baule (Loire-Inférieure) in 1940. Vuillard's parents intended him to have a military career, but under the influence of his lifelong friend, Ker Xavier Roussel, he determined to become an artist. He studied first with Diogène Maillard and then under Robert-Fleury and Bouguereau at the Académie Julian, where Sérusier, Maurice Denis, Bonnard, and Vallotton were his fellow pupils. He also worked briefly with Gérôme at the École des Beaux-Arts.

The early career of Vuillard was similar to that of Bonnard (see p. 206, above), who was his close friend and shared a studio with him. Both belonged to the original group of artists who called themselves Nabis. Like Bonnard, Vuillard first exhibited publicly at the galleries of the dealer Le Barc de Boutteville, and he also showed his work at the offices of the periodical *La Revue Blanche*. The brothers Natanson became much interested in Vuillard and his work, and in 1894 Alexandre Natanson commissioned him to do a series of decorations for his house in Paris, nine large panels showing scenes of the public parks of Paris. Much later, in 1908, Vuillard painted another set of views of Paris for Henri Bernstein. Dr. Vaquez and the novelist Claude Anet also commissioned decorations for their houses, and in 1913 Vuillard was called on to provide paintings for the foyer of the theater of the Comédie des Champs-Élysées. In the last years of his life he carried out a decoration entitled Comedy for the Palais de Chaillot and an allegory, Peace Protecting the Muses, for the Palace of the United Nations at Geneva, his only decorations commissioned by the French government.

The official Salon rejected Vuillard's works at the beginning of his career, but after he had become an accepted artist he exhibited at the Salon d'Automne, which he had helped to found, as well as at the Salon des Indépendants, and at the galleries of Bernheim-Jeune. It was mainly, however, through Jos Hessel that the work of Vuillard became known and sought after. For long years Hessel and his wife were his patrons and devoted friends, and with his mother he spent many summers with them in the country, painting numerous portraits of them and members of their circle. They liked his way of painting and were pleased to be portrayed in his spacious decorative interiors.

Impressed by the art of Toulouse-Lautrec and by the fashionable Japanese print, he had developed very quickly, at the start of his career, a personal manner, characterized by boldly original arrangements, and areas of different patterns placed side by side in an interesting way. He used light colors contrasted with black and applied them to absorbent pasteboard in a way that produced a flat, dull surface.

After the turn of the century, when there was great demand for Vuillard's portraits, his style changed. The small regular strokes were replaced by broader areas of a single tone, often without shading. His charming interiors, with their evidence of quiet activity, gave way to the rich and mirrored apartments that pleased the wealthy bourgeois society of Paris in the early twentieth century. This new style, though still intimate, is less decorative but more closely allied to Impressionism. Vuillard indeed inherited Impressionism, but he recast it for the twentieth century, preserving at the same time all the cheerfulness and bourgeois serenity of the nineteenth.

55·173

Portrait of the Artist with his Friend Varoqui   55·173

This double portrait was painted early in Vuillard's career, probably shortly before 1890. The glass bottle and its reflection in the foreground indicate that the painting is a mirror image. Mirrors and reflections were favorite decorative devices with Vuillard, who used them in a variety of ways. This picture displays a curious combination of clarity and sharpness in the face and left hand of the self-portrait with vagueness in the figure of the friend and in the setting. The implication of subtle mood recalls portraits by Degas. A small oil sketch by Vuillard of the head of his friend belongs to the artist's biographer, Jacques Salomon, and his son Antoine, who were related to Vuillard by marriage.

Signed (at lower left): *E. Vuillard*.

Oil on canvas. H. 36½, w. 28½ in. (92.7 x 72.4 cm.).

REFERENCES: C. Roger-Marx, *Vuillard et son temps* (1945), ill. p. 26, calls it Vuillard à la palette, dates it about 1888 // A. C. Ritchie, *Edouard Vuillard* (exhib. cat.), Museum of Modern Art, New York (1954), pp. 10, 100, ill. p. 29, sees in it the influence of Degas, spells the friend's name Varoquez (in Errata, Varocquez) // A. Salomon, in letters (Oct. 28, 1961, and Oct. 16, 1962), gives the name of Vuillard's friend as Varoqui.

EXHIBITED: Galerie Charpentier, Paris, 1948, *Vuillard*, no. 4 (as Vuillard et son ami Varoquy, 1890); Kunsthalle, Basel, 1949, *Édouard Vuillard, Charles Hug*, no. 35 (as Vuillard à la palette, about 1888); Minneapolis Institute of Arts, 1952, *Great Portraits by Famous Painters*, no. 46 (lent by Sam Salz); Cleveland Museum of Art and Museum of Modern Art, New York, 1954, *Vuillard*, cat. p. 100 (lent by Alex Lewyt).

EX COLL.: Ker Xavier Roussel, Paris (until 1944); Jacques Roussel, Paris (1944–after 1948); [Sam Salz, New York, until 1953]; Alex M. Lewyt, New York (1953–1955).

GIFT OF ALEX M. LEWYT, 1955.

Still Life in the Studio   48.162.4

The picture within this picture shows Antoinette David-Weill (now Madame Citroën) and her nephew, Maurice Lambiotte, playing under a tree at her father's country estate in Mareil-le-Guyon, near Montfort-l'Amaury, west of Versailles. According to Antoine Salomon, Vuillard was working in his studio on the picture of the children when David David-Weill, the great collector, called to bring the artist a pheasant he had bagged that morning. Vuillard put the bird on a stool and set to work immediately painting a picture of it with a background composed of the painting of the children and a sketch for the big tree clipped to a board. The canvas showing the children at play is owned today by Madame

David-Weill in Neuilly, and a study for it belongs to Charles Boyer in Beverly Hills, California.

According to the catalogue of the Vuillard exhibition in 1938, for which the artist himself provided the information, this still life was done about 1926.

Signed (at lower right): *E. Vuillard.*

Tempera on canvas. H. 33¼, w. 41¼ in. (84.5 x 104.8 cm.).

48.162.4

REFERENCES: C. Roger-Marx, *Vuillard et son temps* (1945), p. 79, calls it Faisan posé sur une chaise, dates it 1926 // A. Salomon (in letters, 1961 and 1962), gives information about the painting of the picture.

EXHIBITED: Musée des Arts Décoratifs, Paris, 1938, *E. Vuillard*, no. 193 (as Faisan posé sur une chaise devant un tableau, about 1926; lent by Renand); Wadsworth Atheneum, Hartford (Conn.), 1955, *Twentieth Century Painting from Three Cities*, no. 53.

EX COLL.: Renand, Paris; [F. Kleinberger & Co., New York, in 1947]; Robert Lehman, New York (1947–1948).

GIFT OF ROBERT LEHMAN, 1948.

52.183

Garden at Vaucresson   52.183

This is a representation of the Hessels' house
and garden near Paris, where they spent the

summers until 1925. Jos Hessel called this
property the *Clos Cézanne* (the Cézanne Garden) because he had got it shortly before 1914
in exchange for a picture by Cézanne. Vuillard and his mother rented a modest little
country house near by called the *Closerie des
Genêts* (Broom Flower Garden). When sup-
plying information for the catalogue of his
1938 exhibition, the artist said that he had
begun this picture about 1923 and taken up
work on it again in 1937.

Signed (at lower left): *E. Vuillard.*

Tempera on canvas. H. 59½, w. 43⅝ in.
(151.1 x 110.8 cm.).

EXHIBITED: Musée des Arts Décoratifs, Paris,
1938, *E. Vuillard*, no. 180 (as Jardin à Vaucresson; lent by Jos Hessel); French Pavilion,
World's Fair, New York, 1939, *Contemporary
French Art*, no. 159 (as Le Clos Cézanne à
Vaucresson; lent by Jos Hessel); Paul Rosenberg Gallery, New York, 1943, *Paintings by
Bonnard and Vuillard*, no. 7 (Le Clos Cézanne
à Vaucresson, 1918, 59 x 43½ in.; no lender);
Wildenstein Gallery, New York, 1964, *Vuillard*, no. 59.

EX COLL.: Jos Hessel, Paris; Mme Jacques
Arpels, Paris; [Knoedler, New York].

PURCHASE, WOLFE FUND, 1952.

Matisse

Henri Émile Benoît Matisse. Born at Le Cateau-Cambrésis in 1869; died in Nice in
1954. Matisse was the son of a merchant in fairly comfortable circumstances, who
wished his son to become a lawyer. In 1892, however, young Matisse, who had been
painting as an amateur for two years, persuaded his parents to let him become an artist.
He went to Paris, where he studied under Bouguereau at the Académie Julian, but he
found himself completely at variance with the academic approach. He transferred to
Gustave Moreau and worked with him until 1897, profiting enormously from his

liberal attitude. In Moreau's studio he made the acquaintance of Rouault and Marquet. Matisse copied extensively in the Louvre, mostly the French and Dutch painters of the seventeenth and eighteenth centuries. In 1896 four of his pictures were accepted for exhibition at the relatively new Salon of the Société Nationale, of which he became an associate member. In the course of the next four years he painted in Brittany, visited London, and spent many months in Corsica and Toulouse. During this time he became familiar with the painting of the Impressionists and, encouraged by Pissarro, adopted their technique. His early works were mostly still lifes and landscapes, for which he found few purchasers. The years from 1900 to 1904, though marked by poverty, were years of constant experiment and industry.

In the spring of 1904 Ambroise Vollard gave Matisse his first one-man show. At Saint-Tropez in the summer Matisse saw much of Signac and Cross, and he followed up some earlier experiments in pointillist technique by painting the large figure piece Luxe, Calme, et Volupté in dots of pure, bright color. He was also in close contact with Durand, Marquet, and Vlaminck, and soon became the head of an informal group of artists who from the time of the Salon d'Automne of 1905 were known as the "Fauves" or "wild beasts." Enthusiastic collectors, especially Americans, Germans, and Russians, now began to buy his pictures.

After the first World War Matisse settled in Nice, and from then to 1929 he enjoyed a long period of calm development. His favorite subjects at this time were odalisques or sunny interiors with still life. In these paintings he achieved his purpose—the delight of the eye and the spirit—in almost musical terms. In 1930 he went to Tahiti and also visited the United States, where Dr. Albert Barnes and Miss Etta Cone were devoted admirers of his painting and important patrons. For the Barnes Foundation in Merion, Pennsylvania, between 1931 and 1933 he carried out a series of murals in which the theme of the dance is interpreted with energy and sweep and in a simplified style of almost pure drawing very reminiscent of Greek vase paintings. Matisse's work showed a still greater simplification, both in expression and decorative composition, during the second World War. The culmination of this style is in the series of decorations he made in 1948 for the Dominican Chapel at Vence in the south of France.

Matisse's scale of color had immense variety and range. His visits to the south of France and to North Africa and his familiarity with oriental art intensified his pursuit of rich, decorative effects. He constantly transformed his style, moving from the calculated brilliance of pure tone and expressive line to a happily balanced, serene harmony that is characteristically French. For the sake of the style he thus evolved Matisse willingly sacrificed the normal appearance of human beings and the direct representation of nature. The mood of his pictures is determined by their pictorial language alone, a language of paint textures, luminous tone, graphic arabesques, and the rhythm of colored strokes and lines.

Matisse enjoyed an active career of more than sixty years. Like Picasso he constantly developed and revised both his vision and his means of expression, and he persisted in this deliberate expansion in spite of gaining enough success to tempt him to stop at any one of the various stages in the development of his style. He made countless drawings and engraved illustrations, experimented widely with cut-outs or collages, and created numerous important works of sculpture. Matisse was one of the most influential painters of the twentieth century and might perhaps be called the foremost originator of new color harmonies in all French painting.

53.140.2

A Bouquet on the Bamboo Table

53.140.2

This picture was painted early in 1902 when Matisse was staying with his parents at Bohain-en-Vermandois. The same year it was shown at the Salon des Indépendants and bought by a private collector. The modeling is subtle, and in the emphasis on volumes it reveals the influence of Cézanne. Matisse described the picture in a letter as one of his best works, accounting for what he called its "lack of attractiveness" by explaining that he had painted it during a period of transition from emphasis on values to stress on color, though in it values were still dominant.

Signed (at lower left): *Henri Matisse.*

Oil on canvas. H. 21½, w. 18½ in. (54.6 x 47 cm.).

REFERENCES: A. H. Barr, *Matisse, his Art and his Public* (1951), pp. 41, 50, 558, ill. p. 307, quotes a letter from Matisse giving his evaluation of this picture // G. Diehl, *Henri Matisse* (1954), p. 23, asserts that this picture, which he calls Bouquet d'anémones, was painted in 1903 and that it had been exhibited at the Salon d'Automne and the Salon des Indépendants in 1904.

EXHIBITED: Société des Artistes Indépendants, Paris, Salon of 1902, no. 1212 (as Fleurs dans un vase d'argent); Metropolitan Museum, 1921, *Impressionist and Post-Impressionist Paintings*, no. 64 (lent anonymously); Museum of Modern Art, New York, 1943, *European and American Art*; Buchholz Gallery, New York, 1943, *Early Works by Contemporary Artists*, no. 34 (lent by the Museum of Modern Art); New Jersey State Museum, Trenton, 1947, *Living Artists in Europe and America* (lent by the Museum of Modern Art); Montclair Art Museum (New Jersey), 1948, *History of Still-Life and Flower Painting*, no. 44 (lent by the Museum of Modern Art); Norton Gallery, West Palm Beach (Florida), 1951, *Still-Life Painting* (lent by the Museum of Modern Art); Society of the Four Arts, Palm Beach (Florida), 1952, *Two Centuries of Flower Painting* (lent by the Museum of Modern Art).

EX COLL.: Bernard Goudchaux, Paris (from 1902); Dikran Khan Kélékian, Cairo, Paris, and New York (Cat., *Tableaux de l'école française moderne*, 1920, pl. 46; sale, American Art Association, New York, Jan. 30, 1922, no. 124); Mrs. Wendell T. Bush, New York (1922–

1942); Museum of Modern Art, New York (1942–1951; Cat., *Paintings and Sculpture in the Museum of Modern Art*, 1948, p. 314, no. 499, ill. p. 38).

PURCHASE, ALFRED N. PUNNETT FUND, 1951, FROM THE MUSEUM OF MODERN ART, GIFT OF MRS. WENDELL T. BUSH, 1942.

Odalisque 62.112

Matisse got from his teacher, Gustave Moreau, a lively interest in oriental art. He visited the exhibitions of Moslem art held in Paris in 1903 and in Munich in 1911, and he spent the winters of 1911, 1912, and 1913 in Morocco. In 1911 he also went to Moscow,

62.112

where he was greatly impressed by Byzantine icons.

These experiences probably account for the Moroccan screens that appear in this painting and several others of the same period. The Eastern inspiration is evident also in the subject itself, in the decorative flat patterning of the background, and even of the figure, in the sharp contrasts of shapes and pure bright colors, and in the complete filling of the canvas.

This painting can be grouped with the other odalisques painted between 1923 and 1928 and it seems to be most like the ones done at the beginning of this period.

Signed (at lower right): *Henri Matisse.*

Oil on canvas. H. 28¾, w. 23⅝ in. (73 x 60 cm.).

REFERENCES: J. H. Lipman, *Art in America,* XXII (1934), p. 143, ill. p. 135, dates this picture about 1924, calls it typical of the decorative pictures Matisse painted in his studio in Nice in the period 1917–1925 // *Vogue* (Dec. 15, 1937), ill. in color, p. 53 // M. D. Schwarz,

Apollo, LXVIII (1958), p. 60, ill. // *The Mrs. Adele R. Levy Collection* (exhib. cat.), Museum of Modern Art, New York (1961), pp. 26f., ill. (as painted in 1926).

EXHIBITED: Museum of Modern Art, New York, 1930, *Summer Exhibition, Retrospective,* no. 65 (Odalisque in Armchair, lent by Stephen C. Clark; possibly this picture); Metropolitan Museum, 1957, *Impressionist and Modern Paintings from Private Collections* (lent by Dr. David M. Levy); and *Paintings from Private Collections,* 1958, no. 87, 1959, no. 70, 1962, no. 46 (lent by Dr. David M. Levy); Museum of Modern Art, New York, 1961, *The Mrs. Adele R. Levy Collection.*

EX COLL.: [Valentine Dudensing Galleries, New York, 1927]; Stephen C. Clark, New York (1927–1947); [Durand-Ruel, New York, 1947]; Dr. and Mrs. David M. Levy, New York (from 1947).

GIFT OF THE ADELE R. LEVY FUND, INC., SUBJECT TO A LIFE ESTATE IN DR. DAVID M. LEVY, 1962.

Rouault

Georges Rouault. Born in Paris in 1871; died there in 1958. Rouault, whose father was a cabinetmaker, was directed toward art by his grandfather, who collected lithographs by Daumier and admired such courageous and independent artists as Callot, Rembrandt, Courbet, and Manet. Young Rouault was apprenticed in his teens to a maker of stained glass and subsequently worked for a restorer of old glass, and these early experiences are the basis for his characteristic use of strong, pure, jewel-like colors, separated by heavy lines of black that resemble the leads in medieval glass windows. In 1891 he enrolled in the École des Beaux-Arts, working at first under Delaunay and then with Gustave Moreau, becoming this artist's favorite pupil. Moreau's lasting influence on him is evident in his choice of colors and his preference for literary themes and unusual subject matter. When Moreau died in 1898 Rouault became the curator of the Gustave Moreau Museum in Paris.

In the early years of the twentieth century Rouault, who was deeply religious by nature, experienced a period of disturbing spiritual crisis. His early religious paintings, like the Ordeal of Samson of 1893, had treated biblical themes in an external and conventional way. After 1902, partly as a result of his sympathetic relationship with the impassioned Roman Catholic writer Léon Bloy, he arrived at a more positive and vivid conception of Christian painting, which led him to express his religious feeling by presenting social institutions and vices.

Water color and gouache were Rouault's favorite media up to the opening of the first World War. About 1913 he attracted the attention of the dealer Ambroise Vollard, who handled his work from this time on. Vollard commissioned some book illustrations from Rouault, who produced numerous prints that reveal him as unusually talented in this medium. After 1918 he discarded water color and gouache, working mostly in the oil medium. Just before the beginning of the second World War the fierceness of Rouault's expression gave way to a more serene mood, with satire and caricature replaced by compassion, often embodied in images of Christ. Besides painting, Rouault designed stained-glass windows, enamels, and the sets and costumes for Diaghilev's ballet "The Prodigal Son." His literary output was considerable, including poems, articles, letters, and memoirs published in 1926 as *Souvenirs intimes*. Rouault's work, exhibited since 1910 in numerous one-man shows, is highly prized in both Europe and America. He rigorously determined how much of it should be preserved, destroying several hundred unfinished pictures out of a large group that came back into his possession after the death of his dealer Vollard.

Rouault's subject matter is notable for the constant repetition of a few themes, reworked with insistence and dogmatic conviction. Paintings of prostitutes, judges, and clowns compose a very personal world, in which they are symbolic figures, with faces simplified and striking as masks. His landscapes, often the dismal industrial outskirts of Paris, are also expressive and poetic. Like Goya, Daumier, Rops, and Forain, Rouault resorted to caricature to express his bitter rage against corruption and injustice. His deep unrest and his subjective approach relate him to his contemporaries the Fauves, although he cannot actually be classed with them. He also has in common with them strong lines and rich color. But Rouault used these elements of style to expound his Christian theology, which has a medieval character, recalling Bosch. Although Expressionism has never been strong in France, it is the manifestation of art to which Rouault's work most clearly belongs.

Two Nudes (Filles) 49.106a,b

On each side of a large sheet of paper Rouault has painted two prostitutes in oil colors so freely diluted with medium that the effect resembles water color. The figures on one side of the sheet face toward the right; their outlines, seeping through the paper, provided the framework for the painting of the two very similar figures on the reverse, which naturally face in the opposite direction.

Although Rouault signed each side, he re-

49.106a   49.106b

garded these pictures as sketches, according to his daughter, who believed that they were painted in 1905 or 1906 (letter from Isabelle Rouault, Apr. 26, 1950, in Museum archives). In mood and style they resemble the gouache of 1906 called The Sirens (coll. R. Sturgis Ingersoll, Philadelphia; ill. in *Georges Rouault*, exhib. cat., Museum of Modern Art, New York, 1945, p. 41) and The Prostitutes of 1910 in the Bangerter collection in Montreux (ill. in L. Venturi, *Rouault*, 1959, p. 55). The woman with a pompadour who appears in the Bangerter picture seems to have been the model for the nearer figure in each of the Museum's paintings.

Signed (on each side of the paper, at lower right): *G. Rouault*.

Oil on paper. H. 39⅜, w. 25½ in. (100 x 64.8 cm.).

REFERENCES: G. Charensol, *Georges Rouault* (1926), pl. 15 (obverse), calls it a water color, dates it 1908 // *Rouault (Edizioni d'Arte e Scienza*, Milan, 1945), ill. p. 15 (the obverse), places it in 1908.

EXHIBITED: Hofstra College, Hempstead, New York, 1952.

EX COLL.: [Possibly Galerie Druet, Paris]; Werner Feutz, Switzerland; [Mouradian and Vallotton, Paris, until 1949]; Mr. and Mrs. Alex L. Hillman, New York (in 1949).

GIFT OF MR. AND MRS. ALEX L. HILLMAN, 1949.

Henri Lebasque   53.140.6

Rouault, who was much more interested in general themes than in the details of reality, painted very few portraits. He did this one of the painter Lebasque, who was his friend, during Lebasque's illness, probably about the time that he made the water-color portrait of him in the Granoff collection, Paris, that is dated 1917 (Ref., Courthion, 1963). Rouault usually saw faces as symbolic masks, but here his deep feeling of sympathy has led him to analyze his friend's quality as an individual. The painting is also known as The Sick Man and The Comedian.

Signed (at lower right): *G Rouault*.

Oil on canvas. H. 36¼, w. 28⅞ in. (92.1 x 73.4 cm.).

REFERENCES: L. Venturi, *Georges Rouault* (1940), pp. 51, 74, pl. 49, fig. 57, calls this picture Lebasque Malade, dates it 1914–1915 // M. Wheeler, *Twentieth-Century Portraits* (exhib. cat.), Museum of Modern Art, New York (1942), p. 17, ill. p. 69, dates it 1917, considers it one of Rouault's best portraits // J. T. Soby, *Georges Rouault* (exhib. cat.), Museum of Modern Art, New York (1945), pp. 20f., 116, no. 47, ill. p. 65, observes that it shows a realism rare in the work of Rouault // L. Venturi, *Georges Rouault* (1948), p. 69, pl. 49, fig. 57, dates it 1917, states that Lebasque Malade was the original title, observes that the illness of the model contributes to the intensity of the picture, compares it to the portrait of M. X. of 1911 (pl. 39, fig. 46) // B. Dorival, *Revue des arts* (1953), pp. 234f., considers it one of Rouault's best works; and

53.140.6

Georges Rouault (1956), p. 105, dates it 1917 // P. Courthion, *Georges Rouault* [1963], p. 198, dates it 1914–1930, states that it was also known as The Sick Man and The Comedian, publishes a second portrait of Lebasque, a water color in the collection of Katia Granoff, Paris, dated 1917 (ill. p. 232).

EXHIBITED: Institute of Modern Art, Boston, Phillips Memorial Gallery, Washington (D. C.), and San Francisco Museum of Art, 1940–1941, *Georges Rouault*, no. 54 (lent by the Museum of Modern Art, New York); Pierre Matisse Gallery, New York, 1942, *Figure Pieces in Modern Painting*; Museum of Modern Art, New York, 1942, *Twentieth-Century Portraits*, cat. p. 69; Museum of Modern Art Circulating Exhibition, 1942–1943, *European and American Paintings* (no cat. published); Museum of Modern Art, New York, 1945, *Georges Rouault*, no. 47; Cleveland Museum of Art, Museum of Modern Art, New York, and Los Angeles County Museum, 1953, *Rouault*, cat. p. 28; Galleria d'Arte, Milan, 1954, *Georges Rouault*, no. 31.

EX COLL.: Henri Lebasque, Paris (until 1937); Dr. Franz Mayer, Zurich (in 1938); [Valentine Gallery, New York, in 1939]; Museum of Modern Art, New York (from 1939; Cat., 1948, pl. 320, no. 658, ill. p. 47, with the date 1917).

PURCHASE, JOSEPH PULITZER BEQUEST FUND, 1951, FROM THE MUSEUM OF MODERN ART, THE MRS. JOHN D. ROCKEFELLER PURCHASE FUND, 1939.

The Old Wall   55.21.3

For many years Rouault was interested in depicting in paintings and lithographs the dreariness of the industrial areas on the outskirts of Paris. In 1929 and 1930 he worked on a series of pictures in preparation for a film that never materialized (Ref., Rouault, 1963). This picture is one of the series and appeared in that year in an exhibition in Munich with the title *Le Vieux Mur n'en finissait plus. No. 2 Faubourg* (The old wall went on and on. No. 2 Suburb), a title supplied by Rouault. Another

55.21.3

of the series, also shown in the Munich exhibition, has the same title, but differentiated as No. 1 Faubourg (now in the collection of G. David Thompson, Pittsburgh; Ref., Courthion [1963], ill. p. 422, no. 179). A picture called The Cemetery (in the collection of Philippe Leclercq, Hem, France; Ref., Courthion [1963], ill. p. 227), also done in 1930, probably belongs to the same series.

In the foreground of the Museum's picture a funeral procession seems to be passing, and behind the wall are the crosses of the cemetery.

Formerly called The Funeral.

Signed and dated (at lower right): 1930 — G Rouault.

Gouache and pastel on paper. H. 11½, w. 19¾ in. (29.3 x 50.2 cm.).

REFERENCES: A. M. Frankfurter, Art News, XXXVI (Jan. 8, 1938), p. 24 // Bulletin of the Museum of Modern Art, VII (Apr.-May 1941), p. 7, no. 4, called Landscape with Figures, in list of gifts from a trustee // A. M. Frankfurter, Art News, XL (May 14, 1941), p. 34, ill. p. 11 // B. Dorival, Georges Rouault (1956), p. 70, calls it Le Vieux Mur N'en Finissait Plus // P. Courthion, Georges Rouault [1963], p. 423, fig. 182, p. 463, calls it Le Vieux Mur N'en Finissait Pas [sic] No. 2. Faubourg, dates it 1929, but on p. 463, catalogues it correctly under 1930 // I. Rouault (in a letter, 1963), states definitely that Rouault gave it the title Le Vieux Mur N'en finissait pas (no. 2) (Faubourg).

EXHIBITED: J. B. Neumann Gallery, Munich, 1930, Georges Rouault, no. 30 (as Le Vieux Mur n'en Finissait Plus. No. 2. Faubourg); Valentine Gallery, New York, 1938, 15 Selected Paintings by French XX Century Masters, 16 Gouaches . . . by Rouault, no. 4 (as L'Enterrement, 1930); Art Institute of Chicago, 1942, Twenty-first International Exhibition of Water Colors, no. 9 (lent by the Museum of Modern Art); Museum of Modern Art, New York, 1945, Georges Rouault, no. 61; Renaissance Society, University of Chicago, 1945, Rouault; Museum of Modern Art circulating exhibition, 1946–1947, Landscapes Real and Imaginary; Syracuse University (New York), 1949–1950, Rouault; School of the Boston Museum of Fine Arts, 1950, Group Exhibition; Winnipeg Art Gallery, 1951, European and American Paintings (lent by the Museum of Modern Art); Coe College Art Gallery, Cedar Rapids (Iowa), 1952, exhibition inaugurating opening of new gallery; Cleveland Museum of Art, Museum of Modern Art, New York, and Los Angeles County Museum, 1953, Rouault, cat. p. 29; Leonard Kipnis Gallery, Westport (Conn.), 1955, Georges Rouault.

EX COLL.: [J. B. Neumann, Munich and New York, 1930–1931]; private collection, New York (1931–1941); Museum of Modern Art, New York (1941–1951; Cat., 1948, p. 320, no. 659, ill. p. 48).

PURCHASE, MARIA DE WITT JESUP FUND, 1951, FROM THE MUSEUM OF MODERN ART, ANONYMOUS GIFT.

Twilight (Crépuscule)   56.230.2

According to his daughter, Rouault painted this picture in 1937 for Ambroise Vollard. He gave it the title Crépuscule (Twilight). The four figures in the foreground, however, suggest that it is not only a view of a city at evening but possibly an illustration of a biblical theme. The haloed figure wearing a tunic in the foreground might represent Christ, but it is impossible to determine whether a New Testament text is represented.

Formerly called The Humane Landscape.

Signed (at lower right): *G Rouault.*

Oil on canvas. H. 25¾, w. 38⅞ in. (65.4 x 98.8 cm.).

REFERENCES: P. Courthion, *Georges Rouault* [1963], ill. p. 266, calls this picture Twilight and dates it 1937; p. 464, lists it with incorrect measurements // I. Rouault (in a letter, 1963), states that Rouault made it for Ambroise Vollard, finished it in 1937 and called it Crépuscule.

EXHIBITED: Cleveland Museum of Art and Museum of Modern Art, New York, 1953, *Rouault* (cat. p. 18, as The Humane Landscape, 1928, lent by Mr. and Mrs. Nate B. Spingold).

EX COLL.: [Ambroise Vollard, Paris]; [Sam

56.230.2

Salz, New York, until 1951]; Mr. and Mrs. Nate B. Spingold, New York (from 1951).

GIFT OF MR. AND MRS. NATE B. SPINGOLD, 1956.

Derain

André Derain. Born in 1880 in Châtou (Seine-et-Oise); died in 1954 in Paris. Derain's father wanted him to become an engineer and he studied at the École Polytechnique. He had begun to paint, however, at the age of fifteen and by 1898 was attending the Académie Camillo in Paris, where Eugène Carrière occasionally gave lessons. At this school he met Matisse, who later persuaded Derain's parents to let him take up painting as a career. He did a period of military service and in 1904 studied painting at the popular Académie Julian. In his early years he became a friend of Maurice Vlaminck and for a time shared a studio with him. Derain felt the influence of Van Gogh, Gauguin, Cézanne, and Signac and was himself one of the leaders of the Fauves. In the autumn of 1910, on his first trip to Spain, he met Picasso.

In 1905 Vollard had bought up all the pictures in Derain's studio, and in 1907 Derain made a contract with D. H. Kahnweiler. Nine years later, while Derain was fighting in the war, the first one-man exhibition of his works was held at the gallery of another dealer, Paul Guillaume.

In the course of his career Derain worked at different times in the styles of several of the various movements that took shape at the end of the nineteenth and the beginning of the twentieth century. His early attachment to the Fauves gave place to an interest in Cubism, and then he adopted the Impressionist and Post-Impressionist techniques. Like many of his contemporaries, he was interested in African Negro sculpture. There is great variety in Derain's subject matter; he painted figures, nudes, portraits, landscapes, and still life. He worked in many different mediums, in oil, water color, pastel, and sanguine, and made woodcut illustrations. He designed stage sets, including some commissioned for the Russian ballet.

Although Derain's sensitiveness made him acutely aware of the work produced by his contemporaries, he cannot really be regarded as an eclectic. He had a strong original vision that makes his style highly personal. His best works are characterized by firmness, simplification, and clarity, qualities that mark the paintings of the classical French tradition, in which he takes his place.

54·79

The Table   54·79

In the fall of 1909 Derain began to make an intensive study of still life and from this time on it was one of the important themes in his work. This painting is undated, but it fits very well between a still life of 1910 in a private collection in Paris and another, painted two years later, in the collection of Lady Pamela Berry in London (both ill. in D. Sutton, *André Derain*, 1959, pls. 26 and 27). In the picture of 1912 the jug and the basket of fruit are much rounder and more classically monumental than the crockery in this painting.

Signed (at lower right): *derain*.

Oil on canvas. H. 38, w. 51⅝ in. (96.5 x 129.7 cm.).

REFERENCES: A. Salmon, *André Derain* (1929), ill. p. 13, dates this picture 1911 (in list of illustrations, IV) // C. Zervos, *Histoire de l'art contemporain* (1938), ill. p. 176, dates it 1911 // Alice Derain [Mrs. André] (in a letter to Walter Halvorsen, 1963), asserts that it was painted in 1920.

EXHIBITED: Pierre Matisse Gallery, New York, 1950, *Selections*, no. 4; Galerie Charpentier, Paris, 1950, *Autour de 1900*, no. 68 (La Table de Cuisine, probably our picture); and 1951, *Natures mortes françaises*, no. 43 (La Table); Pierre Matisse Gallery, New York, 1952, *Still Life and the School of Paris*; Museum Fridericianum, Cassel, June–Oct. 1964.

EX COLL.: [Daniel Henry Kahnweiler, Paris, from 1911]; C. Girard, Paris; [Pierre Matisse, New York, from 1950 or before].

PURCHASE, WOLFE FUND, 1954.

Flowers in a Blue Vase   64.161

In the 1920's Derain began to change in his attitudes toward art. He lost some of his admiration for Cézanne and for Cubism and, as Denys Sutton says, "practised several styles simultaneously" in order to adopt the method suitable to each subject.[1] Like the Vase of Roses in the Raeber collection, Basel (1923–1926), this bouquet of flowers of 1925 is painted in a soft and feathery technique reminiscent of Renoir, whose works Derain admired at this time.

Signed (at lower right): *a derain.*

Oil on canvas. H. 21, w. 18½ in. (53.4 x 47 cm.).

Note 1. *Derain* (1959), p. 39.

EXHIBITED: Knoedler Gallery, London, 1927, *Flower Pictures* (1568–1927), no. 30.

Ex COLL.: [Paul Guillaume, Paris]; [Alex Reid and Lefevre, London, until 1927]; [Knoedler, New York, 1927–1928]; A. K. Solomon, New York; Mrs. Edna H. Sachs, New York (1928–1964).

GIFT OF MRS. EDNA H. SACHS, SUBJECT TO A LIFE ESTATE IN THE DONOR, 1964.

64.161

Picasso

Pablo Ruiz Picasso (after about 1901, Pablo Picasso). Born in 1881 in Malaga, Spain; lives in France, at Mougins. Picasso showed signs of talent at an early age and received his first instruction in drawing and painting from his father, José Ruiz Blasco, a teacher in the local art school in Malaga. When he was ten his father took a post in a secondary school at La Coruña in Galicia, and the family moved there. Another move took them in 1895 to Barcelona, where Picasso, who had determined to become a painter, in one day completed the entrance requirement for the art school in which his father then taught. In 1897 he gained admission with equal ease to the Academia de San Fernando in Madrid and received an honorable mention at the Academy's Exhibition of Fine Arts for his painting Science and Charity. He did not, however, attend many classes at the Academy, though he visited the Prado and studied the old masters. After a few months he returned to Barcelona, which became his headquarters for the next few years.

Barcelona, in the last years of the nineteenth century, was a very cosmopolitan and advanced city. Picasso belonged to a group of Bohemian artists and writers who met in the café Els Quatre Gats, and it was there that the first exhibition of his work was held. The Catalan weekly *Joventut* published some of his drawings in 1900. The following spring, when he spent a few months in Madrid, he became the art editor and illustrator of another advanced periodical, the short-lived *Arte Joven*. Later in 1901, after his return to Barcelona, the magazine *Pèl y Ploma* organized an exhibition of Picasso's pastels at the Sala Parés and carried an article praising his work.

Meanwhile, attracted by the vitality and excitement that have always made Paris a center for artists and writers, Picasso had made his first trip there in 1900. This visit was followed by two others, and in 1904 he transferred permanently to France. His work had already been exhibited in Paris. Ambroise Vollard had held a show of his paintings in 1901, and Berthe Weill had given an exhibition the following year. A number of people were thus already aware of his work. Gertrude Stein and her brother Leo, among others, began early to buy his paintings.

Picasso maintained a studio in Paris from 1904 to 1948. In the summers he went frequently to the French Riviera and several times to Spain. He traveled to London for an exhibition of his pictures in 1912 and seven years later went there again when the Ballet Russe first performed "Le Tricorne," for which he had designed the scenery and costumes. In 1936, during the Civil War in Spain, he served briefly as Director of the Prado for the Republican Government, which he championed. Guernica, his famous allegory of the war, was painted in the following year and exhibited in the Spanish Government Building at the World's Fair of 1937 in Paris. Picasso has never revisited Spain since the war. During the second World War he remained in Paris, and in 1944, after the Liberation, he joined the French Communist party. As a delegate to the Communist peace congresses he went in 1948 to Poland and in 1950 to Sheffield, England.

In 1947 Picasso became interested in ceramics at Vallauris, an inland village above Golfe Juan, where pottery has been made for centuries. He began working there, buying a house and settling in 1948. In 1955, however, he left Vallauris for the large villa, La Californie, in Cannes. In 1960 he bought a country house, Mas Notre-Dame-de-Vie, at Mougins.

Picasso's extraordinary vitality, the richness of his imagination, and the speed with which he works combine to account for the large number of his successive styles and their variety. His first pictures, made when he was little more than a schoolboy, are distinguished by their precocious grasp of structure and anatomy and by the intensity of their sober realism. Around 1900, in Barcelona and during visits to Paris and Madrid, the world of cabarets and theaters provided the subject matter for pictures that often recall Toulouse-Lautrec's and occasionally Degas's and Daumier's. The name "Blue Period," roughly assigned to the years 1901 to 1904, is derived from the prevailing blue tone of most of the paintings made at that time. Much of the subject matter in these pictures reveals a melancholy preoccupation with poverty, sickness, and despair. After Picasso moved to Paris in 1904, his happier Bohemian life, the stimulation provided by friendships with Max Jacob, Guillaume Apollinaire, and other contemporary writers, and his fascination with actors and circus performers are all reflected in paintings with a more cheerful and lyrical mood. The pronounced reddish or pink tones in many of these pictures account for the label "Rose Period." The circus pictures of this time show figures of exaggerated slimness and grace, which gave place during the year 1906 to massive forms with a totally different canon of proportions and an emphasis on weight. This classical phase in turn gave way to one of the most important developments of the twentieth century in painting, Cubism, which was born in 1907 in the two right-hand figures of Picasso's large painting the Demoiselles d'Avignon. In the next few years Picasso and Georges Braque developed Cubism to a state of nearly complete, monochromatic abstraction. By the end of 1911 they had begun to vary their effects of texture, form, and color, through the use of *trompe-l'oeil* and *collage*.

About 1915 Picasso began again to produce realistic paintings and drawings, executed with the magnificent draughtsmanship of which he has always been a master. Since that time, for almost half a century he has explored concurrently both the representational and the abstract, and these are in varying degrees merged in his work. He is indisputably the giant of the twentieth century, courageous, spontaneously original, and immensely productive.

A Woman in Green   61.85

This pastel belongs to the group of pictures that Picasso made about 1900 of singers, *diseuses*, and habitués of night clubs and restaurants. It was shown with other pastels at an exhibition held in the Sala Parés in Barcelona, sponsored by the periodical *Pèl y Ploma* in the spring of 1901. These pastels are light and bright in color and extravagantly decorative in treatment, often with a very loose and free use of white, suggesting thin materials and textures. The high-piled coiffure, the stiff and massive collar, the voluminous ostrich cape, and the sharp, pinched features characterize a number of other heads of women in works of the time. The dancer at the left in The Cancan (Zervos, *Pablo Picasso*, I, 1932, pl. 20, no. 41), and the one in El Final del Número (Zervos, I, pl. 15, no. 30) all show the same straight eyebrow as our picture, the same pointed chin and high collar, and could well represent the same woman.

The signature that appears on our pastel still includes "Ruiz," the name of Picasso's father, which the artist dropped after 1901.

Signed (at upper left): *P Ruiz Picasso.*

Pastel on paper. H. 20, w. 13½ in. (sight) (50.8 x 34.3 cm.).

EXHIBITED: Sala Parés, Barcelona, 1901.

EX COLL.: Delmiro de Caralt, Barcelona (1901–1961); [M. Knoedler, New York, 1961].

GIFT OF MR. AND MRS. JOHN L. LOEB, 1961.

61.85

228

FRENCH PAINTINGS III

Harlequin 60.87

Between the pictures of cabaret singers and the typical paintings of the Blue Period, Picasso made in 1901 a series of half-lengths that show a simplified, relatively flat pattern with heavy outlines. In these he seems to be exploring the possibilities suggested in the paintings of Gauguin and Art Nouveau design and composition. In this Harlequin, the Two Acrobats (Ref., Zervos, 1932, pl. 46), and the Courtesan with Jeweled Collar (Ref., Zervos, 1932, pl. 21), Picasso has developed this emphasis on pattern almost to the exclusion of modeling and transitions in color. Others of these half-lengths, though similar in composition, are very different in treatment, some having pointillist brushwork and some showing more solid form.

The picture was signed and dated by Picasso some years after it was painted, but it is impossible to determine exactly when because photographs of it as it looked originally, without a signature, continued to be published after one was added.

Signed and dated (at lower left): *Picasso / 1901.*

Oil on canvas. H. 32⅝, w. 24⅛ in. (82.9 x 61.3 cm.).

REFERENCES: M. K. Rohe, *Die Kunst für Alle*, XXVIII (1912–1913), ill. p. 377, dates this picture 1903, calling it Sitzender Pierrot // E. L. Cary, *New York Times* (July 4, 1926), reprinted in *Brooklyn Museum Quarterly*, XIII, p. 136 // C. Einstein, *Die Kunst des 20. Jahrhunderts* (1926), ill. p. 265, dates it 1906, calls it Pierrot, in a German private collection // *Art News*, XXVIII (July 12, 1930), p. 6, wrongly identifies the anonymous lender to the 1930 summer exhibition as a trustee of the Museum of Modern Art, New York // C. Zervos, *Pablo Picasso*, I (1932), pl. 39, no. 79, catalogues this picture as Harlequin propped on elbows *(sic)*, painted in 1901 in Paris // G. Stein, *Picasso* (1938), pl. 4 (English ed.), frontispiece (French ed.), calls it Harlequin and Matches // A. H. Barr Jr., *Picasso: Forty Years of His Art* (exhib. cat.), Museum of Modern Art, New York, and Art Institute of Chicago (1939), pp. 24, 26f., no. 12, ill., dates it 1901, just before the beginning of the Blue Period, sees in its "decorative, poster-like manner" the possible influences of Van Gogh, Maurice Denis, and Vuillard // R. H. Wilenski, *Modern French Painters* [1940], p. 138, sees in it the influence of Gauguin, erroneously places it in the collection of Q. A. Shaw McKean, Boston (note 3) // R. Gómez de la Serna, *Picasso* [1944], pl. III // A. H. Barr Jr., *Picasso: Fifty Years of His Art* (1946), p. 19, ill. p. 21 // A. Cirici Pellicer, *Picasso antes de Picasso* (1946), pl. 76 // J. Merli, *Picasso* (1948), pl. 64 // W. Hess, *Das Kunstwerk*, IX (1955–1956), no. 3, p. 11, fig. 5 // F. Elgar and R. Maillard, *Picasso* (1956), ill. p. 271 // W. S. Lieberman, *Pablo Picasso, Blue and Rose Periods* (1954), color pl. 13, analyzes the composition // A. Vallentin, *Pablo Picasso* (1957), p. 66 // R. Penrose, *Picasso: His Life and Work* (1958), p. 81, mentions this picture among the important works painted in Paris in 1901 which prove that the Blue Period began before Picasso's return to Barcelona // D. Cooper, *Picasso* (exhib. cat.), Musée Can-

60.87

tini, Marseilles (1959), no. 4, ill., states that the date was added after 1927; and in a letter (1962), reports that according to Picasso the signature was added in Paris in the late thirties.

EXHIBITED: Städtische Ausstellungshalle, Cologne, 1912, *Internationale Kunst-Ausstellung des Sonderbundes Westdeutscher Kunstfreunde und Künstler*, no. 209 (Harlekin, 1903, lent by Edwin Suermondt; possibly this picture); Moderne Galerie (H. Thannhauser), Munich, 1912–1913, *Picasso* (this picture probably included); Brooklyn Museum, New York, 1926, *Special Loan Exhibition of Paintings by Modern French and American Artists* (no catalogue published; lent anonymously, according to museum records); Museum of Modern Art, New York, 1930, *Summer Exhibition: Retrospective*, no. 77 (lent by a New York private collection [Julia Q. Anderson]); Jacques Seligmann and Co., New York, 1936, *Picasso, "Blue" and "Rose" Periods*, no. 3 (lent anonymously); Harvard University, Cambridge (Mass.), 1936, exhibited on the occasion of the Harvard Tercentenary (lent by Henry P. McIlhenny); Boston Museum of Modern Art, 1938, *Picasso; Henri Matisse*, no. 2 (lent by Henry Clifford); Museum of Modern Art, New York, and Art Institute of Chicago, 1939, *Picasso: Forty Years of His Art*, no. 12 (lent by Mr. and Mrs. Henry Clifford); Sociedad de Arte Moderno, Mexico, 1944, *Picasso*, cat. p. 41 (lent by Mr. and Mrs. Henry Clifford); Philadelphia Museum of Art, 1947, *Masterpieces of Philadelphia Private Collections*, no. 50 (lent by Mr. and Mrs. Henry Clifford); Knoedler Galleries, New York, 1947, *Picasso Before 1907*, no. 5 (lent by Mr. and Mrs. Henry P. Clifford); Philadelphia Museum of Art, 1948, *The Collection of Mr. and Mrs. Henry Clifford*, and 1958, *Picasso*, no. 10 (lent by Mr. and Mrs. Henry Clifford); Musée Cantini, Marseilles, 1959, *Picasso*, no. 4 (lent by Mr. and Mrs. Henry Clifford); Knoedler Galleries, New York, 1962, *Picasso, an American Tribute*, no. 15.

EX COLL.: Possibly Edwin Suermondt, Aachen (in 1912); [Der Neue Kunstsalon, Munich, in 1912–1913]; John Quinn, New York (until 1924; Cat., 1926, p. 13, ill. p. 86); Julia Quinn Anderson, New York (1924–1930, or after); Mary Anderson, New York (until 1936); Henry P. McIlhenny, Philadelphia (1936–1937); Mr. and Mrs. Henry Clifford, Radnor, Pennsylvania (1937–1960).

GIFT OF MR. AND MRS. JOHN L. LOEB, 1960.

A Woman Ironing[1] 49.70.2

Studies of working people, and of the sad and the wretchedly poor, were the subjects of most of Picasso's "blue" pictures of the early nineteen hundreds. There are two other pictures, both dated 1904 by Zervos, that show a gaunt young laundress pressing hard on the garment she is ironing (Zervos, *Pablo Picasso*, I, 1932, pl. 111, nos. 247, 248). In one of them, a pastel, the girl is at work in a bedroom, with bent back and curving arms in much the same position as in our painting. In the other, an oil, her bony hands have been brought together on the iron to form, with her sharply raised angular shoulder, a rhomboid form. As its inscription indicates the Museum's picture once belonged to the artist's close friend and biographer Jaime Sabartés, who assigns it an approximate date of 1901 or 1902 (Ref., Sabartés, 1953).

Formerly called Girl Ironing.

Signed and inscribed (at upper right): *a Jacobus/ Sabartes/ Picasso.*

Oil on canvas, mounted on cardboard. H. 19½, w. 10⅛ in. (49.5 x 25.7 cm.).

Note 1. Not reproduced because of terms of bequest.

REFERENCE: J. Sabartés, *Picasso, Retratos y Recuerdos* (1953), ill. after p. 112, dates this picture 1901–1902.

EXHIBITED: Philadelphia Museum of Art. 1944, *History of an American, Alfred Stieglitz: "291" and after*, no. 89; Museum of Modern Art, New York, 1947, *Alfred Stieglitz Exhibition: His Collection*, no. 89; Art Institute of Chicago, 1948, *Alfred Stieglitz—His Photographs and His Collection*, no. 11.

Ex COLL.: Jaime Sabartés, Barcelona (until 1912); Alfred Stieglitz, New York (1912–1946); estate of Alfred Stieglitz, New York (1946–1949).

THE ALFRED STIEGLITZ COLLECTION, 1949.

The Blind Man's Meal   50.188

While he was still at work on this picture Picasso described it in a letter written in French to an unknown correspondent. On the letter he drew a small sketch in sepia of the composition, like the painting in all respects except for the presence of a dog in the lower left-hand corner.

In Barcelona around 1903, during the Blue Period, Picasso painted several pictures of blind people. The blind man who served as model in this picture is seen again in a drawing, seated beside a table, and in a gouache, on a cubic pedestal with his face lifted upwards (Ref., Zervos, 1932, pl. 81, nos. 172, 173). He also appears with a companion in an oil painting (Ref., Zervos, 1932, pl. 100, no. 224), and he was probably the model in the famous etching called The Frugal Repast (A. H. Barr Jr., Picasso: Fifty Years of His Art, 1946, p. 31). There are other representa-

tions of a poor man's meal including the same crock and bowl that are to be seen in our painting (Ref., Zervos, 1932, pls. 87, 94). The striking characteristic of the Museum's picture, as Penrose has observed, is the transfer of all evidence of perception from the refined and bony, sightless face to the extremely sensitive fingers on which the man's awareness of the external world depends.

Signed (at upper right): Picasso.

Oil on canvas. H. 37½, w. 37¼ in. (95.3 x 94.6 cm.).

REFERENCES: C. Zervos, Pablo Picasso, I (1932), p. XXIX, pl. 78, no. 168, dates this picture 1903, states that it was painted in Barcelona // Cahiers d'art, VII (1932), ill. p. 91, with the date 1902 // A. Cirici Pellicer, Picasso antes de Picasso (1946), pp. 151, 154, 158f., pl. 129, dates it 1902 // W. A. Lieberman, Pablo Picasso, Blue and Rose Periods (1954), ill. in color, pl. 19, dates it 1903 // A. Vallentin, Pablo Picasso (1957), pp. 87f. // R. Penrose, Picasso: His Life and Work (1958), p. 90, pl. II, fig. 8; and Picasso (exhib. cat.), Tate Gallery, London (1960), p. 16, no. 18, pl. 6B, dates it 1903, discusses Picasso's treatment of the subject of blindness // J. Richardson, Picasso, an American Tribute (exhib. cat.), Knoedler, New York (1962), no. 13, quotes Picasso's description of this picture from a letter (in the Barnes Foundation, Merion, Pennsylvania) written while he was still working on its composition and had not yet eliminated from it a dog in the lower left.

EXHIBITED: Moderne Galerie (Heinrich Thannhauser), Munich, 1913, Ausstellung Pablo Picasso, no. 10; Buenos Aires, 1934, Picasso (lent by J. K. Thannhauser); Galerie Thannhauser, Paris, 1938; Museum of Modern Art, New York; and Art Institute of Chicago, 1957, Picasso, cat. p. 19; Philadelphia Museum of Art, 1958, Picasso, no. 12; Tate Gallery, London, 1960, Picasso, no. 18; Knoedler Galleries, New York, 1962, Picasso, an American Tribute, no. 13.

Ex COLL.: [Ambroise Vollard, Paris]; [Heinrich Thannhauser, Munich]; private collec-

50.188

tion, Westphalia; [J. K. Thannhauser, New York, by 1934–1950]; Mr. and Mrs. Ira Haupt, New York (1950).

GIFT OF MR. AND MRS. IRA HAUPT, 1950.

The Actor   52.175

During the first winter after Picasso settled in Paris, 1904–1905, he came to know a number of actors and circus people and made many pictures of them. A neighbor in the Montmartre tenement where he lived is said to have been the model for this exaggeratedly tall and emaciated figure standing on a stage close to the prompter's box. There is a pencil study for the painting in the collection of Nelson Rockefeller in New York (ill. in *Picasso*, exhib. cat., Museum of Modern Art, New York, and Art Institute of Chicago, 1957, p. 24).

Signed (at lower right): *Picasso*.

Oil on canvas. H. 76⅜, w. 44⅛ in. (194 x 112.1 cm.).

REFERENCES: H. Hildebrandt, *Kunst und Künstler*, XI (1912–1913), p. 378, places this picture at the end of the artist's Blue Period, when rose became the second major color //

52.175

M. Raynal, *Picasso* (1922), pl. 18, dates it 1904 // O. Schürer, *Pablo Picasso* (1927), pl. 2, dated 1904 // C. Zervos, *Pablo Picasso*, I (1932), pl. 124, no. 291, dates this picture 1905, states that it was painted in Paris // A. H. Barr Jr., *Picasso: Forty Years of His Art* (exhib. cat.), Museum of Modern Art, New York, and Art Institute of Chicago (1939), p. 37, ill. p. 39; and *Picasso: Fifty Years of His Art* (1946), ill. p. 33, states that the Museum's picture was painted in the winter of 1904–1905 in Paris and that D. H. Kahnweiler confirms this // J. A. Gaya Nuño, *Picasso* (1950), pl. 12 // W. S. Lieberman, *Pablo Picasso, Blue and Rose Periods* (1954), color pls. 21, 22 (the painting and a detail), analyzes the composition // F. Elgar and R. Maillard, *Picasso* (1956), ill. p. 273, date this picture in the winter of 1904 // A. Vallentin, *Pablo Picasso* (1957), p. 113, states that it was painted in the winter of 1904–1905 // R. Penrose, *Picasso: His Life and Work* (1958), p. 107, pl. III, fig. 1, dates this painting 1904–1905, states that the model was a neighbor of Picasso's, discusses the color and the handling, considers it the forerunner of the first, or "circus," stage of the Rose Period // A. Blunt and P. Pool, *Picasso* (1962), p. 21, fig. 139 (the Rockefeller drawing), calls it a transitional work, from the Blue Period, observing that the blue is disappearing, melancholy is replacing apathy and immobility, and that there is a greater feeling of movement and vivacity.

EXHIBITED: Städtische Ausstellungshalle, Cologne, 1912, *Internationale Kunst-Ausstellung des Sonderbundes Westdeutscher Kunstfreunde und Künstler*, no. 216 (lent by P. Leffmann); Museum of Modern Art, New York, and Art Institute of Chicago, 1939, *Picasso: Forty Years of His Art*, no. 29 (lent by Rosenberg and

Helft, London) (circulated in 1940 with part of this exhibition to the City Art Museum, St. Louis, Boston Museum of Fine Arts, and San Francisco Museum of Art); Los Angeles County Museum, 1941, *Cézanne to Picasso*, no. 31 (lent by Paul Rosenberg).

Ex coll.: P. Leffmann, Cologne (in 1912); a German private collection (until 1938); [Hugo Perls, New York, 1938]; [Paul Rosenberg, New York, 1938–1941]; [M. Knoedler, New York, 1941]; Thelma Chrysler Foy, New York (1941–1952).

Gift of Thelma Chrysler Foy, 1952.

The Coiffure   53.140.3

As early as 1902, when Picasso made the crayon drawing of a man and a woman with a donkey (Ref., Zervos, I, 1932, pl. 67, no. 136),

53.140.3

he sometimes chose to simplify forms and features in a way that foretold the classical, monumental style in which he often worked at the end of the Rose Period in 1905 and 1906. The artist supports Zervos's date of 1905 for this picture, but Alfred Barr inclines to place it in the following year, perhaps even after Picasso's return to Paris from Gosol (Ref., Barr, 1946, p. 254). The careful welding together of these three figures to form a closely knit composition, the suppression of detail, and the dark outlines that define the contours distinguish this picture from the lyrical works of the Rose Period, such as the Family of Acrobats with a Monkey, which was painted in 1905 (Ref., Zervos, I, 1932, pl. 131).

Signed (at lower left): *Picasso*.

Oil on canvas. H. 68⅞, w. 39¼ in. (175 x 99.7 cm.).

References: A. Level, *Picasso* (1928), pl. 14, dates this picture 1905 // C. Zervos, *Pablo Picasso*, I (1932), ill. p. 141, no. 313, dates it 1905 // *The Fine Arts*, xx (May 1933), ill. p. 4 // J. Merli, *Picasso* (1942), ill. p. 156, dates it 1905 // A. H. Barr Jr., *Picasso: Fifty Years of His Art* (1946), pp. 43, 254, ill., dates it 1906 on stylistic grounds, despite Picasso's support of Zervos's dating // F. Elgar and R. Maillard, *Picasso* (1956), p. 36, ill. p. 275, date it 1905–1906 // A. Vallentin, *Pablo Picasso* (1957), p. 128, dates it late in 1905 or early in 1906, observes that it shows new tendencies in Picasso's composition and coloring // P. Pool, *Burl. Mag.*, CI (1959), pp. 179, 181, mentions it in a consideration of Picasso's change in style about 1905 // A. Blunt and P. Pool, *Picasso* (1962), p. 25, fig. 170, note in it a change in style and mood, find a resemblance in color to a study by Puvis de Chavannes (fig. 169) for a scene in the Pantheon in Paris.

Exhibited: Ausstellungshaus am Kurfürstendamm, Berlin, 1911, *XXII Ausstellung der Berliner Secession*, no. 192; Valentine Gallery, New York, 1933, *Picasso* (lent by Stephen C. Clark); Museum of Modern Art, New York, 1933, *Modern European Art* (no catalogue published); Museum of Modern Art, New York, and Art Institute of Chicago, 1939, *Picasso: Forty Years of His Art*, no. 51, and 1941–1942, circulating exhibition, *Picasso: Epochs in His Art*, shown at Munson-Williams-Proctor Institute, Utica (New York), Duke University, Durham (N. Carolina), William Rockhill Nelson Art Gallery, Kansas City, Milwaukee Art Institute, Grand Rapids Art Gallery (Michigan), Dartmouth College, Hanover (New Hampshire), and Vassar College, Poughkeepsie (New York).

Ex coll.: [Ambroise Vollard, Paris, until c. 1924]; [Hugo Perls, Berlin, c. 1924–c. 1930]; [Pierre Matisse, New York, c. 1930]; Stephen C. Clark, New York (from c. 1930–until 1937); Museum of Modern Art, New York (1937–1951; Cat., 1942, p. 66, no. 478, and 1948, p. 318, no. 594, ill. p. 57).

Wolfe Fund, 1951; acquired from the Museum of Modern Art, Anonymous Gift.

Gertrude Stein   47.106

The American writer Gertrude Stein (1874–1946) posed for a number of portraits. There are thirty or forty drawings and an oil painting of her by Pierre Tal Coat, a painting by Félix Vallotton, and sculptures by Jacques Lipchitz and Jo Davidson. She and her brother had acquired a picture by Picasso before they met him, and soon after the introduction, in the winter of 1905–1906, he began to paint her portrait. Dressed in a brown corduroy suit, she went every afternoon to his studio in the Rue Ravignan and posed there in a large broken armchair, meditating meanwhile on "Melanctha Herbert," the second story in her book *Three Lives*, on which she was working at the time. After some eighty or ninety sessions Picasso became dissatisfied with the head and wiped it out. Spring had come, and Gertrude Stein went off to Italy and Picasso to the little Spanish town of Gosol in the Pyrenees. When he returned to Paris, before seeing his model again, he painted in a new head, the one seen on the portrait today. To objections that the subject did not look like

the picture, the artist answered, "She will." Gertrude Stein declared that she was pleased: "He gave me the picture and I was and I still am satisfied with my portrait, for me, it is I, and it is the only reproduction of me which is always I, for me" (Ref., Stein, 1938, p. 8).

This portrait, like The Coiffure, was painted at an important moment in Picasso's career, when he was moving rapidly from the Rose Period toward Cubism. He had not yet encountered African sculpture, but he very probably knew, and was impressed by, early Iberian sculpture, especially the examples of bas-relief from Osuna that had been put on exhibition at the Louvre in the spring of 1906 (Ref., Sweeney, 1941).

Oil on canvas. H. 39⅜, w. 32 in. (100 x 81.3 cm.).

References: *Camera Work* (June 1913), special number, pl. v // R. Fry, *Burl. Mag.*, xxxi (1917), pp. 163, 168, illustrates this portrait with Raphael's Donna Gravida to show that the new aesthetic principles of the twentieth century correspond in aim with those of an earlier period but contrast with those that dominated the nineteenth century // C. Zervos, *Pablo Picasso*, 1 (1932), pl. 167, no. 352, dates this portrait 1906 // [G. Stein], *The Autobiography of Alice B. Toklas* (1933), pp. 7, 14, 26, 55–57, 60, 64–66, 70, 142, 150, ill. opp. p. 56, describes the painting of this portrait and the feelings of both the sitter and the artist about it, notes that Picasso's attention had not been drawn to African art until after the portrait had been finished // G. Stein, *Picasso* (1938), reprinted in 1946, pp. 7f., 16, 21, states that this picture marked the end of the Rose Period // A. H. Barr Jr., *Picasso: Forty Years of His Art* (exhib. cat.), Museum of Modern Art, New York, and Art Institute of Chicago (1939), pp. 56, 59, ill. // J. Cassou, *Picasso* (1940), ill. in color p. 41 // R. H. Wilenski, *Modern French Painters* [1940], pp. 200, 214, 219, observes that this portrait is one of the first of the pictures in which the influence of Negro sculpture is apparent // J. J. Sweeney, *Art Bull.*, xxiii (1941), pp. 191–198, fig. 1, states that it was begun in the

autumn of 1905 and that the final version of the head was painted when Picasso returned to Paris from a summer visit to Spain in 1906, while Gertrude Stein was still in Italy; traces the style of the head to a stone bas-relief (fig. 2) installed in the Louvre in 1906 // J. Merli, *Picasso* (1942), p. 53 // M. Wheeler, *Twentieth Century Portraits* (1942), p. 13, ill. p. 52 // B. Dorival, *Les Étapes de la peinture française contemporaine*, II (1944), p. 230, dates this portrait in the middle of the Rose Period, citing it as an example of the coexistence of two opposite styles at the same time in Picasso's work // A. H. Barr Jr., *Picasso: Fifty Years of His Art* (1946), pp. 46, 50, ill., relates it in style to other works by Picasso // L. Stein, *Appreciation, Painting, Poetry and Prose* (1947), p. 174, claims that Picasso used Negro art as a source in completing this portrait, which he finds "incoherent" // D. Sutton, *Picasso, . . . Époques Bleue et Rose* (1948), unpaged, compares this with the self-portrait of 1906 // P.-O. Zennström, *Picasso* (1948), pp. 45f., 49, fig. 12 // F. Fels, *L'Art vivant* (1950), ill. p. 225, along with Félix Vallotton's portrait of Gertrude Stein done in 1907 // G. Rosenthal, *Baltimore Museum of Art News* (April 1951), p. 1, mentions this picture, publishes portraits of Gertrude Stein by other artists // W. S. Lieberman, *Pablo Picasso, Blue and Rose Periods* (1954), color pl. 33, discusses this portrait on page opposite the plate and in the unpaged text // W. Boeck and J. Sabartés, *Picasso* (1955), pp. 136, 489, no. 70, ill. p. 460, no. 35 // J. Camón Aznar, *Picasso y el Cubismo* (1956), pp. 331f., fig. 272 // F. Elgar and R. Maillard, *Picasso* (1956), pp. 46, 49, 51f., ill. p. 275, relates this portrait to other pictures done by Picasso at about the same time // R. Penrose, *Portrait of Picasso* (1957), p. 32, fig. 67, illustrates it with a photograph of Gertrude Stein taken about 1906 (fig. 66) // A. Vallentin, *Pablo Picasso* (1957), pp. 128–130, 136f., states that Picasso delegated Sagot to ask Gertrude Stein to pose // J. Golding, *Burl. Mag.*, c (1958), p. 159, ill. p. 154, fig. 14 (detail) // R. Penrose, *Picasso: His Life and Work* (1958), pp. 115f., 119, 154, 290, pl. IV,

fig. 1, discusses the portrait fully, observes that at this time it was unusual for Picasso to paint from a model // A. B. Saarinen, *The Proud Possessors* (1958), pp. 176, 184, ill. after p. 200 (with a photograph of it as it hung in 1907 in the Steins' apartment at 27 Rue de Fleurus in Paris) // L. G. Buchheim, *Picasso* (1959), pp. 49, 135, ill. p. 48, observes that it was begun in the style of the pink period but marks the beginning of a new period // J. Golding, *Cubism* (1959), pp. 52, 76, pl. 79 B, discusses Picasso's use of the conventions of Iberian sculpture, slightly modified in form, in painting the face // H. P. Roché, *L'Oeil* (Mar. 1959), ill. p. 39, a photograph taken by Man Ray in 1922 of Gertrude Stein sitting beside this portrait // F. Gilot and C. Lake, *Life with Picasso* (1964), pp. 68–70.

EXHIBITED: Petit Palais, Paris, 1937, *Les Maîtres de l'art indépendant*, no. 11 (lent by Gertrude Stein); Museum of Modern Art, New York, and Art Institute of Chicago, 1939, *Picasso: Forty Years of His Art*, no. 65 (lent by Miss Stein); Knoedler Galleries, New York, 1947, *Picasso before 1907*, no. 33; San Francisco Museum of Art and Portland Art Museum (Oregon), 1948, *Picasso, Gris, Miro*, no. 3; Yale University Art Gallery, New Haven (Conn.), and Baltimore Museum of Art, 1951, *Pictures for a Picture of Gertrude Stein . . .*, no. 29; Musée des Arts Décoratifs, Paris, 1955, *Picasso*, no. 12; Museum of Modern Art, New York, and Art Institute of Chicago, 1957, *Picasso*, cat. p. 29; Philadelphia Museum of Art, 1958, *Picasso*, no. 36.

EX COLL. Gertrude Stein, Paris.

BEQUEST OF GERTRUDE STEIN, 1946.

A Woman in White 53.140.4

This is one of the numerous pictures in which Picasso's model was his young wife Olga Koklova, whom he had married in 1918. There is an oil sketch, possibly made in preparation for this painting (Zervos, V, pl. 2), and another of a seated acrobat (Zervos, v, pl. 9), in both of which the model poses with arms crossed as in this picture. These two works, like the Woman in White and many others from 1923, show deliberate gentleness and refinement in the conception as well as the rendering, which differentiates them sharply from the related but much more brutally massive classical figures of 1921 and 1922.

Signed (at lower right): *Picasso*.

Oil on canvas. H. 39, w. 31½ in. (99.1 x 80 cm.).

REFERENCES: G. Pène du Bois, *The Arts*, XVII (1931), p. 611 // H. F. MacKenzie, *Understanding Picasso* (1940), pl. XI, connects this picture with others of the same period and discusses the sources of Picasso's classical style // R. H. Wilenski, *Modern French Painters* [1940], p. 300, analyzes the works of 1923, finds this picture reminiscent of Masaccio // J. Merli, *Picasso* (1942), ill. in color opp. p. 184 // A. H. Barr Jr., *Picasso: Fifty Years of His Art* (1946), pp. 128f., ill., dates this picture 1923 // J. A. Gaya Nuño, *Picasso* (1950), p. 19, pl. 29 // C. Zervos, *Pablo Picasso*, v (1952), pl. 1, no. 1, dates it 1923 // F. Elgar and R. Maillard, *Picasso* (1956), p. 107, ill. in color p. 134 // A. Vallentin, *Pablo Picasso* (1957), p. 262.

EXHIBITED: Musée Galliera, Paris, 1926, *Salon du Franc* (as Une Femme en chemise, not listed in cat.; see *Beaux-Arts*, IV, 1926, p. 288); McLellan Galleries, Glasgow, 1927, *A Century of French Painting* (exhibition organized by Reid and Lefevre, London), no. 55; Kraushaar Galleries, New York, 1927, *Modern French Paintings, Water-Colors and Drawings*, no. 17; Museum of Modern Art, New York, 1930, *Painting in Paris*, no. 73 (lent from a private collection), and 1931, *Memorial Exhibition: The Collection of the Late Miss Lizzie P. Bliss*, no. 101; Addison Gallery, Andover (Mass.), 1931, *The Collection of Miss Lizzie P. Bliss*, no. 78; John Herron Art Institute, Indianapolis (Indiana), 1932, *Modern Masters from*

the Collection of Miss Lizzie P. Bliss, no. 74; Art Institute of Chicago, 1933, *Century of Progress*, no. 407 (lent by the Trustees of the Estate of Miss Lizzie P. Bliss through the Museum of Modern Art); Museum of Modern Art, New York, 1934, *The Lillie P. Bliss Collection*, no. 48, and 1934–1935, *Modern Works of Art*, no. 129; Smith College Museum of Art, Northampton (Mass.), 1935, *Paintings from the Lillie P. Bliss Collection* (lent by the Museum of Modern Art); Museum of Fine Arts, Dallas (Texas), 1936, *Texas Centennial Exhibition*, cat. p. 37 (lent by the Museum of Modern Art); Museum of Modern Art, Boston, 1938, *Picasso; Henri Matisse* (lent by the Museum of Modern Art); Art Gallery of Toronto, 1938, *Paintings of Women*, no. 57 (lent by the Museum of Modern Art); Museum of Modern Art, New York, 1939, *Art in Our Time*, no. 160; Museum of Modern Art, New York, and Art Institute of Chicago, 1939, *Picasso: Forty Years of His Art*, no. 179, included in the section of the exhibition circulated in 1940–1941 to Cincinnati Museum of Art, Isaac Delgado Museum, New Orleans, Minneapolis Institute of Arts, and Carnegie Institute, Pittsburgh (Pa.); Sociedad de Arte Moderno, Mexico City, 1944, *Primera Exposición: Picasso*, cat. p. 42 (lent by the Museum of Modern Art); Denver Art Museum (Colorado), 1945, *Picasso* (lent by the Museum of Modern Art); Cleveland Museum of Art, 1966, *Fifty Years of Modern Art*.

EX COLL.: [Paul Guillaume, Paris; bought at auction, after exhibition *L'Art français au service du franc*, Musée Galliera, Paris, Oct. 29, 1926; as Une Femme en chemise]; [Étienne Bignou, Paris]; [Alex Reid and Lefevre, London, by 1927]; [Kraushaar Galleries, New York, 1927]; Lizzie P. Bliss, New York (1927–1931); estate of Lizzie P. Bliss, New York (1931–1934); Museum of Modern Art, New York (1934–1951; Cat., 1942, pp. 67–69, no. 487, ill., and 1948, p. 318, no. 607, ill. p. 59).

ROGERS FUND, 1951, ACQUIRED FROM THE MUSEUM OF MODERN ART, LIZZIE P. BLISS COLLECTION.

53.140.4

Metzinger

Jean Metzinger. Born in Nantes in 1883; died in 1956 in Paris. In 1903 Metzinger went to Paris, where he studied in various academies, painting in a Neo-Impressionist manner and then becoming interested in Fauvism. By 1909, however, he could be classed as a Cubist. He first showed his work at the Salon d'Automne of 1906 and from then on contributed to the principal Paris exhibitions.

Metzinger, with Picasso and Braque, was among the creative leaders in the Cubist movement and was an important agent in making known the first discoveries of these other two artists. He started writing about painting in 1910 and in that year published *Notes sur la peinture*, proclaiming Cubism as the new art. In 1911 Metzinger contributed paintings to the first collective exhibition of the works of Cubist painters which were brought together in a special gallery, Salle 41, of the Salon des Indépendants. In the same year Guillaume Apollinaire applied to this movement the term *cubisme*, which then came into general usage. In 1912, with Albert Gleizes, Metzinger published *Du Cubisme*, the first work on the aesthetics of the movement. He also helped to organize the "Section d'Or" exhibition of 1912.

The active development of Cubism ceased in 1914 with the beginning of the first World War. Though by this time Metzinger had ceased to play an important part in the movement, he continued to figure in European exhibitions. Between 1921 and 1924 he returned to representational art, which he called "constructive realism," and from that time on he painted both realistic and abstract pictures.

59.86

Still Life   59.86

In 1915 Juan Gris painted Still Life before an Open Window, a picture combining still life with a view. Metzinger apparently had the one by Gris in mind when, two years later, he turned sharply from his preceding works to paint the Museum's picture. It resembles Gris's not only in the use of the window but also in the placement of light and dark masses, the rugs under the table, and the imitation of wood, and even in some of the shapes of the objects, especially the triangles.

Signed and dated (at lower right): *Metzinger / 11–17.*

Oil on canvas. H. 32, w. 25⅝ in. (81.3 x 65.1 cm.).

REFERENCE: *Dictionary of Modern Painting* [1964], ill. p. 234 in color, dated 1917.

Ex coll.: Léonce Rosenberg, Paris; [Galerie Fricker, Paris, until 1957]; Joseph H. Hazen, New York (1957–1959); [The New Gallery, New York, 1959].

Purchase, Funds received from the M. L. Annenberg Foundation, the Joseph H. Hazen Foundation, and Joseph H. Hazen, 1959.

Modigliani

Amedeo Modigliani. Born in Leghorn (Livorno) in 1884; died in Paris in 1920. Modigliani came from a highly cultivated and intellectual family, with a mixed Spanish and Italian heritage. His mother, a professional journalist and a woman of great intelligence and energy, conducted a small school of languages for young women. She permitted young Amedeo, who in his teens survived several serious illnesses, to abandon his study of the classics and embark on the career of an artist. He entered the school conducted in Leghorn by Guglielmo Micheli, a landscape painter who had studied with Giovanni Fattori. In 1901, he went south to Capri, visiting Rome, Florence, Venice, and Naples. In 1902 he studied painting in Florence under Fattori. The years between 1903 and 1906 were spent largely in Venice, attending classes irregularly at the Institute of Fine Arts, visiting churches to study paintings, and sketching and painting independently.

The decisive step in Modigliani's career was his move, early in 1906, to Paris. He had wished for some years to become a sculptor and enrolled first in the private school of sculpture run by the Italian Filippo Colarossi. For the next ten years he produced stone and wood carvings as well as paintings. The influences of African Negro sculpture and early Cubism blended in the arrestingly personal style of the carved stone heads that he produced in these first years in Paris. He soon acquired as a friend a young doctor, Paul Alexandre, who became his patron and for some time was the only purchaser of his works. Indeed, during all of his brief career Modigliani found few buyers and only after his death were his astonishingly original works appreciated. Paul Guillaume and subsequently Léopold Zborowsky, who became his sole dealer in 1916, helped to mitigate the abject misery in which poverty, tuberculosis, and an abnormal consumption of alcohol and drugs held the gifted young Italian captive. Despite the troubles of the last years of his life Modigliani managed to produce many portraits and innumerable drawings. In 1908 and 1910 he showed a number of works at the Salon des Artistes Indépendants, and the year before his death pictures by him were exhibited in a group show in London. His first one-man show, consisting of thirty-two works, took place at the end of 1917.

Modigliani was one of the foremost members of the School of Paris, an assemblage of artists who had emigrated from many different countries. Living first on the Butte Montmartre and afterward across the river in Montparnasse, he mingled intimately not only with struggling artists like Soutine but also with the numerous poets and philosophers who belonged to the same circle. He had a number of friendships with women, whose faces are recorded for us in portraits that are highly stylized but deliver, paradoxically, an astounding analysis of character.

Modigliani's style was founded on his study of the works of the old masters and on his awareness of his contemporaries, Cézanne, Matisse, Picasso, and Derain. But he had a very strong individuality, and these influences were submerged in his peculiarly personal combination of mass with line, which produced a body of subtle and beautiful work.

Portrait of a Young Girl   60.118

This young woman, whose nearly blank eyes are so surprisingly expressive, is seen again in a full-length portrait in the Albright Gallery in Buffalo. The Albright model has been called The Young Servant Girl and has also been more specifically identified as Marie Feret, a peasant working as a servant at Cagnes, who was painted by Modigliani when he was in the south of France for his health in 1918. This picture has been called Le Col Marin

60.118

(The Sailor Collar); the collar the model is wearing, however, does not conform to what is usually called a sailor collar.

Signed (at upper right): *modigliani*.

Oil on canvas. H. 23¾, w. 18¼ in. (60.3 x 46.4 cm.).

REFERENCES: J. N. Rosenberg, in foreword to *New Pictures and the New Gallery* (1923), ill. (unnumbered plate), tells that this picture, called Jeune Fille, was bought by Mr. Iklé at the New Gallery sometime between Nov. 14, 1922, and June 30, 1923 // A. Pfannstiel, *Modigliani* (1929), "catalogue presumé," p. 33, calls it Le Col Marin, giving its height wrongly as 65 cm., includes it among the paintings done in 1917 // A. Basler, *Modigliani* (1931), ill. p. 17, calls it Le Col Marin, 1917 // P. Descargues, *Modigliani* (1951), pl. 29, calls it Le Col Marin, 1917, giving its height wrongly as 65 cm. // A. Pfannstiel, *Modigliani et son oeuvre* (1956), p. 121, no. 202, repeats the information in the first edition (Ref., 1929) referring to the photograph of it in Descargues (Ref., 1951, pl. 29), but adds wrongly that the painting was at that time in a private collection in Paris.

EXHIBITED: Metropolitan Museum, 1957, *Impressionist and Modern Paintings from Private Collections* (lent by Charles F. Iklé).

EX COLL.: [Léopold Zborowsky, Paris, until 1922]; [Bernheim-Jeune, Paris, 1922/23]; [The New Gallery, New York, 1922/23]; Charles F. Iklé, New York (from 1922/23).

GIFT OF CHARLES F. IKLÉ, 1960.

56.184.2

Jeanne Hébuterne 56.184.2

Modigliani met Jeanne Hébuterne at the studio of some friends at Carnival time in 1917, when she was only nineteen. She bore him a daughter in November 1918 and was about to have another child when the painter died. The following day she flung herself from the roof of her parents' house. This portrait, which has been dated 1917 or 1918, was probably painted before her first child was born.

Signed (at upper right): *modigliani.*

Oil on canvas. H. 36, w. 28¾ in. (91.5 x 73 cm.).

REFERENCES: J. Lassaigne, *Panorama des arts* (1946), ill. p. 11 // P. Descargues, *Modigliani* (1951), pl. 42 // Mrs. N. B. Spingold (in a letter, 1952), gives the provenance of this picture // P. D'Ancona, *Modigliani, Chagall, Soutine, Pascin* [1953], p. 23, discusses a picture that is probably this one but states erroneously that it is dated 1918; p. 25, illustration of this picture with the date 1917 // A. M. Frankfurter, *Art News*, LII (Mar. 1953), ill. p. 25 // A. Pfannstiel, *Modigliani et son oeuvre* (1956), p. 153, no. 290 (probably this picture,

although a reference is given [Basler] for a reproduction of another) // A. Ceroni, *Amedeo Modigliani* (1958), p. 69, cat. no. 152, color pl. 152, dates it 1918 // C. Roy, *Modigliani* (1958), p. 83, ill. in color p. 108 // J. Russell, *Modigliani* (exhib. cat.), London and Edinburgh (1963), p. 21, no. 45, pl. 30 (in color), dates it in the late summer or autumn of 1918.

EXHIBITED: Galerie Bing, Paris, 1925, *Modigliani*, no. 4 or no. 19; Arthur Tooth & Sons, London, 1938, *Amedeo Modigliani*, no. 20; Paul Rosenberg Gallery, New York, 1953, *Collectors' Choice*, no. 26 (as painted in 1918; lent by Mr. and Mrs. Nate B. Spingold); Metropolitan Museum, 1960, *The Nate and Frances Spingold Collection*; Tate Gallery, London, and Royal Scottish Academy, Edinburgh, 1963, *Modigliani*, no. 45.

Ex COLL.: [Léopold Zborowsky, Paris]; Libaude, France (until c. 1932); [Adolphe Basler, Paris, c. 1932]; [Galerie Bing, Paris]; Collection de Monsieur R. B. (sale, Hôtel Drouot, Paris, salle 1, June 3, 1937, no. 18, as *Déshabillé au Fauteuil*, 92 x 73 cm.); George[s?] Hyordey; [Galerie Bing, Paris, until 1951]; [Jacques Lindon, New York, 1951]; Mr. and Mrs. Nate B. Spingold, New York (from 1951).

GIFT OF MR. AND MRS. NATE B. SPINGOLD, 1956.

The Italian Woman 56.4

The large and placid dark-eyed woman who sat for this portrait was described as early as 1930 as an Italian woman. It would be interesting to identify her with Rosalia, an Italian who kept a little restaurant in the Rue Campagna-Première, where Modigliani was one of her favorites (Lunia Czechowska, in Ref., Ceroni, 1958, p. 28).

Signed (at upper right): *modigliani.*

Oil on canvas. H. 40⅜, w. 26⅜ in. (102.6 x 67 cm.).

REFERENCES: M. Dale, *Formes* (Oct. 1931), ill. after p. 122, calls this picture Italian Woman // U. Apollonio, *Cahiers d'art*, XXV (1950), ill. p. 173, calls it La brune // A. Pfannstiel,

56.4

Modigliani et son oeuvre (1956), pp. 154f., cat. no. 297 // A. Ceroni, *Amedeo Modigliani* (1958), p. 60, cat. no. 110, dates it 1918.

EXHIBITED: Galerie Georges Petit, Paris, 1930, *Cent Ans de peinture française*, no. 52 (as l'Italienne); Demotte Galleries, New York, 1931, *Amedeo Modigliani*, no. 20 (as painted in 1917, formerly in the Bradly collection, Paris, lent by Chester Dale); Palais des Beaux-Arts, Brussels, 1933, *Modigliani*, no. 76 (lent by the Chester Dale collection); Kunsthalle, Basel, 1934, *Modigliani*, no. 66 (lent by the Chester Dale collection); Philadelphia Museum of Art, 1943, *Paintings from the Chester Dale Collection*, pl. 21 (as painted about 1915); Society of the Four Arts, Palm Beach (Florida), and Lowe Gallery, Miami (Florida), 1959, *Amedeo Modigliani*, no. 22 (Woman in Black, probably this picture; lent by the Chester Dale collection); World's Fair, Brussels, 1958, *Fifty Years of Modern Art* (cat. published in 1959), no. 221.

EX COLL.: Bradly, Paris; [Georges Petit, Paris, 1930]; Chester Dale, New York (by 1931).

GIFT OF THE CHESTER DALE COLLECTION, 1956.

Soutine

Chaim Soutine. Born in Lithuania in 1893; died in Paris in 1943. Soutine came from the little village of Smilovitchi near Minsk. He was one of the numerous children of a humble and very poor tailor, who intended his son to become a cobbler. At the age of thirteen the boy left home to take some drawing lessons in Minsk and in 1910 went to Vilna, where he spent three years at the local art school. In 1913 he arrived in Paris and there, during two years of extreme poverty, studied painting at the École des Beaux-Arts, in Cormon's studio. He soon became acquainted with many of the foreign-born artists congregated in Paris, including the sculptors Zadkine and Lipchitz and the painters Chagall and Modigliani. In 1919 Soutine met the dealer Léopold Zborowski and at his suggestion spent most of the next three years in Céret, a small town in the Pyrenees, and in Cagnes, on the Riviera. When he returned to Paris in 1922 with about two hundred pictures Zborowski brought him to the attention of the American collector Dr. Albert Barnes, who bought in one transaction a large part of Soutine's stock of paintings. Although this good fortune relieved Soutine of his struggle to secure the bare necessities of life, chronic bad health and a temperamental disposition toward self-torment and bitter revolt continued to exact a toll of misery and anguish as long as he lived.

Although his paintings are immensely subjective in style and subject matter, Soutine studied the old masters, and their influence made successive impressions on his work. He admired El Greco and Tintoretto, and, nearer to his own time, Cézanne and Bonnard. The artists to whom he was especially attracted, however, were Courbet and Rembrandt, whose painting of a slaughtered ox incited him to make a similar picture. He also used Rembrandt's *Hendrickje Bathing* as the basis for a painting.

Soutine infused all his paintings with his characteristic turbulence. He did landscape, portraits, and still life, approaching each in an equally subjective way. In his landscapes, especially those painted at Céret, buildings are shown toppling, and the topography is convulsive, as if in volcanic upheaval. The still lifes—carcasses of beef, plucked fowl, and plates of herring—are almost anthropomorphic in their tragedy. His portraits nearly always show distortion, but from this malformation there emerges a poignant distillation of individual personality and extreme pathos. Soutine relied for his aesthetic effects on very varied surfaces with some passages of heavy impasto, on a very individual, unconstrained brush stroke, and on his brilliant command of color, juxtaposing strong, jewel-like tones in original and startling combinations. More than any of the painters who were his contemporaries in Paris, he gave a concrete form to the emotional violence that lies at the heart of Expressionism. Although there is little or no resemblance in their work, Soutine and Vincent van Gogh have much in common; aliens from society, both showed an utter disregard for current conventions in painting.

Landscape with Figures   64.147

This convulsive landscape, dominated by the interlaced branches of a twisting tree, resembles closely many of the pictures that Soutine painted between 1919 and 1922 at Céret, a small village in the Pyrenees. In comparison with most of the scenes that he painted soon afterward at Cagnes in the Alpes Maritimes, it is more agitated and more thickly painted.

Signed (at lower right): *Soutine.*

Oil on canvas. H. 26, w. 21½ in. (66 x 54.6 cm.).

REFERENCE: M. Tuchman (in a letter, 1965), dates it about 1919, agrees that the style of this picture is that of the landscapes Soutine painted at Céret.

64.147

EXHIBITED: Redfern Gallery, London.

Ex COLL.: [Paul Guillaume, Paris, bought from the artist]; private collection, England (until 1960); Alex Maguy, Paris (in 1960); [Jacques Lindon, New York, in 1960]; Peter I. B. Lavan, New York (1960–1964).

GIFT OF MR. AND MRS. PETER I. B. LAVAN, SUBJECT TO A LIFE ESTATE IN THE DONORS, 1964.

Portrait of a Child in Blue   56.230.3

In this portrait Soutine has captured with tender understanding the curious combination of defiance and helplessness that characterizes childhood. The relative absence of brutality and the pattern in values formed by the areas of hair, flesh, and costume relate it to the paintings of valets he made in 1929, especially the one belonging to Mr. and Mrs. Leigh Block of Chicago (M. Wheeler, *Soutine*, 1950, ill. p. 80).

Formerly called Portrait of a Young Girl.

Signed (at upper right): *Soutine.*

Oil on canvas. H. 39¼, w. 25½ in. (99.7 x 64.8 cm.).

REFERENCE: *Met. Mus. Bull.*, XVI (1957), ill. p. 45.

EXHIBITED: Metropolitan Museum, 1960, *The Nate and Frances Spingold Collection.*

56.230.3

Ex COLL.: [Jos Hessel, Paris]; Jean Monteux, Paris; [Jacques Lindon, New York, until 1951]; Mr. and Mrs. Nate B. Spingold, New York (1951–1956).

GIFT OF MR. AND MRS. NATE B. SPINGOLD, 1956.

Books and Periodicals Abbreviated in the Catalogue

Art Bulletin. *The Bulletin of the College Art Association,* Providence and New York, 1913+

Burl. Mag. *Burlington Magazine for Connoisseurs,* London, 1903+

Degas sales. *Catalogues des tableaux, pastels et dessins par Edgar Degas et provenant de son atelier,* Paris, Galeries Georges Petit. Four sales: May 6-8, 1918; Dec. 11-13, 1918; April 7-9, 1919; July 2-4, 1919.

Gaz. des B.-A. *Gazette des Beaux-Arts,* Paris, 1859-1939; New York, 1942+

Gogh letters. Gogh, Vincent van, *The Complete Letters of Vincent van Gogh,* Greenwich, Connecticut, 1958.

Lemoisne. P. A. Lemoisne, *Degas et son oeuvre,* 4 vols., Paris, 1946-1949.

Mag. of Art. *Magazine of Art,* Washington, 1909-1953.

Met. Mus. Bull. *Bulletin of The Metropolitan Museum of Art,* New York, 1905+

Met. Mus. Miniatures. The Metropolitan Museum of Art "Miniatures," New York.

Rev. de l'art. *Revue de l'art ancien et moderne,* Paris, 1897-1937.

Robaut. A Robaut, *L'Oeuvre de Corot,* 5 vols., Paris, 1905.

Thieme-Becker. U. Thieme and F. Becker, *Allgemeines Lexikon der bildende Künstler,* 37 vols., Leipzig, 1907-1950.

Index of Collectors

VOLUMES I, II, AND III

A

B

C

X

Y

Z

Index

VOLUMES I, II, AND III

C

W